Commercial Perfume Bottles

Jacquelyne Y. Jones-North

Photography by Duane A. Young

With Price Guide

Schiffer Publishing Ltd

1469 Morstein Road
West Chester, Pennsylvania 19380

Title page:
Lucien Lelong's "Jabot" came in a frosted
glass bow bottle. The perfume was introduced
in the United States in 1939. (2" and 4").

Printed in the United States of America.
ISBN: 0-88740-108-2
Published by Schiffer Publishing Ltd.
1469 Morstein Road, West Chester, Pennsylvania 19380

This book may be purchased from the publisher.
Please include $2.00 postage.
Try your bookstore first.

THIS BOOK IS DEDICATED TO:

Robert Du Grenier
Ken Leach
Madeleine France
Priscilla McOstrich
Laurens Tartasky
Richard J. Peters
Thomas J. North

and
In memory of my beloved Grandmother
Alma Mattie Henderson

Duane Young Photography

The photographer of this book, Duane Young, owns and operates a professional commercial and portrait photography studio in Dallas, Texas.

His Award Winning style of photography in commercial and portraiture has gained him recognition in the United States.

Mr. Young enjoys challenging assignments that allow him to use his creative abilities. To contact him call information for Duane Young Photography.

Lighting provided by Novatron of Dallas.

Rental equipment provided by Light Tec Dallas.

Additional photography was provided for this book by Elizabeth A. McCarron.

Acknowledgements

To all those who were involved in the making of this book, I owe profound thanks: Madeleine France, Plantation, Florida; Laurens and Lorraine Tartasky, Colorado; Mr. and Mrs. V. James Cole, New York; Mr. & Mrs. Marshal Garber, New York; Priscilla McOstrich, New York; Gallery #47 (Manhattan Art & Antique Center), New York; Ken Leach, New York; Richard J. Peters, New York; Gay Taylor, New Jersey; Museum of American Glass at Wheaton Village, Millville, New Jersey; E. Lee Rowe, Baltimore, Maryland; Carr-Lowry Glass Co., Baltimore, Maryland; The Color Lab, Dallas, Texas; Robert Messina, Dallas, Texas; Novatron Lighting of Dallas, Dallas, Texas; Larry Neve, Dallas, Texas; Edith Sacell, New York; Ralph Taylor, New York; Camille Grace, Gladstone, Missouri; STUFF, Gladstone, Missouri; Clayton Antiques, Clayton, Missouri; Jeri Schwartz, Stamford, Connecticut; George Corly, Dallas, Texas; Janis Helmer, Dallas, Texas; Glen Campbell, Moline, Illinois; Cocktails and Laughter Antiques, Arlington, Virginia; Elizabeth A. McCarron, New York; Gloria Barbour, Oklahoma; Pauline de Morcia, Dallas, Texas; Mel Mitchell, Dallas, Texas; Gene Galloway, Dallas, Texas; Wilhelmina Bruton, Dallas, Texas; Robert Du Grenier, New York; Huntington Galleries, Huntington, West Virginia; Robert Rowe, Huntington, West Virginia; Carl Johnson; Charles Wheatly; Jack Webb; Ft. Worth Public Library, Ft. Worth, Texas; New York City Public Library, New York; Justin Jones, Dallas, Texas; Ernestine Jones, Dallas, Texas; Quata Young, Dallas, Texas; New York Experimental Glass Workshop, New York; Catherine Barré, New York; Philippe Dahais, New York; David Kratz, New York; Saint Gobain Desjonquères, New York; Verreries Bross, New York; Coty Inc., New York; Tim Mason, Dallas, Texas; Mike Hulme, Dallas, Texas; Gunther Knop, New York; Bernard Lee, New York; Joseph Markowski, New York; Marjorie Ambrogio, New York; Ellen J. Taylor, Pennsylvania; and Peter Schiffer, Pennsylvania.

With a special thank you to:
Gloria C. Young
Gail Sargent
Nancy and Tom De Rosa
William T. Nixon
Jo Ellison and
6th Floor Government Publications Desk—Dallas Public Library

Frontispiece:
In store tester rack held a variety of Houbigant perfumes.

Contents

Flask form bottle highlighted with brown staining, moulded with a kneeling draped nude surrounded by flowers and foliage, held the perfume "Flausa" by Roger & Gallet. Bottle marked—R. Lalique. Numbered stopper. Circa 1910's. (4-7/8").

The perfume house of Roger & Gallet was founded in Paris in 1862 by M. Armand Roger and Charles Gallet. The perfume "Bouquet des Amours" was created by Roger & Gallet in 1898. The simple bottle shown, adorned with chubby cupids on the label, came in an odd-shaped blue box. (3-3/4").

The Spanish perfume house of Myrurgia
launched its perfume "Suspiro de Granada"
in the U.S. in 1929. The opaque black glass
flacon came encased in a gay red, black, and
gold lacquer case decorated with frivolous
pompons. (3-1/4").

Foreword

BY KEN LEACH

Both dealer and collector will be pleased to see this long awaited book. It successfully employs an asthetic format to present vital information, much as the perfume bottle embellishes the desirability and appeal of the scent it contains.

Ms. North has combined information gleaned from collectors, research libraries, and the sadly incomplete files of glass and perfume companies to present us with this beautifully illustrated analysis which will serve as an invaluable guide to various levels of collecting, while entertaining us in its pictorial variety.

The bottles shown here cover a century of imaginative design. Although perfume formulas have changed little throughout history, their containers have evolved from pharmaceutical jars to true works of art.

Beginning this century we saw a profusion of companies competing in the marketplace. Offering basically the same fragrances, focus was necessarily placed on more exciting presentation. Some companies employed top designers such as Lalique and Baccarat to evoke a mood and tempt the eye. When successful, a lasting image would be created, the flacon often being the major factor in the purchase price of the scent.

It is interesting to see a bottle, and picture the circumstances surrounding its creation. Whether it be literature, fashion, archeological discoveries or our fascination with other cultures, one can often recognize the artist's inspiration.

These enticing packages with their intriging names have the same effect on todays collector as they did on the original buyer. For decades the perfume gift, given or received, has been a charming and durable token of affection. We see a bottle that once held a favored scent, and it triggers our mind to images of the past.

Throughout our history scent bottles of all types have been collected, but with the proliferation of commercial bottles this century, there is a vast new world of discovery, diversity, and possibility. We find an explosive new interest in collecting commercial bottles, which now have been moved from the vanity to more revered displays throughout the home. Those who are newly inspired, as well as the long time collector, are finding great reward in the search for and acquisition of bottles.

With more information available, the demand has increased for quality bottles in each category. Many new collectors are bypassing the less expensive bottles and seeking only those in the top level, while a few established collectors are purchasing at prices inconceivable only years ago.

Some approach collecting as a hobby, waiting for the occasional bottle that falls under their predetermined price limit. Without care this can lead to an accumulation of minor examples with no direction. The more advanced collectors begin the same way, but soon develop a need for quality rather than quantity. They reach a level of selectivity that requires serious commitment. Very good investments have been made, but the primary factor is ultimately the pleasure of collecting.

Feeling like a prospector who has struck gold, there is a sudden rush of adrenalin when you discover a bottle that you have been searching for. Regardless of the circumstances, take time from your excitement to examine your find. Make sure it has the correct stopper, and is in acceptable condition. A pleasant day can be made of shopping the countryside, but bottles of the highest quality are limited and usually come from the specialists in the field. Frequently the uninformed dealer will ask an inflated price on a piece he thinks to be unique. Under these circumstances you may find creative stopper matching and unintentional misrepresentation. [For example, at a recent antiques show we witnessed a dealer unpack 30 bottles and 30 stoppers, randomly assembling each with no attention to proper match.]

Refer to your book to verify how a particular scent was bottled, packaged, or advertised and find a bottle dealer you can trust to know when a piece is correct, what is a fair price, and how it is regarded in the world market. Assume your dealer has access to the most desirable bottles and is looking for the unusual quality in each category.

Collecting is an adventure and with an experienced guide you will travel through a remarkable world. New discoveries are made every day. It is never too late to start collecting!

3 Clear bottle decorated with a simple red ribbon used by Floris of London for its popular "Red Rose" scent (3-1/2").

1 Frosted glass draperies bottle for "Indiscret" by Lucien Lelong was introduced in the United States in 1936. The bottle was made by Verreries Brosse. (6-3/4", 8").

2 Beautiful pale blue flacon moulded with a design of flower petals and a bee-shaped stopper was used by Coty for "Au Coeur Des Calices". Bottle marked—R. Lalique. Numbered stopper. (2-3/4").

4 Beautiful crystal flacon decorated with a gold enamelled scene of an oriental lady walking in a garden was made by Baccarat for Cadolle. The same Baccarat bottle with a different gold enamelled scene was used by Houbigant for "Parfum d'Argeville. Circa 1913. (5-5/8").

5 Flacon originally designed by Rene Lalique in 1929 for a Molinard perfume was reissued in 1980 for "Molinard De Molinard". (12-1/2").

6 Frosted glass key-shaped bottle with a long dapper and ground stopper held "Chamart". Marked France on label. (4").

Introduction

In today's collectibles market, there is a rapidly growing interest in the commercial perfume bottle. A fundamental factor in the luxury, prestige, and pleasure of perfume has been the beauty, form, or novelty of its container. The bottle was the symbol made permanent and visible of the ultimate quality and characteristics of a fragrance. The decoration and designs that have been used for commercial perfume bottles are almost limitless. Each historic art or decorative style movement in the last hundred years has extended its influence over the design of bottles made during its reign. Thus commercial perfume bottles are, in truth, mirrors of their era.

For each new perfume, eau de toilet, or cologne marketed by a perfume firm, a wide range of containers were needed from small sample bottles to deluxe presentation bottles. It was in the last century that the practice of commissioning the design of a bottle to hold a particular perfume by a specific company began. Two advances in bottle making helped make it possible to standardize the bottles used for perfumes and colognes. The first advance was the accomplishment of merchanizing the mould blown glass method of manufacture and the second was the invention of an automatic bottle making machine.

The mechanizing of the mould blown glass method of manufacture for bottles began in the 1880's. The glass was gathered automatically or by the glassworker's rod and placed in the blank mould where it was blown by compressed air or by the glassblower. The blank was then hand transferred from the blank mould to the second finishing mould. It was the introduction of precision-cast metal moulds in the semi-automated method of manufacture that allowed a new sophistication and variety in bottle design. After cooling, the bottle surface was polished with felt polishing wheels or by hand with cork to bring forth the sparkle and clarity of the glass. Each bottle had a stopper hand ground to an exact fit by a skilled operator. Even today, the highest quality perfume bottles are still made semi-automatically.

The invention of an automatic bottle making machine was patented in 1891 by J. Michael Owens. The machine accomplished every step from shaping the molten glass to cooling the completed bottle. By the early 1900's much of the commercial bottle manufacturing in the United States had become fully automated. As advances were made in automatic production, a greater range of shapes became available, but the semi-automatic technique was still the only way to manufacture prestigious, heavy weight flacons.

Advances in the perfume trade from 1870 on were also taking place. Chemists were discovering amazing synthetic fragrance chemicals to replace many of the expensive natural essential oils needed in perfume manufacturing. The new synthetics revolutionized the perfume industry by extending considerably the perfumer's choices. They also helped lower the price of the finished product, thus greatly expanding the number of people who could afford to purchase it. The first perfume blended with a synthetic ingredient was "Fougère Royale" by Houbigant, launched in 1882. From about 1900 on, the majority of perfumes were made with a combination of both synthetic and natural aromatics.

The golden age of the perfume bottle that occurred around 1907 to the Second World War was the direct result of the cumulative advances mentioned above and the partnership of two geniuses, Rene Lalique and Francois Coty. Until this era, most of the commercial flacons were rather plain cylindrical, square, or rectangular shapes to provide room for prominent display of the perfumer's label. Around 1907 Coty, inspired by a vision of his beautiful scents housed in exquisite bottles with engraved labels and packaged in luxurious boxes, sought out Rene Lalique, one of the greatest designers of the 20th Century. The association of Lalique and Coty uplifted the perfume and its flacon into the category usually reserved for rare and precious works of art. The bottles Lalique created for Coty were the first of their kind and expressed in a visual way the theme of the fragrance they housed. The bottles were also cost-effective, supplying a quality design at a reasonable price. The successful collaboration between Coty and Lalique brought about sweeping changes in packaging by the perfume industry and was copied the world over.

The twentieth century was to see the long-lasting marriage between high fashion and perfume occur. The French couturier that first started the trend of marketing fragrances to harmonize with his clothing designs was Paul Poiret, a name that evokes the Art Deco period. In 1910 Poiret created the company Parfums Rosine, named after his small daughter, to produce perfume.

With the ending of World War I the fragrance industry entered a period of unprecedented growth that continued throughout the 1920's and 1930's. Many key factors contributed to the vogue for perfume including: vastly increased advertising, lower cost and greater accessibility, women holding jobs in ever-icreasing numbers, the shattering of the tabu against nice women using cosmetics, a change in the stereotype of the ideal woman from the passive, demure Victorian to the sophisticated, assertive flapper, and the popularity of moving pictures which created a desire for glamour. Also, other Paris fashion houses started to follow the lead set by Poiret in 1910 and began introducing perfumes under their own labels. Among the fashion designers that introduced fragrances in the 1920's were Chanel, Lanvin, Molyneux, Worth, Nicole Groult, Weil, Callot, Bechoff, Jean Patou, J. Suzanne Talbot, Martial et Armand, Lucien Lelong, Drecoll, Lenief, Kondazian, and Reboux. Some houses created a single perfume, while others evolved whole collections. Practically all of the large houses became known as parfumeurs de luxe, as well as dressmakers, and many houses of lesser size and fame added their contributions to the perfumes of the 1920's. The fitting-room in Paris was not considered complete without its atomizer bottle of the house perfume.

For the most part, the couturiers and perfumers during the 1920's and 1930's dressed their perfume creations in elegant containers. During this time it was quite common for the most respected painters, sculptors, and decorators to design flacons for the perfume trade. A short list can include such illustrious artists as Gallé, Lalique, Dali, Léger, Picart, Lepape, Pegnet, Helleu, and Marie Laurencin. The chic, imaginative flacons were made and/or designed by companies in France like Baccarat, Lalique, A. Jollivet, C. K. Benda, Lucien Gaillard, J. Viard (or J. Villard), Sue et Mare, LM & AL, Sabino, Verreries Brosse, Boutet de Monvel, Pochet et du Courval, Daum Nancy, and Cristallerie d'Art de Choisy le Roi. Beautiful commercial perfume flacons were also made by glass houses in Austria, Germany, Murano, England, and Czechoslovakia. In the United States the glass companies of Wheaton and Carr-Lowry produced high quality bottles for the perfume trade. The final cost of the bottle may have been many times the cost of the perfume it held. The best made French perfume bottles usually had matching numbers of marks on both the bottle and stopper. They were placed there by workmen in the glass houses and indicate that the bottle and stopper were hand ground to fit each other.

The years following World War II were to experience a decline in the quality and packaging of bottles used to house perfume. There were a few exceptions like Dior, but most perfume firms would not pay the ever-increasing cost of first-rate flacons with hand ground stoppers. Gone also were the opulent, luxurious, dramatic colors, designs, and hand finishes that had reached their heyday in the 1920's and had made these superb flacons genuine works of art. By the 1960's, interchangeable, machine ground glass to glass stoppers had become the norm and plastic screw tops became common to see on even the better scents.

7 Special limited edition Christmas flacon called "Edition 1946" by Lancôme came cradled in a lavish package decorated with scenes of the Nativity. Numbered stopper. (4-1/8").

Opposite page:
9 Francois Coty commissioned Rene Lalique in 1907 to design this beautiful, slender flacon, intaglio moulded with four classically dressed women and quatrefoil stopper for the perfume "Ambre Antique". The perfume was introduced in the U.S. in 1913. Bottle marked—R. Lalique. (6").

8 Crystal pillow-shaped bottle with a bull-dog stopper held the scent "Toujours Fidele" by D'Orsay, introduced in Europe in 1912. The flacon can be found marked either Baccarat or Duam Nancy. (3-1/2").

The Bottle Designers and Makers

LALIQUE

To a collector of fine glass the name Lalique invokes an almost instant vision of lyrical, artistic, well-designed glass of the highest quality. Collectors of perfume bottles are familiar with finding the Lalique signature on exceptional flacons that once seen they instantly covet for their personal collections. The fame and prestige that Lalique glass enjoys was firmly grounded on Rene Lalique's mastery of techniques he refined as a jeweler and later converted to the production of glass.

Rene Lalique was born in the French village of Ay on June 4, 1860. His artistic gifts became apparent at an early age. By twelve he had won an important design award at the Lycee Turgot in Paris where he studied drawing for four years. In 1876 his father died, necessitating his learning a trade. Lalique apprenticed himself to a Paris silversmith, Louis Aucoc, and enrolled as a student at the Ecole des Arts Decoratifs.

In 1878, Lalique left Paris and went to England to study at the London Art College at Sydeham for two years. It was in London that Lalique began to develop the unique, naturalistic style that was to become his signature as a jeweler. Art students of the time were being influenced by William Morris and the Pre-Raphaelites, and the emerging Art Nouveau style.

In 1880 Lalique returned to Paris in order to freelance as a jewelry designer for several world-famous firms. By 1885 he was able to open his first atelier in the Place Gaillon. He continued working for other houses for a time, but felt the creative urge to manufacture his own designs. It was during this time period that Lalique earnestly explored the potential of inexpensive materials outside those traditionally used by jewellers. In studying enameling, he invented superior ways of working with this material. Enamel being related to glass heightened his interest in the medium. Lalique set up his first small furnace to experiment with glass in the early 1890's in the Rue Therese, his new and larger quarters.

During the nineties, Lalique exhibited his jewelry all over Europe, winning personal success with his designs. The triumph of his pieces led to so many orders he was overwhelmed. During this period his illustrious clientele included Samuel Bing, an art dealer; the Armenian oil magnate, Calouste Gulbenkian; and the famous actress Sarah Bernhardt. Lalique was awarded the Croix de Chevalier de la Legion d'Honneur in 1897 and at the Paris Exposition of 1900 his exhibition of jewelry, ivory, and bronze work won him international acclaim.

In 1902 Lalique went looking for new fields to explore and conquer. Renting a small workshop at Clairfontaine, he equipped it and hired four glass workers. One of a kind perfume bottles encased in silver were some of Lalique's earliest attempts.

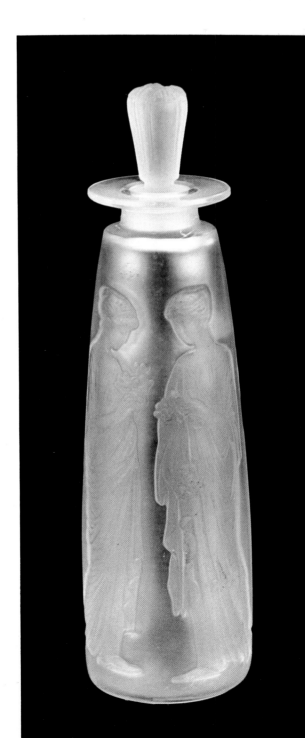

13. One of the earliest perfumes marketed by Roger & Gallet in America was "Fleurs d'Amour" created in France in 1902. The square crystal bottle with cut glass stopper had a lovely gold embossed label showing cupid holding a bouquet in one hand and throwing flowers with the other. Polished bottom. (4-1/2", 3-1/2").

10 Fancy pressed glass bottles with original Lundborg labels and fancy cardboard box. The Lundborg perfumery was located in London, England. Circa 1900. (4-1/2").

11 Figural cologne bottles were made in hundreds of patterns, in America and Europe during the Victorian period. The boy playing a drum bottle held "Ylang-Ylang" extract. Bottle marked C & T. (6").

12 Victorian high button shoe bottle held cologne by an unknown maker. (3-1/4").

14. Art Nouveau style, gold embossed label with a lady holding a flower to her nose ornamented the simple, clear flask that held the perfume "Ideal" by Houbigant which debuted in France in 1900. No marks. (6-1/4").

15 Metal and glass lantern bottle was patented on April 25, 1882. It was used to hold "Fire Fly Bouquet" by Jesse Oakley & Co. New York. (3-1/4").

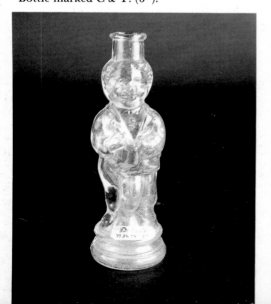

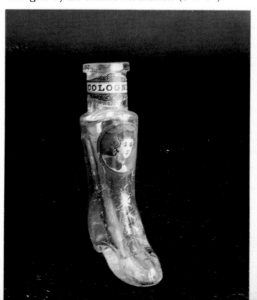

16 Colgate & Co., widely known for its soaps and toothpaste, marketed perfumes for many decades. The perfume "Monad Violet" in a plain cylindrical bottle was first introduced in 1901. (3").

17 Cork and metal crown-stoppered clear glass bottle held the Colgate perfume "Caprice", first marketed in the United States in 1883. (5-1/4").

18. Trade card for "Florida Water" by Murray & Lanman copyrighted in 1881.

19 Sprinkler top bottles for colognes and toilet waters were used frequently during the first quarter of this century. Many of them can be found with the original labels on them.

20 A rare and beautiful three bottle set with brass closures, enamelled with Egyptian characters, held rose and sandelwood scents by Ahmed Soliman of Cairo. Leather and satin case. (7-1/2").

21 Clear glass bottle with moulded bottom and soft kid leather at the neck held the perfume "The English Violet" by the Frederick Stearn Co. of Detroit, Michigan. The paper used to cover the coffret looked like green marble. Circa first quarter 20th century. (5-3/4"). Photo by Elizabeth A. McCarron.

23 Late 19th century Statue-of-Liberty bottle was used by the Wenck Perfumes Manufacturing Co. of New York. Marked Pat. App. For. (6-1/8"). Photo by Elizabeth A. McCarron.

22 Street lamp perfume bottle of metal and glass held "Beacon" by Tappan. The label said "The quality of this perfume is excellent." Herman Tappan of New York received a patent design on this bottle in 1892. (6-1/8"). Photo by Elizabeth A. McCarron.

Fate took a hand in 1907 when Francois Coty commissioned Lalique to design the labels for his perfume bottles. Lalique went one step further; he also designed the bottles! This relationship went on to become one of the most enduringly successful of all his commercial ventures. The glassworks of Legras and Cie executed the first bottles, but by 1909 he was manufacturing them himself at his glassworks in Combs, forty miles from Paris. Before this, perfume had been available in hand-made bottles that were sometimes more expensive to manufacture than their contents. Lalique found a way of mass-producing such bottles so that they appeared luxurious while being affordable to both the rich socialite and poor shopgirl alike. Involved in this process was what Lalique called "demi-crystal", more malleable and responsive than lead crystal and semi-automatic machinery. Demi-crystal had a lead content of around 12 percent, about one-half the lead content required under French law before glass can be labeled crystal.

The first flacon design Lalique made for Coty was known as "Libellule". This extremely rare bottle displayed an embossed dragonfly across the entire front of the bottle. A bottle for the scent "Amber Antique" which came in frosted glass ornamented with figures of Grecian women was also among the earliest. Lalique designed a fabulous bottle in 1909 for the Coty's perfume "L'Effleurt de Coty". The rectangular flacon is moulded on one side with a female nude rising from the center of a flower blossom; the stopper is of Egyptian revival design.

Between 1910 and 1940 Lalique manufactured millions of bottles for French and American perfumers including: Jay-Thorpe, Lournay, D'Orsay, Arys, Lentheric, Corday, Delettrez, Fioret, Gabilla, Lengyel, Molinard, D'Heraud, Coty, Guerlain, Isabey, Lalo, Forvil, Roger et Gallet, Rigaud, Vigny, Worth, Houbigant, Lucien Lelong, Rosine, and Volnay.

His son, Marc Lalique, made bottles for Rochas, Nina Ricci, Raphael, and Lancome, starting in the forties after World War II. This is not to say that the Laliques designed and made all the bottles for the above companies, but they produced at least one for each of the companies listed.

Lalique used all colors of glass but the largest portion of his perfume bottles are of clear or frosted crystal. The hardest to find colors are red, blue, green, amber and black. Enameling, hand staining, and sandblasting contributed also to their beauty. Art Nouveau influenced much of his work which can be seen in the graceful nudes, insects, fish, flowers, birds, and animals on his flacons. The 1920's saw Lalique designs becoming more geometric and streamlined. He was an early leader of the Art Deco movement.

The mass produced flacons for perfumers were so successful that Lalique made them a part of his own personal line. Garnitures de toilette, sets of co-ordinated containers designed for the dressing table for powder, cream, etc. were also included. Since the mid-nineteenth century, dressing table sets of silver, cut crystal, and other expensive materials had been sold. The relatively inexpensive sets mass-produced in glass by Lalique were a wholesale success. There are at least six different patterns in the garniture sets. They include "Myosotis", a forget-me-not pattern; "Perles" with ropes of pearls; "Epines", a relief design of thorny branches; "Fleurettes", another flower design; "Duncan", with nude figures; and "Dahlia". The "Dahlia" pattern is still in production today after being revived by Marc Lalique after World War II.

In his lifetime, Rene Lalique was crowned by the world as the most important designer of the 20th Century. He died at the age of eighty-five on May 5th, 1945. Marc Lalique, who since the 20's had been in charge of production and the business end, took over the firm and assumed all design and production responsibilities. With the death of Marc in 1977, his daughter Marie-Claude became the President of Cristal Lalique.

24 Mould blown, milk glass perfume bottle with clear cut glass stopper was made in the midwestern U.S. about 1870. "Lightner's White Rose Perfume" is lettered on the underside of the glass label which is set into a reserve space in the body of the bottle. (19 cm.) Photo courtesy Huntington Galleries; gift of Mr. R E. Wells.

25 Green velvet, plum-shaped, turn-of-the-century presentation box held "Wild Plum Blossom" by B. D. Baldwin Co. of Chicago. (3").

26 Crystal flacon with a snail motif was designed by Raymond Guerlain for the perfume "Mouchoir de Monsieur" by Guerlain, presented in 1904. Bottle made in France. (4-1/2").

27 Named after a famous French general, "La Rose Jacqueminot", marketed in France in 1905 was the first commercial success for the Coty perfume house. Numbered stopper. (6").

28 Guerlain of Paris launched the perfume "Champs Elysèes" in 1904. The turtle-shaped faceted crystal bottle by Baccarat was presented around 1914. (4-1/2").

29 Paul Poiret, the foremost fashion designer of the Art Deco period, was the first couturier to bring together the art of fragrance and fashion. Poiret named his perfume house "Rosine" after his daughter. The perfume "Nuit de Chine" came in an oriental-inspired bottle. Numbered stopper. Bottle made in Murano. U.S. Introduction 1923. (3-1/2").

30 Long green pressed glass bottle with a cork and metal stopper held "Eau de Cologne" by John Taylor & Co. of Toronto, Canada. A 1918 tax stamp is attached to the bottle. (9").

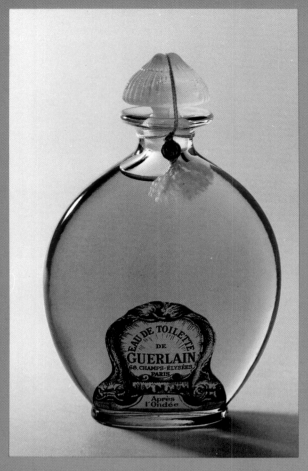

31 Clear flacon with a frosted glass stopper held "Apres L'Ondee" eau de toilette by Guerlain. (6-1/2'').

32 J. Grossmith & Son of London started using the perfume name "Shem-El'Nessim" in 1907. (4-1/2'').

33 Oriza L. Legrand introduced the perfume "Deja Le Printemps" in the U.S. in 1922. The deluxe crystal flacon marked Baccarat had a metal stopper cover shaped like a butterfly resting on a flower. (4-5/8'').

34 The Andrew Jergens Co. of Cincinnati, Ohio first started making "Ben Hur" perfume in 1904. This frosted glass bottle for "Ben Hur" was used in the late teens or early 20's. The perfume was named after the popular novel "Ben Hur", written by Louis Wallace in 1880. Moulded bottom. (3-7/8''). Photo by Elizabeth A. McCarron.

35 A fancy red and gold embossed label enhances the frosted glass bottle for "Rose" perfume by the J.M. Pitkin Co. of Newark and New York. Circa first quarter 20th century. (3-1/4").

BACCARAT

Incomparable crystal perfume bottles made for the luxury perfume industry, signed Baccarat, are among the most avidly sought by discriminating collectors today. The Cristalleries de Baccarat was founded in 1822 in France and from the beginning produced beautiful, hand-made perfume flacons. Three of Baccarat's earliest clients for crystal commercial flacons were the famous Parisian perfume houses of Houbigant, Violet, and Pinaud. The first commercial flacons were rather plain cylindrical, square or rectangular shapes to provide room for prominent display of the perfumer's label. Usually only the cut glass stopper provided any recognizable difference.

Baccarat followed the trend set by Coty and Lalique in the years just preceding the first World War. Baccarat began to make bottles in the late Art Nouveau style with fanciful moulded stoppers for clients like D'Orsay, Roger & Gallet, and Lenthéric. Before long the bottles also took on more imaginative shapes.

During the twenties, Baccarat began producing flacons in the Art Deco style under the influence of George Chevalier, a sculptor. Hired by Baccarat after World War I, Chevalier was to exert a powerful design influence on Baccarat until 1970.

During the golden age of the perfume bottle, that occurred just before World War I to around 1945, Baccarat made flacons for such companies as Elizabeth Arden, Arys, Atkinson, Boujois, Bichara, Corday, Coty, Delettrez, D'Orsay, Caron, Fontanis, Gabilla, Grenoville, Guerlain, Richard, Jaeckel, T. Jones, Lenthéric, Molinard, Myon, Oriza, L. Legrand, Jean Patou Ramses, Roger and Gallet, Rimmel, Silka, Schiaparelli, Violet, Volnay, Ybry, Yardley and Houbigant.

VERRERIES BROSSE

Founded in 1854, the French company of Verreries Brosse et Cie originally built its excellent reputation on quality handcrafted bottles, glass, and crystal. In 1919, Emile Barre bought out the remaining partners and became sole owner of Verreries Brosse. Barre, recognizing the importance of the revolution taking place in perfume packaging in hte 1920's, converted his entire factory to the manufacture of customized, luxury perfume bottles. Brosse was soon supplying high-quality semi-automatic bottles to such noted perfumers as Coty, Guerlain, Patou, Lanvin, Chanel, Bourjois, Ciro, Vigny, Bienaime, Oriza L. Legrand, Baruch, Mury, Grenoville, Forvil, Lubin, Roger & Gallet, Lenthéric, Worth, Caron, Clark, Loiret and D'Orsay. In 1963 Brosse switched from hand grinding stoppers to precision machine grinding. In 1976 Verreries Brosse patented two new stopper innovations. The first is a ring made of polypropylene with horizontal joints placed on the stopper dowel. The second is a polypropylene coating of the stopper dowel designed with internal friction teeth. Today Brosse makes the highest quality, stoppered, semi-automatic bottles for such firms as Giorgio of Beverly Hills, Hermes, Desprez, Carven, Chanel, Guy Laroche, Warner, Yves St. Laurent, Nina Ricci, Ungaro, Gres, and Guerlain. The Brosse trademark on a bottle is a VB or VB or BR.

36 Presented in France in 1906, the perfume "Apres L'Ondee" by Guerlain came in a crystal Louis XVI flacon. (3-1/2").

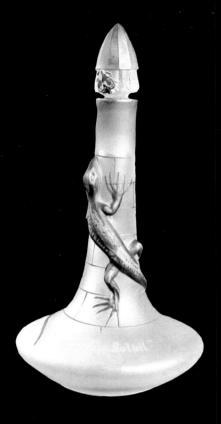

37 Rare flacon with a lifelike lizard stalking a fly perched on the stopper held the Lubin perfume "Au Soléil". Lubin claimed the use of the name "Au Soléil" since 1912. Bottle marked—Lubin Paris. Numbered stopper. (6").

38 Octagonal crystal flacon, hand-painted with 18k gold, was used for both the Guerlain perfumes "Sillage", introduced in 1907, and "Apres L'Ondee", introduced in 1906. (3-1/8").

39 The scent "Eau de Coty" was first created by Francois Coty in 1909. The oval bottle with frosted stopper received U.S. patent 63,351 on November 27, 1923. (7-1/4").

40 Clear glass bottle with frosted stopper held "Bouquet" by Melba. Acid mark—Bottle made in Bohemia. Circa 1900-1917. (3-1/2").

41 Rectangular flacon moulded on one side with a female nude rising from the center of a flower was created by Rene Lalique for Coty's perfume "L'Effleurt de Coty". It was put into commercial production in 1910. Marked—Lalique. Numbered stopper. (4-1/2").

42 Crystal bottle similar to a bottle used by Guerlain has blue enamelled decoration. Bottle marked—Crystal Nancy. Numbered stopper. (4-1/2'').

43 Another flacon used for the perfume "Nuit de Chine" by Rosine. Bottle marked—R. Lalique. Numbered stopper. Photo by Elizabeth A. McCarron. (3-1/4'').

44 Three moulded, brown stained, reclining nude women embellish the bottle and stopper of "Buda" by Tokalon of Paris and New York. The perfume "Buda" was sold in the U.S. in the early 1920's. Polished bottom. (3-5/8''). Photo by Elizabeth A. McCarron.

SAINT GOBAIN DESJONQUERES

The firm of Saint Gobain was founded in 1665 under the patronage of the French King Louis XIV. This glasshouse has been making flacons for perfumers for centuries. In the 1950's Saint Gobain acquired the Desjonquères glass company. The Desjonquères factory was completely destroyed by bombs during World War II. After the war, under the Marshall Plan, the factory was rebuilt and equipped with modern fully-automatic machinery with the help of the Wheaton Glassworks of New Jersey. In 1979 Saint Gobain Desjonquères introduced a plastic covered dowel stopper. An exciting innovation developed by Saint Gobain Desjonquères was fully automatic lead crystal introduced in 1984 with the "Diamella" by Yves Rocher bottle. Saint Gobain Desjonquères is now the largest producer of perfume bottles in the world. They can number among their clients Halston, Guy Laroche, Cardin, Gucci, Dior, Avon, Yardley, Estee Lauder, Warner, Kenzo, Elizabeth Arden, Givenchy, Yves Saint Laurent, Chanel, Niki de Saint-Phalle, Ted Lapidus, and Rochas. Occasionally you can find the Saint Gobain Desjonquères trademark S or SGD on the bottom of bottles made by this firm.

POCHET ET DU COURVAL

The French glassworks of Pochet et du Courval, located in upper Normandy about 84 miles northwest of Paris, has a long history of making quality perfume bottles. The company was founded in 1623 by letters patent from the Comtesse d'Eu. In 1930 Pochet built its first semi-automatic factory and the demanding perfume industry became their exclusive clientele. In 1971 Pochet built a modern fully automatic facility, the Verrerie de Guimerville. Today Pochet provides both traditional semi-automatic and high-quality fully-automatic flacons for the commercial perfume market. Pochet et du Courval's trademark on bottles is a H P or HP. Pochet makes flacons for such prestigious firms as Cardin, Coty, Jean Desprez, Lagerfeld, Christian Dior, Jean Patou, Carven, Leonard, Balmain, Louis Feraud, Oscar de la Renta, Cartier, and Molinard.

LUCIEN GAILLARD & J. VIARD

Lucien Gaillard, a contemporary of Rene Lalique, was a superb designer of Art Nouveau style objects, including perfume flacons. Gaillard, a Frenchman, worked in his family's business and was primarily interested in metalwork until around 1900. It was then that the famous designer Rene Lalique encouraged Gaillard to try his hand at jewelry design. Gaillard was very successful in the attempt and won first prize at the Société Des Artistes Francais in 1904 for his Lalique-influenced Art Nouveau jewelry.

Lucien Gaillard expanded his design sphere to include a variety of everyday articles, such as parasol handles, hairpins, and flacons, made from precious and non-precious materials. Fine and unusual craftsmanship, combined with a strong sense of design, were hallmarks of his work. Gaillard designed flacons used by such notable French perfume houses as Clamy and Violet.

Another imaginative French glass designer of the 1920's was a sculptor named J. Viard. He was part owner and chief designer for an art glass company called C. & J. Viard and Viollet le Duc, located at 25 Rue Chevalier Desire in Montreuil Ceine. The firm made both Art Deco and Art Nouveau style bottles, some with stained or enamelled decoration, for such companies as Richard Hudnut, Isabey, Favolys, and Langlois. Some of the bottles were simply marked with an acid stamp—made in France; others were signed J. Viard or J. Villard.

45 Metal and glass telephone bottle held the perfume "Number Please". The bottle received a patent on April 30, 1907. (4-3/8").

46 Classic Baccarat clear crystal flacon held "Rue De La Paix" by Guerlain, launched in 1908. The flacon was also used for other Guerlain scents. (3-3/4").

47 Paul Rieger of California first marketed his "Flower Drops" perfume in a choice of odors around 1910. Ads of the time claimed his special perfume lasted 50 times longer than ordinary perfume. The petite glass bottle of perfume came in a wooden screw top case which could later be used as a needle holder. (case 3").

50 Flower shaped frosted glass and cork stoppered bottle held a Narcisse perfume. (1-1/2").

51 Black glass flacon with the four side moulded with a caryatid at each corner and the stopper moulded with stylized flowers wa for Ambre" by D'Orsay. The bottle wa illustrated in a 1920 French fashion magazin called "L'Illustration des Modes". Bottl marked—R. Lalique. Numbered stopper (5-1/4").

48 Clear glass bottle with an elaborate gold stopper in the Art Nouveau style held the perfume "Jasmin Revant" by Bourday. Cork stopper. (3").

49 Brilliant cut crystal flacon by Baccarat used for the perfume "L'Or" by Coty. Numbered stopper. Circa 1912. (8-1/2").

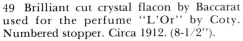

54 Colgate & Co. introduced an oriental perfume called "Florient" in 1912. The clear glass bottle had a frosted stopper. (2-3/4").

52 The perfume "Bouquet Antique" by Ciro came in a bottle decorated with black enamelling, with a flower stopper. European introduction 1923, American introduction 1925. (3-1/4").

53 Raymond Guerlain designed the crystal flacon with the heart-shaped stopper for the Guerlain perfume "L'Heure Bleue" first launched in France in 1912. Bottle marked—Baccarat. (3-1/4").

55 When Coty trademarked the perfume name "Styx" in the U.S., he claimed use of it from 1912. This flacon, moulded with vertical ribs, had a circular stopper created by four bees, their wings spread and touching. Bottle marked—Lalique. (4-1/2").

56 Clear and frosted crystal flacon by Baccarat held the Grenoville perfume "Bluet". Grenoville claimed use of the name "Bluet" for perfume since 1910. (3-7/8").

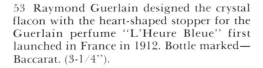

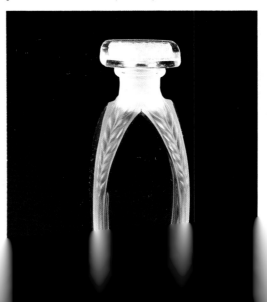

57 Richard Hudnut, sometimes called the father of the American cosmetics industry, introduced the perfume "Three Flowers" in 1915. (6-3/4").

59 The Imperial Crown Perfumery Co. was started in the 1850's in St. Louis, Missouri. The company won the grand prize for perfumes in 1904 at the Louisiana Purchase Centennial Exposition. The pressed glass, six-sided bottle with a crown-shaped stopper has a 1914 tax stamp attached to it. (8-1/4").

61 Solon Palmer, an American perfume house started in 1847, marketed the perfume "Gardenglo" in 1913. The American-made bottle had a cut glass top. (3").

58 Eagle decorated helmet-shaped perfume bottle has a metal screw top. Circa 1910's. (3-1/2").

60 The popular Houbigant perfume "Quelques Fleurs" was launched in Europe in 1913. Bottle marked—Houbigant. (5-1/4").

62 Crystal bottle with gold enamelling shaped like a French water pump has beautiful detailing. Maker and perfume unknown. Circa 1910's. (4-1/4").

WHEATON GLASS CO.

Theodore Corson Wheaton, an energetic and far-sighted man, was the original founder of the Wheaton Glass Co. Born in Tuckahoe, New Jersey, in 1852, Theodore became an apprentice to a pharmacist and physician named Dr. Way in South Seaville, New Jersey. Having found his calling in life, he enrolled in the Philadelphia College of Pharmacy and Science at the age of 21. After graduation in 1876, Theodore promptly enrolled in the Medical College of Pennsylvania. He was awarded his M.D. degree in 1879.

Dr. Wheaton returned to South Seaville after graduation and established his first practice as a country doctor. Restless, he moved his family in 1882 to a growing industrial city, Millville, New Jersey. Between 1883 and 1892, along with a busy medical practice, Dr. Wheaton opened and operated three drugstores and a general store.

In 1888 Dr. Wheaton became interested in and helped finance a glass factory in Millville that specialized in pharmacists' and physicians' glassware. By 1890 he was the sole owner and the company was named the T. C. Wheaton Company after him. The factory, under his supervision, grew steadily and by 1898 was operating three twelve-pot furnaces. In 1899 the son of Dr. Wheaton, Frank Hayes Wheaton (who was to become a legend in the glass industry) joined the firm.

The company continued to grow and prosper. In 1914 the grinding room was expanded and presses were installed to make ointment jars and stoppers. By 1915 the plant occupied twenty acres. When World War I cut off the supply of glassware from Europe, business boomed. By 1918 the T. C. Wheaton Co. employed over 450 people.

After the death of Dr. Wheaton in 1931, Frank H. Wheaton was elected president and chairman of the board. In 1935 he began expanding and modernizing the plant. New offices and a larger grinding room were added. The first automatic equipment was installed between 1937 and 1938 which required additional mould and batch making facilities. Frank H. Wheaton worked at the company until 1983, when he died at the age of 102.

By the 1930's the T. C. Wheaton Company was making cosmetic and perfume containers for Elizabeth Arden and Shulton. Some other companies Wheaton made perfume bottles for are Coty, John Fredericks, Adrian, Marie Earle, Lucien Lelong, Hattie Carnegie, Veolay, De Raymond, Raquel, Prince Matchabelli, Mary Chess, Guerlain, and Bourjois. The grinding department for decorative stoppers had become the largest in the country. Many of these containers were sprayed with color in the decorating department. Some of the bottles were signed with the Wheaton trademark of a W inside a circle.

A new enterprise called the Wheaton Glas Co. was formed after World War II by the third generation of Wheatons, led by Frank H. Wheaton, Jr. This new company specialized in perfume bottles, cosmetics containers, glass-tubing, and ampules. The two companies operated side by side for years, often sharing the same customers. In 1966 the two companies merged and became the Wheaton Glass Co. Today the company, still family-owned and controlled, produces bottles for such leading firms as Avon, Estee Lauder, Warner, Lancome, Coty, Dana, Max Factor, Elizabeth Arden, Revlon, Jovan, and Houbigant. Wheaton now operates over 40 divisions around the globe.

63 Kerkoff of Paris started using the name "DJer-Kiss" for perfumes and toiletries around 1908. The perfume was very popular in the U.S. in the teens and 20's. The pressed glass sachet bottle marked ED—736. (3-1/2").

64 Moulded leaf pattern frosted glass flacon has a flower-shaped stopper with tiny lady-bugs crawling across it. Grey staining heightens the details. Acid mark—France. (4-3/4").

66 Controlled bubble bottle shaped like an apple, with a metal stopper cover, held the scent "Le Fruit Défendu" by Rosine, introduced to the U.S. in the early 1920's and in Europe in 1918. This white and gold quilted Deco box replaced the original silver box with an embossed leaf pattern. Paper label—made in France. (2-1/2").

65 F. Salathé and Company of New York started importing Fioret of Paris perfumes into the United States in 1921. The package for "Sweet Pea" by Fioret had a glass pendent signed R. Lalique hanging from it. The square crystal bottle with an engine-turned, gilt metal, hinged top is acid marked 'Cristal Nancy'. (6-1/8").

68 The perfume "Un Air Embaume" by Rigaud, popular for over forty years, was introduced in the U.S. in 1915. The clear and frosted glass bottle, which can also be found in pink, was decorated with moulded nudes on the sides. A December 1913 "Harper's Bazaar" magazine also showed the bottle was used for a perfume called "Dolcemia" and claimed the 'odd-shaped bottle decorated by Lalique'. Ground bottom. (4-3/4").

67 Crystal flacon with a frosted glass sphinx head stopper by Baccarat held the perfume "Nirvana" by Bichara of Paris. Numbered stopper. (6").

69 Rare, art glass, amphora-shaped bottle, with scarab stopper was made for Caron. (5-1/2").

CARR-LOWRY

The Carr-Lowry Glass Co. of Baltimore, Maryland was founded in April 1889 by two enterprising men, Samuel J. Carr and William W. Lowry. Both men had gained experience in the field as salesmen for other glass manufacturers. From its inception until 1958, a special division of the glassworks made excellent quality, attractive hand-ground, stoppered commercial bottles for the perfume trade. In the beginning all the bottles were made by hand, often by expert craftsmen trained in New Jersey glasshouses. In 1933 the firm installed its first semi-automatic machinery, and in 1944 became a subsidiary of the Anchor Hocking Glass Corporation. To stay competitive, in 1958 Carr-Lowry switched to fully automatic bottle manufacturing and closed its hand-grinding department.

One of Carr-Lowry's oldest clients, going back to the year 1893 when it was the California Perfume Co., is Avon. The glass company was a pioneer in producing sculptured bottles with difficult shapes and designs. Today, the company enjoys a worldwide reputation as a leader in the field of perfume and cosmetic containers in both flint and opal glass. Among the many companies Carr-Lowry manufactures fully-automatic bottles for are Lagerfeld, Avon, Chanel, Geoffrey Beane, Guerlain, Elizabeth Arden, Estee Lauder, and Warner.

70   Bryenne of Paris created the perfume "Chu-Chin-Chow" in 1918 and marketed it in the United States in 1923. The enamelled, cobalt and milkglass Mandarin bottle came in a green and gold pagoda-shaped box. Bottle signed C K Benda. (2-1/2").

71   A Baccarat crystal Buddha holding "Subtitlité" perfume by Houbigant is enshrined in a black moire box lined in red silk. The perfume, introduced in Europe about 1919, was launched in the U.S. in 1923. (1-1/2 oz.).

The Perfume Manufacturers

ADRIAN

Gilbert Adrian was born Adrian Adolph Greenburg in Connecticut in 1903. His schooling included the *School of Fine and Applied Arts* in New York and in 1922 study in Paris. While in Paris he met Irving Berlin. When he returned to the United States he designed costumes for George White's "Scandals", Greenwich Village "Follies", and "Music Box Revues". Adrian went to Hollywood in 1923 to design costumes for Rudolph Valentino. In 1925 he began to design costumes for Metro-Goldwyn-Mayer. Adrian soon became the top Hollywood designer. He created costumes for such stars as Rosalind Russell, Greta Garbo, Katherine Hepburn, and Joan Crawford. His creations had an enormous influence on style conscious women of the era. An example is a gown designed for Joan Crawford which was copied by dress manufacturers. Macy's department store alone sold more than half a million copies.

In 1941 Adrian opened his own chic fashion salon for custom-made and ready-to-wear clothing in Beverly Hills. In 1944 Adrian launched two perfumes and colognes, "Saint" and "Sinner". The design of the bottles followed the column design prominently featured in the Adrian salon and in Adrian advertising. The bottles for "Saint" and "'Sinner" were made by Wheaton.

ANGELIQUE

Charles N. Granville and N. Lee Swartout started Angelique in 1946 in Wilton, Connecticut. The name Angelique was the name of a friend of Mrs. Granville. One of the company's all-time best sellers was a floral perfume called "Black Satin" introduced in 1946. The name "Black Satin" was suggested by Sylvan Rich, president of Martini Frocks. The fashion tie-in with its connotation of sophistication and richness was obvious. The clear tower shaped bottle was topped with a block of clear plastic and set upon a dais of black and gold. It was covered with a cylinder topped with black satin and encased in a package of black and gold. Angelique later introduced three related perfumes: White, Gold, and Red Satin.

The company gained a reputation in the perfume trade for its exciting promotional stunts such as releasing scented "snow" from an airplane and dropping perfumed bubbles pumped by machines from a fleet of twelve airplanes over the city of Los Angeles. Angelique perfumes were sold in the United States and Canada.

ANJOU

The Campana Co. of Batavia, Illinois started Parfums Anjou in 1944. The ancient, history shrouded province of Anjou in France was the inspiration for the company name. The first perfume introduced was "Devastating", a spicy floral scent, in 1944. The packaging was in green satin, called devastating green, and the prism bottle had a polished crystal stopper. "Apropos", a fresh, green, woodsy scent was introduced in 1948 in four sizes in a box embossed with a reproduction of a French brocade. Both "Apropos" and "Devastating" were also marketed in faceted bottles with lucite caps. "Side Glance" introduced in 1952 came in a clear multi-faceted bottle, packaged in checked grey and black.

ELIZABETH ARDEN

Florence Nightingale Graham who became Elizabeth Arden was born on a farm in Woodbridge, Canada, the youngest of five children. Florence left school before the age of eighteen to become an apprentice nurse. Dissatisfied with nursing, she then held a succession of minor, dead-end jobs.

The turning point in her life came when she left Canada about 1909 for New York to join her brother William. Florence took a job as secretary with the New York office of a London cosmetic firm, Eleanor Adair. At the Adair's shop she learned basic formulas for making cosmetics and facial massage.

In 1910 Florence Graham decided to open her own beauty salon. She created for herself a new name, Elizabeth Arden (inspired by "Elizabeth and Her German Garden" and Tennyson's "Enoch Arden") for her new firm. She borrowed $6,000 dollars from a relative, which was repaid within a few months, for excellent interior decorators. The salon approached skin and hair care scientifically and emphasized massage treatments to tone up flabby skin.

Arden's first treatment product was a light and fluffy cleansing cream which she called "Amoretta". A young chemist, A. F. Swanson created it for her around 1914. "Ardena" skin tonic was the second product put on the market. Soon the Arden line included rouges and eyeshadow. In the beginning Arden salons sold fragrances by other perfumers such as Babani of Paris, but soon Elizabeth Arden was having perfumes blended in France especially for her company.

The business grew very quickly and her first branch salon opened in Washington, D.C. in 1914. Arden's New York salon moved to larger quarters on Fifth Avenue in 1915. By the early 1920's over 600 shops in the United States carried her products. Arden's first foreign salon opened in Paris in 1922. By 1929 Elizabeth Arden was internationally famous and wealthy.

Florence Graham was five feet four inches tall, with a petite figure, hyacinth eyes, and reddish brown hair. She married a silk manufacturer Thomas Jenkins Lewis in 1915 which gave her U. S. citizenship. Thomas Lewis became the manager of her wholesale business and was general manager of the firm from 1918 until their divorce in 1934. She married in 1942 Russian-born Prince Michael Evlanoff, a naturalized American citizen, whom she divorced in 1944. Her sister Gladys, who became through marriage Madame la Vicomtesse de Maublanc, was in charge of the Arden salon in Paris.

Elizabeth Arden's all-time best selling perfume is "Blue Grass" introduced in 1934. Arden's love of horses was surpassed only by her desire to produce beauty. Her stable of race horses, under the colors of Maine Chance Farm included winners in the Kentucky Derby and other top races. While visiting Grasse, France in 1934, Miss Arden discovered a floral perfume that reminded her of the rolling, blue grass, Kentucky countryside. So the delightful classic perfume was christened "Blue Grass".

Elizabeth Arden perfumes were packaged, for the most part, in bottles made in France by such companies as Baccarat and Verreries Brosse. Two

72 Smith & Scott of Bermuda marketed Lili brand perfumes in the U.S. from 1931. The bottles were redesigned in 1939. The bottle of Easter lily design was made by Wheaton. Photo courtesy of the Museum of American Glass at Wheaton Village.

73 Square glass flacon with brown staining, moulded with two draped figures, was used by D'Orsay for an unknown scent. Bottle marked—R. Lalique. Circa 1913. (3-1/2").

74 Beautiful Czechoslovakian bottle with rare nude figural dapper is similar to the bottle shown in a 1930 ad for "Ramsès" eau de toilette.

75 Stairstep black opaque glass bottle received a patent on November 25, 1919. It held a perfume called "Christmas Ever". Wood and cork stopper. (3-1/2").

76 Clear crystal flacon with a frosted glass stopper held "L'Origan" by Coty, created in 1905 and introduced in the U.S. in 1909. Bottle marked—R. Lalique. (4").

77 Caron of Paris created the perfume "Le Narcisse Noir" in 1912. The famous clear, squatty bottle with the black flower stopper was widely copied by other firms. (2-1/2", 3-1/2", 5-1/2").

80 Frosted and clear glass commercial perfume bottle made in Russia for an unknown perfumer. (4-1/2").

78 Simple clear bottle with gold stripes and a green glass with gold stopper held the perfume "Narcisse" by Richard Hudnut. Acid mark—Made in France. (2").

79 The stopper of this blue stained bottle is a graceful nude woman kneeling on a snake. It held the Lubin perfume "Eva". Numbered stopper. Circa 1920. (3-7/8").

81 Langlois of New York and Boston marketed the perfume "Cara Nome" in 1918. American made clear and frosted bottle. (6").

82 Guerlain marketed the perfume "Pois de Senteur" in 1917. The bottle has the Guerlain trademark embossed on the reverse side of the bottle. Bottle marked—France. (4-1/2").

very sought after bottles are the fan shaped flacon for "Cyclamen" introduced in 1938 and the hand holding a torch flacon for "It's You" introduced in 1939.

HARRIET HUBBARD AYER

Harriet Hubbard Ayer Inc. was founded in 1886 in the United States by America's first beauty columnist, Harriet Hubbard Ayer, who was famous for her beauty, charm, and culture. Harriet Hubbard was born in Chicago about 1849 into a well-to-do, socially prominent family. She received her formal education at Chicago's Convent of the Sacred Heart. At the tender age of sixteen she was married to Herbert Copeland Ayer, son of a rich Chicago iron dealer. As a wealthy society matron she traveled abroad, read widely, and pursued artistic interests. Because of a growing estrangement between her and her husband, Harriet and her two daughters moved to New York in 1882 and a divorce was granted in 1886.

In 1886 Harriet Hubbard Ayer started her business with the manufacture and sale of a facial cream she claimed to have uncovered in Paris. She advertised that the cream had been used by Madame Recamier, a famous beauty of Napoleon's day and used the Recamier name on the label with her own. Ayer creams and cosmetics were soon used by such professional beauties of the day as Adelina Patti, Lillian Russel, and Lilly Langtry.

In 1896, Arthur Brisbane, editor of the *New York World* persuaded Harriet to write a column of beauty advice for the Sunday's woman's page. The articles were a success and she became the country's highest paid, most popular newspaper woman.

Harriet Hubbard Ayer was also an early social activist. She taught emigrant mothers how to properly care for their babies in the New York slums. Harriet also joined the "Rainy Daisies", a women's group who campaigned against the unhygienic trailing skirts of the era.

Harriet Hubbard Ayer Inc. trademarked many perfume names starting in 1922. Among the company's most popular perfumes were "Yu", a spicy odor introduced in 1938 in a deco crystal bottle sumptuously packed in gold, rose lacquer, and black; "Golden Hour", introduced in 1945 in a gold plated ceramic candle shaped bottle in a box covered with blue suede paper; and "Golden Chance", introduced in 1948 in a bottle that was fashioned after an old fashioned inkwell finished with a gleaming cap. One of the prettiest Ayer bottles was for "Muguet" introduced in 1932. The bottle shaped like a fan of crystal had a carved stopper and base.

BABS CREATIONS

Babs Creations, Inc. was started in 1939 at 146 West Fifty-Second Street in New York. The company specialized in colognes and perfumes to sell for one dollar or less. Imitating the successful "Shocking" by Schiaparelli packaging, Babs also marketed its perfumes in unique bottles, showcased on pedestals and sometimes covered by glass domes.

Babs' first and longest selling perfume and cologne was called "Yesteryear" introduced in 1939. Designed by Walter Hershfield, the bottle was shaped like a lovely Victorian Lady holding an umbrella. She held in her hands a nosegay and around her waist she wore a velvet sash.

In 1940 Babs presented both "Gay Whirl" and "Forever Yours". "Gay Whirl" eau de toilette had a dainty, pink plastic ballerina stopper poised atop a carpeted glass staircase. "Forever Yours" perfume had two graceful painted metal hands tenderly holding a glass heart bottle with a small golden chain hanging from it. Tiny cuffs of pink velvet and lace accentuate the hands screwed to a wrought metal base.

In 1941 Babs marketed "Tic-Toc" perfume and "Hurdy Gurdy" cologne. The "Tic-Toc" bottle was shaped like an 18th century miniature clock decorated with metal filigree set on a pressed fiber base. "Hurdy Gurdy" was presented in the form of a miniature street organ with a monkey chained to the handle.

83 The Pari Ti Corporation of New York compounded and bottled the perfume "Tuya" from South America in three sizes. The name was trademarked in 1942. This bottle, made by Wheaton, was shown in 1946 ads. Photo courtesy of the Museum of American Glass at Wheaton Village.

HENRI BENDEL

The firm of Henri Bendel, an influential couture and retail store was founded in New York by Henri Bendel in 1897. The son of Austrian emigrants, he was born in Lafayette, Louisiana. Bendel learned French as his first language and English as his second. He received his formal schooling at St. Charles College in Grand Coteau. Bendel opened his first retail establishment in Morgan City, Louisiana. In 1896 he opened a wholesale millinery business in New York. Business was good so Bendel quickly expanded his business to include custom made gowns and furs. He relocated his retail establishment in 1912 to W. 57th Street where he added a ready-to-wear department. For many years Henri Bendel stocked the largest assortment of French couture fashions in the United States. The first perfume Henri Bendel marketed was "Un peu d'elle" introduced in 1915.

BLANCHARD

Howard Kestenbaum and his brother Eugene J. Kestenbaum started Parfums Blanchard in New York in 1930. "Rigoletto" was the first perfume marketed in 1930. Blanchard's best selling perfumes were "Gardenia" introduced in 1932, and "Jealousy", a sophisticated fragrance, introduced in 1943. All Blanchard perfumes were created and bottled in the United States except for "Climax" introduced in 1952. "Climax" was a French import, created in France although bottled in this country.

BOURJOIS

In 1863, while America was in the midst of a violent Civil War, in Paris Alexandre Napolean Bourjois was establishing his famous cosmetic and perfume house. M. Bourjois soon gained renown for his face powders and theatrical make-up. Among his distinguished clientele was the famous actress Sarah Bernhardt. In 1890 he invented the first dry rouge. Bourjois is also responsible for the first powder compact ever marketed. Among his earliest perfumes were "Manon Lescaut", "La Rose Pompon", "Etoile D'Amour" introduced in 1903 and "Ashes of Roses" introduced in 1909. In 1928 the famous perfume in the distinctive cobalt blue bottle called "Evening in Paris" was born. The name and color scheme were the inspiration of a young Parisian perfume artist named Jean Helleu. The idea of blue and silver for the package was inspired by the blue depth of the Parisian sky at dusk with the stars just appearing on the horizon.

One of the most sought-after Bourjois perfume bottles by collectors is "Kobako". The perfume "Kobako" introduced in 1936 was in a bottle of Oriental design, a replica of an ancient Chinese rock crystal snuff bottle, moulded into frosted glass and encased in an Oriental red embossed plastic box. The bottle made in France was by Verreries Brosse. The bottle and perfume originally came in four sizes.

HATTIE CARNEGIE

Hattie Carnegie, a world famous American designer, was born Henrietta Kanengeiser in 1889 in Vienna, the second of seven children. When their home was destroyed by fire her father, an artist and designer, moved his family to America. In the U.S. the family name was changed to Carnegie in emulation of Andrew Carnegie, the wealthiest man in the world at that time. Hattie was forced to leave school at the age of thirteen in order to take a job as a cash girl at Macy's when her father died. Her major interest was designing, however, and despite the fact that Hattie couldn't sew and was never to learn, she went to work for a milliner trimming hats.

Hattie started her first enterprise in 1909, shortly before she was twenty, with a friend Rose Roth. Hattie designed the hats while Rose designed the dresses. In 1913 the business had become so successful that the shop was moved near fashionable Riverside Drive. Around 1917 Hattie bought out her partner's share of the business.

84 This bottle by Wheaton was used by Para Ti for "Tuya" cologne. Circa 1946. Photo courtesy of the Museum of American Glass at Wheaton Village.

85 Clear bottle with a cobalt blue flower stopper probably held a Narcisse perfume. (2").

89 Madame Gabilla, the first successful woman perfumer, started blending her scents commercially in Paris in the 1890's. She created the perfume "Mon Cheri" in 1910. Everett-Gould Inc. of New York launched the perfume in the United States in 1920. Bottle made in France. Numbered stopper. (3-1/8").

88

86 Deco bottle with silver enamelling is marked Baccarat. The orange box is marked 'Madhva Paris'. Numbered stopper. Circa 1923. (4-3/8"). Photo by Elizabeth A. McCarron.

87 & 88 Four-sided, clear and frosted glass flacon, moulded at each corner with a cicada, with leaf-shaped stopper was used by Roger et Gallet for the perfume "Cigalia". The wooden box has matching cicadas on it. Two sizes were available. Bottle marked—R. Lalique. Circa 1920's. (5").

90 Amberina glass, heart-shaped flacon with a flame stopper has the name of the perfume "Coeur de Feu" written across it in gold. The bottle came on a gold painted wooden base. Circa 1920's. (4-1/4'').

91 Rare Guerlain set in an antique eighteenth century hand-made leather box, custom fitted by Louis Vuitton. The set included two lipsticks, powder and puff, and two perfumes "Sillage" and "Apres L'Ondée". Circa 1920. Photo by Elizabeth A. McCarron.

92-94 Wonderful flacon for the perfume "Gai Paris" by T. Jones is moulded with a picture of the Champs Elysee on front and the Moulin Rouge on back. The sides are moulded with trees and the stopper with a court jester's paraphernalia. Numbered stopper. Photos by Gunther Knop.

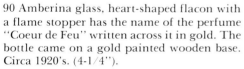

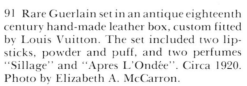

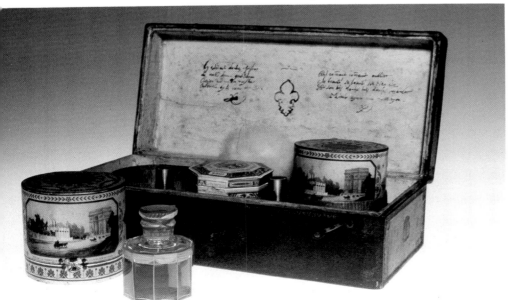

95 Illustration from a 1920 French fashion magazine, "L'Illustration des Modes", for "Grace" by D'Orsay.

The fashionable world patronized the shop making it a resounding success. In 1919 she made her first buying trip to Paris. Hattie was to travel to Europe several times a year from that time forward bringing back quantities of couture clothes. The majority of clothes sold by her were still of her own design however. Hattie, following the trend of fashionable New Yorkers, moved her business to a building she bought on East Forty-Ninth Street. In the early days of the Depression she added a ready-to-wear line to her shop and in 1934 she launched "Spectator Sports", a wholesale enterprise.

Hattie Carnegie was a small, slender, feminine lady with beautiful reddish-blond hair. She was married briefly in 1918 to an Englishman and again briefly married in 1922. In 1928 she married a childhood sweetheart, Major John Zanft, an agent for motion picture stars. This was a happy marriage that lasted until her death in 1956.

Following the trend set by European designers, Hattie Carnegie introduced her first perfume around 1928. Called simply "Hattie Carnegie" the black bottle made in France was shaped like an inkwell and decorated with small gold nosegays. The interesting portrait bottle used to hold different Carnegie scents was designed by Tommi Parzinger in 1937 and made by the Wheaton Glass Co. In 1944 her unique portrait bottle was washed in twenty-two karat gold to hold Perfume "49". In 1943 Carnegie put her perfumes on the wholesale market.

CARON

The well-known perfume house of Caron was started in 1903 by Ernest Daltroff. Daltroff was fascinated by scent, so he purchased a perfumery in Asnières not far from Paris. He also bought out the rights and shop of one Anna-Marie Caron and kept the name, thinking it would sound and look better on packaging. In 1904 Daltroff met Fèlicie Vanpouille, a young dressmaker. She designed the bottle for the Caron perfume "Chantecler" in 1906. Vanpouille gave up dressmaking and became Daltroff's lover and active business partner, taking charge of design and packaging. Many of the beautiful flacons used by Caron were designed by Ms. Vanpouille. In 1941 Fèlicie Vanpouille, after the death of Ernest Daltroff, became the sole owner of the firm they had built.

The Caron company, right from the start, exported their products abroad. Throughout its history the vast majority of its products went from France to foreign markets such as the U.S., England, and South America. In 1923 a branch company was opened in New York. It was not until the 1930's that Caron perfumes were easily attainable in France itself.

The first perfume to bring success and recognition to Caron was "Narcisse Noir" (Black Narcissus) introduced in 1912. The easiest to recognize of Caron's perfume bottles, the squatty clear bottle with an opaque black glass flower stopper was made and designed by Baccarat. The unpatented "Narcisse Noir" bottle was widely copied by other perfume firms. There would be differences in the stopper color or design but at first glance the copies would fool the eye. The copied bottles used by other companies almost always held a Narcissus perfume. Caron learned a valuable lesson and from then on usually patented their bottle designs.

Three of the most sought after Caron bottles by collectors are "Adastra", a handsome bronze bottle with a sunflower stopper; "Alpona", an opaline bottle decorated with a golden sun; and "Voeu de Noël" (Christmas Wish), a double flower bottle. All three perfumes were first premiered in America in the French pavilion at the New York World's Fair in 1939.

CARVEN

Following the end of the second World War in 1945, a trio of perfume-minded and experienced Frenchmen named Maurice Pinot, Georges Baud, and Jean Prodhon combined their talents together to start Carven Parfums in Paris. The strong friendship between the founders was forged during the war when they shared the trials of confinement in a prison camp in

Germany. The firm was named after the famous dressmaker Madame Carven, a good friend of the founders.

The trio unanimously decided that their first perfume should not only be luxurious but also be a symbol of youth to offset the real pain and suffering that had swept the globe during the war. Thus the perfume "Ma Griffe" (My Signature) was born and presented in 1946 in a clear, uncluttered bottle and packaged in a fresh green and white striped box. Warren Kane was appointed U.S. distributor of "Ma Griffe" and marketed it in America about 1950.

CASWELL-MASSEY

The oldest pharmacy and perfumery in the United States is Caswell-Massey which has operated under a succession of names and in several locations. The business was first established by Dr. William Hunter in 1752 in Newport, Rhode Island. Dr. Hunter, born in Scotland around 1729, studied medicine and pharmacy in Edinburgh in 1746. At the age of twenty-one he emigrated to Rhode Island where he set up a surgery and opened the first all drug shop in America. At the shop he concocted both perfumes and prescriptions. Dr. Hunter was a famous patron of the arts. He gave the portrait painter Gilbert Stuart his start and employed Charles Feke, youngest son of Robert Feke, the finest colonial painter before Copley. He was also the first doctor to lecture on human anatomy in the colonies. Dr. Hunter was an ardent Tory, so after his death in the Revolutionary War, his widow put the shop under the name of his clerk Charles Feke, to prevent confiscation. The firm continued to prosper, particularly among Newport society. With the death of Feke in 1822 the ownership passed to Rowland Hazard. In the 1850's Hazard took Phillip Caswell into partnership and the name became Hazard and Caswell. About one hundred years ago a Canadian named William Massey became a partner and the firm got its present name. A New York City shop was opened before the Civil War and the Newport shop was closed in 1906.

The firm is now in the hands of two brothers, Ralph and Milton S. Taylor, who purchased Caswell-Massey in 1936. They are both graduates of the Columbia School of Pharmacy and Ralph Taylor studied perfumery with the authority Edwin Sagarin. In 1916, a thirteen-year-old Ralph Taylor was employed by Caswell-Massey to sweep the shop and wash out bottles in the basement. Ralph Taylor has adapted many of the original antique fragrance formulas to modern tastes and has also created new scents including that for "Tricorn". Mr. Taylor also custom designs perfumes for people who demand a unique, personal scent.

Caswell-Massey has been in continuous operation for over two hundred years and a list of its clientele reads like a "Who's Who of American history". Some of the names included are George Washington, Dolly Madison, Sarah Bernhardt, the Marquis de Lafayette, Jenny Lind, Katharine Hepburn, Greta Garbo, John Kennedy and Paul McCartney.

CHANEL

Gabrielle "Coco" Chanel, one of the leading designers of haute couture in the twentieth century, was born in the early 1880's near Issoire in the French province of Auvergwe. Orphaned at an early age, Chanel was raised by her grandmother. At seventeen Chanel left her grandmother's home and went to Deauville along with her sister to work for a milliner. She and her sister moved to Paris in 1914 where Chanel opened a small hatshop. She often went horseback riding, a passion since childhood, in the Boise de Boulogne early in the morning. Since the cocks were crowing at that time of day, she earned the nickname "Miss Cocorico", later shortened to "Coco".

In 1916 Chanel designed and presented her first fashion collection. By the mid-1920's she had established her reputation internationally and was generally considered to be the most important figure in the world of haute couture. As a couturier, she usually emphasized a comfortable, easy-to-wear, classic costume consisting of a cardigan with turned-up sleeves, a

96　The perfume "Shai" by Rosal of Miami, Florida was trademarked in 1943. This bottle by Wheaton was shown in a 1946 ad. Photo courtesy of the Museum of American Glass at Wheaton Village.

97 Frosted glass flacon of disk form moulded with a pattern of overlapping petals held the perfume "Auteuil" by Lalo of Paris. Bottle marked—R. Lalique. Numbered stopper. (1-6/8").

98 Novelty soaps were big sellers in the 1920's and 1930's. This European creation named "Cleopatra" was imported by the Irving W. Rice Co. of New York in 1923. She came in four assorted headdresses. Photo by Elizabeth A. McCarron.

99 Clear crystal flacon with a frosted glass stopper moulded with a design of two butterflies and berries held the scent "Paris" by Coty introduced in 1921. Numbered stopper. (2-7/8").

100 Frosted glass bottle with the shoulders moulded with graduated thorns, the stopper moulded with salamanders, was used by Coty to hold a variety of eau de colognes. Circa 20's. (9'').

102 Houbigant launched the perfume "Mon Boudoir" in the U.S. in 1919. The simple crystal bottle with a gold decorated stopper is marked Baccarat. (3-1/2'').

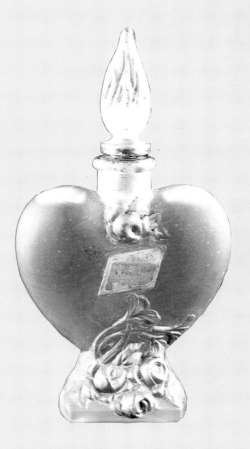

101 Vigny of Paris presented the perfume "Le Chick Chick" to the American market in 1923. The delightful bird bottle had a gold metal stopper cover. (5-1/4'').

103 Gold trimmed frosted glass heart bottle decorated with moulded roses, with a flame stopper was used by the De Vaudrey Company. The perfume was called "Coeur Perdue". (4-6/8'').

full-cut skirt, loads of costume jewelry, short cut hair, and a sailor hat. At the height of her career, Chanel was the wealthiest designer in France. When her clients shifted their allegiance to Schiaparelli, she retired in 1938. She made a comeback in 1954 because she felt that men had taken over Paris fashion.

It was a collaboration between this sophisticated and distinguished couturiere and one of the foremost perfumers of all time, Ernest Beaux, that was responsible for the creation of the world's most famous perfume, "Chanel No. 5". The memory that inspired the perfume was of Monsieur Beaux's participation in the last campaign of World War I in the most Northern area of Europe. There raises, in the last spring, a richly delicate fragrance of extreme freshness from the birch forests, cool lakes and flower-filled meadows. An unforgettable impression was retained by Monsieur Beaux and he wanted to recreate it in a perfume. He numbered various perfume creations for reference from 1 to 5 and 20 to 24. Monsieur Beaux felt that "No. 5" recaptured his memory the best and was already his favorite. When in 1921 Chanel was presented with all of them she also picked "No. 5" as her favorite among the perfumes. Since Chanel felt that 5 was her lucky number and the name "No. 5" would bring it good fortune, the name was simply continued.

The package and bottle design for "No. 5" caused a revolution. The bottle was so austere and so simple, it made almost all the other elaborate perfume packages look over-dressed and fussy. The clear bottle, made by Brosse, had a simplicity and purity of line that is considered a classic today. In 1959 the bottle was honored by being placed in the New York's Museum of Modern Art's permanent collection.

CHARBERT

Herbert H. Harris founded Parfums Charbert in New York in 1933. The successful firm aimed its perfumes and cosmetics toward a largely middle class audience. Most of Charbert's perfumes were created and blended in Paris, adding to their sales appeal. Very early in the company's history a drum became its symbol and trademark. The first perfumes put on the U.S. market were "Breathless" and "De toi je chante" (Of thee I sing) in 1933. Many Charbert perfumes were bottled in a jewel cut drum flacon. A favorite with collectors is "Grand Prix" presented in 1938 in a miniature lady's riding boot made of leather. By pulling one of the little slide straps the top was removed and by pulling the other slide strap the bottle was raised from its white satin-lined case.

Another interesting presentation Charbert did in 1937 was two large cologne bottles with cut glass stoppers of "Gardenia" and "Lavender" held by a metal rack which had a lock and key which could be reused as a liquor stand. Introduced in 1947, "The French Touch" was originally packaged in turquoise and black and bottled in a simplified version of the crystal drum bottle. "Consent" introduced in 1953 used the same bottle but was packaged in an attractive white and black box dotted with gold. The most luxurious presentation used by Charbert was for "De Toi Je Chante" in 1934. The golden-hued mirror flacon was encased in a velvet covered box with a large long tassel hanging from it.

In 1940 Charbert presented "Cologne Trumpet". Designed in glass, the trumpet was bugle-shaped, topped with a brass 'mouth-piece', had a brass handle, and was lavishly tasseled with bright red, white and blue trappings. The box had wide strips of red, white, and blue.

CHARLES OF THE RITZ

Charles Jundt founded the cosmetic company of Charles of the Ritz in New York City in 1916. The company was named after the founder and the Ritz part of the name came from the exclusive Ritz-Carlton which was the hotel in which he first operated a salon. The first Charles of the Ritz perfumes presented were "A", "B", and "C" introduced in 1927. A very successful company, by the 1950's the line was being sold in over 20 countries.

104 "5 Fleurs" flacon made by Brosse.

104—105
Original pictures used to illustrate a 1930's "Forvil" catalog, showing many flacons made by Lalique and Brosse.

A charming bottle of white decorated with pink in the shape of an antique barber bottle patented in December of 1940 was used for many years to hold "Moss Rose" cologne. Another long-time seller for Charles of the Ritz was "Spring Rain" sold in a parasol shaped bottle with a wooden handle stopper that was patented in 1941. "Directoire" introduced in 1948 came in an urn shaped bottle made in France packaged in gold and white, designed so the paper looked like fine white leather. The toilet water was sold in a modernized obelisk bottle. The scent "Love Potion" introduced in 1941 came in a crystalline bottle that suggested the shape of an 18th century bust of cupid and was topped with a stopper in the form of a dimpling cupid's head with wings in gilded glass. The bottle came in a tall, oval, red satin box.

The elegantly presented perfume "Ishah" (Woman) introduced in 1954 was packaged in Mediterranean blue with a trim of gunmetal soutach braid inspired by the costume designs of the ancient Near East. "Ishah" was bottled and packaged in France.

MARY CHESS

Mary Chess was started in 1930 by Grace Mary Chess Robinson (Mrs. Avery Robinson) in her small apartment kitchen on Lexington Avenue in New York. She personally compounded all her first products with the assistance of her cook and maid. Mrs. Robinson incorporated her business and trademarked the name Mary Chess in 1932. Her first small shop on 66th Street was opened in 1933. The shop specialized in perfume and perfume related items such as sachets, perfume lamps, scented jewelry, and even scented paint. Saks Fifth Avenue became a client selling Mary Chess items in its store and her business boomed. The first Mary Chess shop on Park Avenue opened its doors in 1938. The company became internationally famous with branches in Montreal and London.

The wonderful chess piece bottles designed by Grace Chess Robinson came into use during the late 1930's but were not patented until 1941. The bottles were inspired by the Mary Chess name and were adapted from an antique 17th century chess set. In the United States the bottles were made by the Wheaton Glass Co. Another unusual Mary Chess bottle was a frosted crystal replica of the Plaza Fountain that held "Souvenir d'un Soir' presented in 1956.

"White Lilac" was the first perfume introduced by Mary Chess and was the company's all-time best seller. The perfumes named for flowers were true florals and the others were floral blends.

CIRO

Parfums Ciro, originally named Guy T. Gibson Inc. was started in New York by J. S. Wiedhopf and Guy T. Gibson in 1921. The parent firm was in New York with a salon in Paris. All Ciro perfumes were made, bottled, and then packaged in France. Three of the first perfumes marketed were "Doux Jasmin" (Sweet Jasmine), "Chevalier de la Nuit" (Knight of the Night), and "Maskee" (The Clown) in France in 1923. The perfume "Maskee" was sold in a clown bottle in a black satin box with a whimsical figure of the clown in gold on it. The perfume "Doux Jasmin" came in a plain cylinder bottle with a colored glass button stopper. "Gardenia Sauvage" (Wild Gardenia) was introduced in 1928 in a bottle of modern design with a beehive stopper. The perfume "Camelia de Maroc" introduced in 1936 was inspired by the thirties vogue for camelia flowers as corsages.

Ciro's "Danger" bottle was probably one of the first truly modern creations in the perfume field. The inspiration for this was a Baccarat vase, designed to suggest oblong blocks of crystal, displayed at the French Exposition of 1936. "Danger" made its appearance in 1938 in a Baccarat bottle which embodied the grace and artistic feeling of the vase. Two other bottles made by Baccarat for Ciro were for the perfumes "Reflexions" introduced in 1933 and "Surrender" in 1931. The jewel faceted clear crystal bottle for "Surrender" was originally presented nestled in a mirror-lined, decorated velvet box.

105 The flacons for "Anémones" and "Trois Valses" were by Lalique.

106 "Le Golliwogg" by Vigny bottle with the white collar as the stopper and the glass head holding the perfume. Bottle made in France. (2").

107 Perfume pin in the shape of "Le Golliwogg" by Vigny. (1-1/8").

108 "Le Golliwogg" by Vigny has a black glass head stopper topped with real seal fur for hair. Bottle design and name are based on a character created by Florence K. Upton around the turn of the century. The bottle was made by Verreries Brosse. The perfume was introduced in America in 1922 by the Lionel Trading Co. of New York. (3-1/2").

109 "Jack-Junior-Jill" set of "Le Golliwogg" perfume came in a black drop front box with a pink satin lining. (2-1/2").

111 Holiday theme, free-blown bottles made in Germany. Circa 1920's. (Santa 3-1/4'', rabbit on egg 2'', Christmas tree 3-1/2'').

10 Cute, puppy dog, pressed glass bottle with hand-painted face held the perfume "Allez...Hop!'' by Jovoy of Paris. It was sold in a dog basket package. Circa 1924. (4-1/2'').

112 Novelty hand-blown bottles set consisting of a Mother Elephant chained to her two babies. Circa 1920's. (Mother 5'').

113 Very thin and fragile free-blown novelty bottles made in Germany held various floral scents. Their popularity in this country reached its peak between 1922-1927. (Elephant 2-1/2'', horse 3'', camel 2'', rabbit 2'').

114

115

A Ciro bottle that is a favorite with collectors is "New Horizons" introduced in 1941. The "New Horizons" bottle has clean simple lines with a graceful curve that suggests the horizon itself. The stopper is in the form of an Art Deco inspired eagle. The original box was curved to match the bottle.

JACQUELINE COCHRAN

The famous American aviatrix and business executive was born in Pensacola, Florida about 1912. An orphan, she left her foster parents and struck out on her own at an early age. By the age of twenty-three, she had acquired both a pilot's license and a cosmetics firm. She married the wealthy American financier Floyd Bostwick Odlum. As a pilot, Miss Cochran received over 200 trophies and awards. In 1938 she was the first woman pilot to win the Bendix Transcontinental Race. During World War II she was head of the Women's Air Force Service Pilots. In 1960 Ms. Cochran was the first woman pilot to break the sound barrier.

Among the perfumes her firm marketed were "Shining Hour" introduced in 1941 and "Pursuit" in 1949. Her beauty products were not nationally distributed until 1938, hitherto they were sold only to the patrons of her salons.

CORDAY

The French firm of Corday was founded in 1921 in the city of Paris. The firm took its name from the famous French revolutionist Charlotte de Corday. In 1793, Charlotte assassinated Jean Paul Marat, whom she held responsible for the reign of terror, in his bath. She was captured by Marat's friends and guillotined.

In 1924 the Lionel Trading Co. of New York started importing Corday perfumes to the U.S. Among the perfumes imported starting in 1924 were "Jet" presented in a fountain shaped bottle boxed in a trellis decorated container; "Serre Fleurie" in a bottle shaped like an urn of flowers; "Toodle-oo" in an egg-shaped bottle with a bird stopper resting in a nest made of feathers; "Kai Sang" in a black glass Chinese inspired bottle; and "Toujours Moi" (Always Me).

The scent that was to become Corday's signature perfume "Toujours Moi" was used for many years in Notre Dame and other famous cathedrals in Paris as an incense. Becoming fascinated with this Oriental fragrance, in 1923 Charles Oppenheim persuaded Corday its originator to market it as a perfume. René Lalique designed the distinctive bottle of a stylized flower dripping nectar in little drops. Mrs. Oppenheim contributed the name from an idea she had on a boat returning from Europe. In 1951 "Toujours Toi" was introduced in the United States in the same bottle used for "Toujours Moi".

The firm of Baccarat made many of the beautiful crystal flacons used by Corday including those for "Orchidee Bleué" (Blue Orchid), "Femme du Jour" (Woman of the Day), "La Plus Belle", "L'Heure Romantique" (Romantic Hour), "L'Ardente Nuit", "Voyage a Paris" and "Possession". The perfume "Possession" introduced in 1939 was inspired by Rodin's masterpiece in marble "The Kiss".

Corday started a new trend in the industry in 1935 in the selling of its perfumes in small dram units. The Corday scents were sold in petite, dram size, inexpensive bottles that were reproductions of the original deluxe sizes. The idea was a complete success with consumers and was soon copied by many other perfume houses.

In 1934 Corday introduced in the U.S. four colognes in colored glass bottles, green for "Brut", amber for "Sec", blue for "Lilas" and rose for "Lavande". In 1937 "Orchidee Bleue" cologne in a modified cabochon bottle and "Voyage A Paris" cologne in a replica of the perfume flask but turned on its side and given a long neck were introduced to this country.

Three other exceptional presentations by Corday were for "Tzigane", "Zigane" (Gypsy) and "Rue de La Paix". The perfume "Tzigane" introduced in 1938 came in an interesting, modernistic, moulded, frosted glass bottle by R. Lalique in a coffret which took the form of a violin. In 1949 "Zigane", was introduced in a violin shaped bottle with matching box. A miniature metal lamppost with three fragrances forming the lamps with a ceramic ashtray base called "Rue de La Paix" was presented in the U.S. in 1952. Another handsomely presented perfume was "Fame" introduced in 1947 in a drop front, hinged top box covered with embossed paper in pastel tones in a clear glass modern bottle. Another perfume called "Jet" by Corday introduced to the U.S. in 1940 came in a crystal flask with a black stopper, in a box of dazzling white satin and black velvet.

COTY

The renowned perfume and cosmetic house of Coty was founded by Francois Sportuno of Corsica in Paris in 1904. Born into a middle class family, Sportuno had the benefit of a good education. After his schooling he became a secretary to a prominent French political figure. At night, in his spare time, Sportuno learned to compound colognes and fragrances from his friend, an apothecary named Raymond Goery. Sportuno soon discovered he had the priceless perfumer's 'nose' for fragrance. He furthered his education in the perfume trade by a visit to the Grasse distilleries. Sportuno dreamed of creating a partnership between perfume and its presentation. He felt that fine perfume should be marketed in a luxurious manner with opulent boxes, richly engraved labels, and beautiful, well-made flacons.

Sportuno opened his first business in Paris at 61 Rue la Boétie with money borrowed from his family and a few of the essential oil houses who recognized his genius. About this time Francois Sportuno changed his name to Coty, thinking it would be easier for his customers to say and remember. Coty proceeded to develop a collection of floral perfumes, popular with women at the beginning of this century. Coty, with the help of Givaudan, an important essential oil house, created a refined rose perfume called "La Rose Jacqueminot" in 1905. He approached a large department store called the Louvre in Paris, attempting to sell his perfume. He was turned away by the store's buyer before he had an opportunity to demonstrate his rose perfume. However, by purpose or accident, Coty happened to break a bottle of his perfume in the store, allowing the clientele to experience the remarkable scent. The store revised its decision and began to sell Coty perfumes when customers wanted to know where the perfume could be bought. Soon all the department stores in Paris carried Coty perfumes to meet the consumer demand. By 1910 Coty was acknowledged worldwide as the number one perfumer in the world.

Coty was to instigate changes in the packaging of perfume that was to revolutionize the entire industry. He originated the idea of packaging perfume in silk-lined boxes covered with beautiful embossed papers or leather. Coty was also the first perfumer to use unique, highly recognizable flacons for his perfumes to convey an image of luxury and prestige to the customer. Coty teamed up with the innovative designer Rene Lalique so that the bottles being mass produced for his perfumes were of the highest quality. Coty also commissioned several flacons to be made by Baccarat, including the one for "L'Or" perfume. Coty was also among the first to market small bottles of his perfumes at prices the working class could afford.

COUNTESS MARITZA COSMETIC CO.

Louis F. Margolies founded the firm of Countess Maritza in New York in 1940. The name Maritza came from a river that flows between Greece and Turkey and Countess was added for prestige and glamour. The first scent introduced was "Silent Night" in the early forties. The perfume and cologne "Rare Jewel" introduced in 1948 was packaged in a regal blue hinged box with a picture of the famous Cullinan diamond, the largest in the world at the time, reproduced in its natural size on the top. Countess Maritza marketed several toilet waters including "Forbidden Moment", "Queen Christina", "Sonata", and "White Mist".

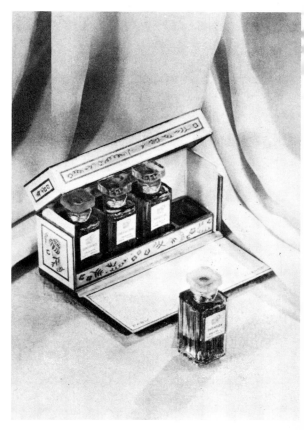

116

114-116 Three original catalog pictures used to illustrate an "Orianys of Paris" catalog.

51

117 Rare metal flacon with decorative chain and a button stopper made out of ivory held "Aladin" by Rosine. Bottle marked—Aladin Rosine. U.S. introduction 1923.

118 Richard Hudnut first created the perfume "Yanky Clover" in 1898. This bottle was probably used in the 1920's.

120 Lucien Gaillard designed this clear glass flacon moulded with a Greek key design, with a figural stopper reminiscent of a religious statue for the perfume "Tanagra". Bottle marked—L.G. (5-3/4").

119 Frosted glass flacon moulded with a realistic flower design with matching stopper, enhanced with brown staining, held "Anthemis" by De Clamy of Paris. Acid mark—Lucien Gaillard. (2-3/8").

122 Spiral design metal filagree adorns the clear glass bottle for "Le Balcon" by Rosine. It was packaged in a suede leather drawstring bag. Circa 1923. No marks. Bottle probably made in Murano. (2-3/4").

123 "Nuit de Noel" introduced in 1922 by Caron was bottled in opaque black glass and packaged in a green-tasselled cardboard box covered with paper imitating shagreen. Acid mark—France. Numbered stopper. (4-5/8").

121 Richard Hudnut first created the perfume "Yanky Clover" in 1898. Bottle shown was probably used in the 1920's.

124 Square crystal flacon moulded with the perfume name "Chose Promise" and maker 'Fioret Paris', has a draped woman highlighted with brown staining on the rectangular stopper. It came in a green leather case lined in gold velvet. Bottle marked—R. Lalique. Numbered stopper. Circa 1920's. (5-1/8").

125 Deluxe Eau de Cologne bottle made by
Lalique.

125-126 Original pictures used to illustrate a
1930's "Forvil" catalog, showing many flacons
made by Lalique and Brosse.

JEAN D'ALBRET

Guillame d'Ornano founded the house of Jean d'Albret in Paris in the 17th century. The perfume "Ecusson", which means shield or coat of arms, was the first fragrance marketed by this house.

The history of this perfume goes back to about 1572, to the Court of Jeanne d'Albret, mother of France's King Henri IV. It was the fashion of the day, among both men and women, to have their own personal scent recipes. "Ecusson" was blended for a connoisseur of perfumes, Marshal Alphonse d'Oramo, by his alchemist for his exclusive use.

It wasn't until the early fifties that the French firm of Jean D'Albret marketed "Ecusson" in the United States. "Casaque" introduced in 1956 in the U.S., was once a favorite of author George Sand.

LILLY DACHE

Lilly Daché, a famous American milliner, was born on a farm in Beigles, France. Lilly hated school and played hooky so constantly that her parents arranged an apprenticeship to an aunt in Bordeaux who was a milliner when Lilly was fourteen. When Lilly was fifteen her aunt contracted an apprenticeship for her at Réboux's in Paris. She was a midinette there for four years.

In 1924 Lilly Daché arrived in New York with fifteen dollars and the names of two stores, R. H. Macy and Henri Bendel. Macy's promptly hired her as a salesclerk in millinery, but she was fired one week later because the intricacies of writing sales slips was beyond her. Her next job was for a hole-in-the-wall milliner on 77th Street, which she bought ten weeks later for one hundred dollars. Her designs became so popular that the waiting crowds of women attracted the attention of the police who would come to see whether there was a fire. After moving several times to larger quarters, Lilly finally bought her own nine-story building on East 57th Street which contained workrooms, showroom, and living quarters.

In 1929 Lilly Daché met Jean Desprès on a blind date arranged by a mutual friend. Jean Desprès, a Frenchman who worked for Coty, was to become an executive vice president for the firm. In 1932 they married and from that day on they never missed a day lunching and dining together.

Lilly Daché's major contributions to the fashion field were colored snoods, draped turbans, visored caps, and brimmed hats moulded to the head. She began designing dresses to go with her hats by 1949. She also designed lingerie, hosiery, gloves, and loungewear. Lilly Daché closed her business in 1968 upon her husband's retirement from Coty.

In 1941 Lilly Daché added perfumes to her product line with the help and advice of her husband. Her perfume "Dashing" came in a poodle-shaped bottle. The perfume "Drifting" came in a surreal bottle shaped like a woman's breasts spouting from green leaves with a bright pink feather-topped stopper.

DAGGETT AND RAMSDELL

In 1890 V. Chapin Daggett and his partner Clifford Ramsdell opened their first apothecary shop on lower Fifth Avenue in New York City. They were soon producing skin care products which became famous. A well-known user of their cremes was the actress Lillian Russell. Daggett and Ramsdell didn't market a perfume until 1937 when "Sonata" was introduced. In 1946 the fragrance "Gay Manhattan" was presented in a golden metal sphere which was perfume bottle and atomizer all in one.

DE HERIOT

Hollywood, California was the home of De Heriot Perfumes Inc. founded by Harriett Hessin in 1935. The inspiration for the company name came from Heriot, a former Premier of France, and the 'DE' prefix was the suggestion of the toilet goods buyer of J. W. Robinson's, Ethel Usher. The firm became noted for its imaginative gift packaging and promotion. The first perfume introduced in 1935 was "La Premiere" in a beautiful cut glass bottle. The scent "Célèbre" presented in 1950 came in a clear glass bottle with cut glass top in a quilted box.

CHRISTIAN DIOR

That great master of fashion, Christian Dior started his parfum house just one year after opening the doors of his fashion salon in 1946. Born in 1905 in Granville, France, Christian Dior was the second of four children born to Maurice and Madeleine Dior. His parents were members of a family that had gained wealth as chemical manufacturers. Dior's advanced education was directed toward a career in the diplomatic service, although at thirteen he already displayed a talent for designing by creating costumes for fancy dress balls given by his parents at their summer home. Dior attended the *Ecole des Sciences Politiques* and later traveled extensively in Europe.

Influenced by friendships he had formed with numerous artists, Dior renounced his diplomatic aspirations to become an art dealer in 1928. His art gallery was among the first to show and promote surrealist paintings. He exhibited pictures by his friends Salvador Dali, Christian Bérard, and Jean Cocteau.

The world-wide Depression of the 1930's brought a sharp decline to the Dior family fortune. Christian Dior found it necessary to earn a living. He became an illustrator of haute couture for *Le Figaro Illustrated*. He began designing hats several of which were bought by the house of Agnès which caused a sensation. Dior was soon desiging other accessories and eventually gowns. He became an apprentice to the well-known designer Robert Piquet in 1938.

When World War II broke out, Dior entered the French Army. After the fall of France he spent a year and a half on his father's farm helping him. Dior returned to the world of fashion in 1941 when he became a designer for Lucien Lelong.

In 1946 Dior opened the doors to his own elegantly decorated salon in Paris at No. 30 Avenue Montaigne, a four-story house. Marcel Boussac, a French millionnaire textile manufacturer, provided the financial backing for the enterprise. Dior's first showing in 1947 premiered the so-called new look, featuring a long, full-cut skirt. It totally revolutionized women's dress and reestablished Paris as the center of the fashion world.

In 1948 Charles of the Ritz introduced in the United States two of Dior's perfumes "Miss Dior" and "Diorama". Both perfumes were presented alike in the classic Baccarat urn and graceful obelisque bottle. The dramatic packages were in grey and gold with a Directoire motif. The rarest of materials like crystal, gold, satin, and velvet were employed in the packaging and presentation of Dior perfumes in keeping with his standards of quality.

D'ORSAY

D'Orsay Parfums was founded about 1830 during an era of elegance that swept France in the nineteenth century by a great dandy, Count Alfred D'Orsay, in Paris. A gifted man of the arts, one of his greatest talents was his remarkable genius for blending perfumes. In his laboratory the Count personally trained his chemists to create and blend perfumes and gave them formulas which were kept scrupulously for generations. There is no surviving record of the name of the first perfume marketed by D'Orsay but it was sold in both France and England. D'Orsay perfumes were not introduced into the United States until the next century about 1912 or 1913.

D'Orsay Parfums marketed crystal bottles of outstanding design and beauty created in character with the quality of the fragrance they contained. The flacons were made by such famed glass houses as Lalique, Baccarat, Sue et Mare, Nancy, and Brosse. "Toujours Fidele" (Always Faithful) introduced in Europe in 1912 was one of D'Orsay's longest selling

126 Eau de Cologne bottle used by Forvil.

127 Clear and frosted glass flacon decorated with moulded roses stained pink held "Rose d'Ispahan" by Corvse of Paris. Numbered stopper. (5").

128 Flattened spade-shaped flacon moulded with a cupid within a red-stained heart held the perfume "L'Amour Dans le Coeur" by Arys. Bottle marked—R. Lalique. Circa 1920's. (9.75 cm.).

129 Frosted glass flacon moulded with a design of pinnated leaves with a standing woman figural stopper was used by Arys for an unknown scent. Bottle marked—R. Lalique. (4-1/8").

130 Frosted glass flacon moulded with a triangular design, festooned with enamelled blue dots, and finished with a figural stopper held "Glyciane" by Favolys. Bottle marked— J. Viard. Circa 1920's. (3-1/2").

131 Several perfumes by J. Giraud Fils of Paris were marketed in the United States in the early 1920's. (2-3/4").

132 The perfume "Narcisse" by Vivienne came in a hand-painted bottle. Circa 1920's. (4").

perfumes. It came in a clear pillow-shaped crystal bottle with a figural dog stopper. The bottle can be found marked either Baccarat or Nancy.

Some of the perfumes first marketed in the U.S. were "Leur Coeurs", "Cyclamen", "Panier de Roses", "Nelly", "Les Fleurs" and "Poesie" (Poetry). The perfume "Leur Coeurs" was sold in a heart shaped bottle by Baccarat. The scent "Panier de Roses" came in a decorative basket in a Lalique bottle of flared glass moulded with trellis work and entwined rosebuds at the rim and on the stopper. The perfume "Nelly" came in a circular Baccarat bottle of flattened demi-lune form, moulded with female masks and flowers alternating with printies around the rim. The slender, conical Lalique bottle for "Poesie" was lightly moulded with dancing nymphs against a ground of flowers.

Lalique also designed the bottles for the D'Orsay perfumes "Ambre" and "Le Lys". The square "Ambre" flacon was of opaque black or clear glass moulded with a caryatid at each corner and the stopper was decorated with stylized daisies. A 1920 French magazine stated that other D'Orsay scents could also be purchased in this bottle. The flacon for "Le Lys" was moulded with an all-over design of stylized flowers heightened with brown enamel. Lalique also designed a tester for D'Orsay of block rectangular form moulded with a design of intertwining brambles. Each of the five receptacles had a briar rose stopper moulded with a name of a different D'Orsay scent.

A masculine perfume by D'Orsay called "Dandy" introduced in 1926 became a popular scent with the flappers of the era. The opaque black glass cubistic flacon was designed by Sue et Mare. A portrait of Alfred D'Orsay was embossed on the stopper of a chubby little clear crystal bottle made for "Milord" introduced in the U.S. in 1933. The D'Orsay seal was used on an oval crystal bottle for "Duo" introduced in the U.S. in 1930.

Verreries Brosse made many of the D'Orsay bottles including the ones for "Belle de Jour" and "Intoxication". Introduced in 1938, "Belle de Jour" (Belle of the Day) was a spicy fragrance which came in an unusual milky white glass sculptured bottle with a hand holding a bouquet of ribbon as a stopper. The box was a shiny black with a ribbon engraved on it. The stimulating perfume "Intoxication" introduced to the U.S. in 1942 came in a handsome, clear, jewel cut flacon.

133 Two flacons by Brosse for "5 Fleurs" and "Les Yeux Doux" by Forvil.

MARY DUNHILL

Mary Dunhill was started in 1934 by Alfred Dunhill of London Inc. in New York. Mary Dunhill was the daughter of Alfred Dunhill, internationally famous tobacconist of 30 Duke Street, London. She had for many years maintained her own establishment at 39 Craven Road, Lancaster Gate, London. The first perfume marketed by the company was called "Frou Frou de Gardenia" in 1934. Mary Dunhill's best selling fragrance "Flowers of Devonshire" was introduced in 1936 in an attractive bottle in a box of blue and silver with a tiny bouquet of flowers.

Inspired by the amulets of good luck charms worn by the women of the East, "Amulet" was presented in 1938. A little metal talisman, impregnated with the scent was attached to the box and could be worn as a bracelet. Another perfume called "Escape" was introduced in 1943. The bottle was a copy of an old medicine bottle dramatized by a golden key on it and the aquamarine satin box embossed with gold had a heart-shaped padlock closing. S. A. Ogden designed a purse bottle for Mary Dunhill in 1937 called "Scentinel". Perfume could be carried in safety in this tightly stoppered inner glass vial in the gleaming metal round case of sterling silver or gold plate.

EISENBERG ET SONS

The firm of Eisenberg, which originally sold ladies' ready-to-wear dresses, was started by Jonas Eisenberg, an Austrian immigrant, around 1914 in Chicago. His two sons in 1930 began to design and manufacture under their own label a line of ladies' clothing and fashion jewelry. The exclusive line was strictly limited to one department store in about five hundred cities throughout America.

The firm opened a cosmetics division in the thirties and in 1938 introduced two perfumes designed to enhance the dresses made by Eisenberg of Chicago. The perfumes which were blended in France were called "847A", an exotic scent, and "847B", a delicate fragrance. Advertisements for the perfume claimed the name of the perfume had numerological fashion power and wearing it might change your luck. A frosted glass mannequin bottle used to house the perfume was designed by the Eisenbergs.

EVYAN

Evyan Perfumes was founded in the U.S. in the 1930's by Baron Walter Langer von Langendorff and his wife Lady Evyan. Dr. Walter Langer was a brilliant chemist with three doctorate degrees who emigrated to the United States from Austria in the thirties. Dr. Langer believed that a creative, innovative American perfume house could challenge the well established French firms.

In 1943 Parfumes Hartnell introduced and distributed two Evyan perfumes "White Shoulders" and "Menace" in four sizes. Both were beautifully packaged in boxes of real lace over silk in turqouise and peach. The innovative lace motif was designed by Lady Evyan herself, inspired by her personal collection of rare, heirloom pieces.

Evyan's all-time, best-selling perfume "White Shoulders" was the result of years of careful experimentation and research. An appropriate, suitable name for the romantic perfume was sought after. The name "White Shoulders" was the result of a compliment given Evyan one evening at a dinner party for intimate friends. One of her guests commented on her lovely white shoulders displayed to advantage in an off-the-shoulder evening frock, and thus the perfume was named.

J. FLORIS LTD.

Juan Flaminias Floris from the island of Minorca founded J. Floris Ltd. in London in 1730. Floris became famous for its true natural flower fragrances. In 1820 King George IV showed his approval of the firm by bestowing a Royal Warrant. The Royal Warrant was reaffirmed by William IV, Queen Victoria, Edward VII, George V, and George VI. The firm also supplied in 1863 perfumes and nosegays to Florence Nightingale. The perfume "Red Rose" introduced in London in 1730 was the first one in the line to be promoted.

DOROTHY GRAY

Dorothy Gray Limited was founded in New York City by Dorothy Gray in 1916. There were Dorothy Gray salons in London, Paris, and New York. Many famous beauties of stage, screen, and society were patrons of her famous beauty salons. By the 1920's cosmetics, perfumes, and colognes were marketed under the Dorothy Gray name. In 1928 Dorothy Gray opened a building on Fifth Ave. in New York.

A flower bouquet perfume called "Elation" was introduced in 1936 in two sizes. It came in a handsome cut glass bottle packed in a smart white kid case. A heart shaped bottle which fit into a bright red stand held "Flutter", a romantic scent marketed in 1938. "Nosegay", also presented in 1938, came in a classic vase shaped bottle with a flowered stopper. Dorothy Gray created "Lady in the Dark" perfume in 1941 to be worn with furs. It came in a glass plumed flacon in a round box with a large pom-pom on the top. A wedgwood blue and white vase bottle with packaging to match held "Wedgwood" perfume introduced in 1953. In 1947 a pretty bottle and box decorated with masks held "Savoir Faire".

134 Two flacons by Brosse for "Trois Valses" and "A Vos Ordres" by Forvil.

135 The perfume "Emeraude" by Coty was introduced in the U.S. in 1923. The square crystal flacon had a brass stopper cover. (3-3/4'').

136 Purse bottles with brass covers, introduced in the United States in 1923, were marketed by Le Blume and Kerkoff. (2-3/4'').

137 Heart shaped bottle with moulded coral pattern by Rene Lalique was used by Parfums De Volnay of Paris. The bottle shown was pictured in a 1922 U.S. Volnay advertisement. The ad stated that most of the Volnay containers were designed by Lalique. (3-1/2'').

138 Pressed glass, pillow-shaped bottle has as a figural stopper a young lady sitting cross-legged. Scent unknown. Circa 1920's. (3-1/2'').

139 The Lionel Trading Co. marketed the perfume "Severem" by Jovoy of Paris in America in 1923. The novel, clear glass camel bottle had a frosted glass figural stopper.

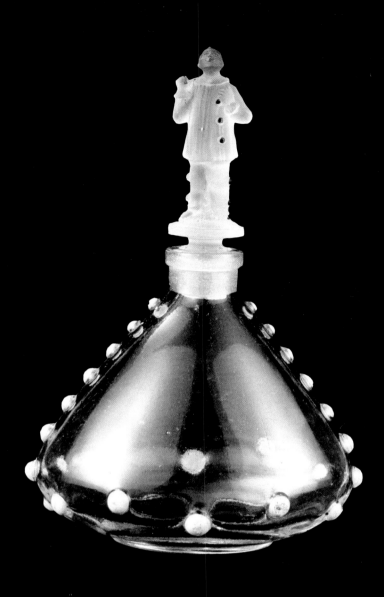

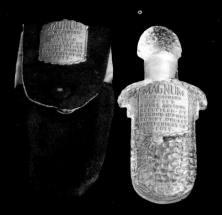

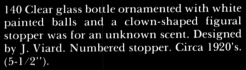

140 Clear glass bottle ornamented with white painted balls and a clown-shaped figural stopper was for an unknown scent. Designed by J. Viard. Numbered stopper. Circa 1920's. (5-1/2").

141 Frosted glass bottle with melon ribbing, moulded with a leaf design, had a flower-shaped stopper. Perfume unknown. Paper label—made in France. (2-3/4").

143a The perfume "Besame" by Myrurgia came in a flacon moulded with an all-over leaf design with matching stopper. Numbered stopper. (3-1/2").

143b Peggy Hoyt, a fashionable French milliner of the teens and twenties, started using the trademark engraved on this bottle in 1915. The clear crystal bottle by Baccarat with a blue stained stopper held "Flowers—The Perfume of Aristocrats." (4"). Photo by Elizabeth A. McCarron.

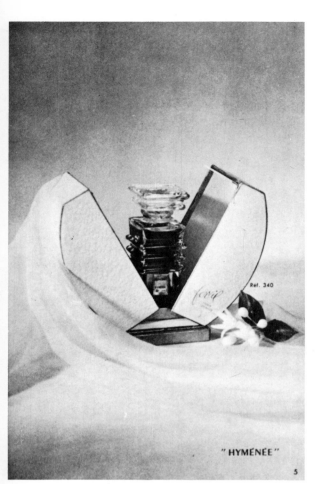

144 "Hyménée" flacon made by Brosse for Forvil.

GOURIELLI

The House of Gourielli was founded in New York City in 1942 by a leader in the cosmetics field, Helena Rubinstein and Prince Artichil Gourielli-Tchkonia, a Georgian nobleman. Helena Rubinstein married Prince Artichil, who was several years younger than she, in 1938. Madame Rubinstein and her husband launched the Gourielli Apothecary just around the corner from the Rubinstein Salon on Fifth Avenue.

The first perfume marketed was romantically called "Something Blue" in 1943. The advertising for this scent was directed toward hopeful brides-to-be. The label was a lace fringed heart and a heavenly blue sachet to wear for luck was included with the perfume. In 1947 the bottle was changed to a Paris designed heart shape with a cupid moulded in the center. Gourielli's best selling perfume was "Five O'Clock" introduced in 1947. The inspiration for the bottle was the classic cocktail shaker. In 1953 a flower formula from Grasse called "Fourth Dimension" was presented in an ultra-modern manner, in a beautiful spiral bottle with a piece of sculpture. In 1954 the bottle was changed to an hour-glass design in cut crystal.

GUERLAIN

The name Guerlain has been associated with fine perfumes for over 150 years. The original founder of the company was Pierre Francois Guerlain from Picardy. Guerlain studied in England and was qualified in both medicine and chemistry. He opened his first shop selling smelling salts, soaps, and fragrances in 1828 in Paris on the Rue de Rivoli. He became so successful that in 1848 the shop was moved to the fashion center of Paris on the Rue de la Paix. Guerlain was appointed perfumer to the Court of Napoleon III and Empress Eugénie in 1853. "Eue Imperiale" was created especially for the Empress by Guerlain around 1853. Guerlain also numbered among his exclusive clientele the Prince of Wales, the leading members of all the royal houses of Europe, and many of the famous writers, artists, and musicians of the era. His son Aimée Guerlain applied for their first U.S. trademark for the perfume "Eau Imperiale" label on February 25, 1875. The firm of Park and Tilford of New York became Guerlain's first agents in the U.S. in 1884.

Pierre Guerlain's sons Aimée and Gabriel took over control of the firm in 1890. In 1889 Aimée created "Jicky", one of the first modern perfumes to contain synthetic oils. Gabriel Guerlain contributed by designing the bottle made by Baccarat. The perfume "Jicky" was originally created as a man's scent, but the fashionable ladies of the era loved it so much they began wearing it.

Jacques Guerlain, Pierre Guerlain's grandson, became a creative director for the firm early in this century. He is responsible for some of Guerlain's best selling perfumes. Jacques created "J'Heure Bleue", introduced to the U.S. in 1913, and "Shalimar", introduced to the U.S. in 1926. The flacon for "Shalimar" was designed by Raymond Guerlain who was inspired by an old piece of silver belonging to the family. Baccarat was chosen to execute the beautiful crystal bottle with its sapphire blue stopper.

A beautiful collection of perfume bottles can be made just from the bottles produced for Guerlain. The most sought-after bottle is the one for "Champs Elysées" made and designed by Baccarat. Collectors have nicknamed it the "turtle" bottle. Shaped like a turtle in clear faceted crystal, the bottle has a flat space on the front on which a label was placed. The bottle was introduced about 1914.

Since the beginning of the firm in 1828, Guerlain has marketed over 200 different perfumes. Also, Guerlain has the distinction of being the only perfume house in the world that has been owned and controlled by the same family for five generations.

ANN HAVILAND

Gaston T. de Havenon founded Haviland Laboratories Inc. in New York City in 1939. The first perfumes marketed by the company were "Lily of the Valley" and "Perhaps" introduced in 1939. The first mention of an Ann Haviland perfume though was in 1935. It was "Daphne" perfume which was made exclusively for Jay-Thorpe, a fashionable shop in New York City. The perfume "Perhaps" was the company's all-time best selling fragrance because of its packaging and lasting quality.

HOUBIGANT

The firm of Houbigant, one of the biggest perfume producers in the United States today, was originally founded in 1775 by Jean-Francois Houbigant in Paris. Houbigant opened his master perfumer's shop at 19, Faubourg Saint-Honoré under a sign meaning 'The Flower Basket'. France was under the rule of Louis XVI at the time, and Houbigant sold wig powder, perfume, pommade, fans, and gloves. He soon became the fashionable perfumer and enjoyed the patronage of both the nobility and clergy. Armand-Gustave Houbigant, Jean-Francois' son, took over control of the business in 1807. Regimes and clienteles changed but the firm served them all beautifully. In 1880 Houbigant began to manufacture its perfume in Neuilly-Sur-Seine, a suburb of Paris. Also in the 1880's, Houbigant was appointed court perfumer to the Czar of Russia.

Among Houbigant's most successful perfumes were "Ideal" introduced in 1900, "Coeur de Jeannette" introduced in 1899, and "Quelques Fleurs" created by Robert Bienaimé in 1912. The perfume "Ideal" was important because of the early use of synthetics and "Quelques Fleurs" started the trend toward lighter floral perfumes. Many of the bottles used by Houbigant were made by Baccarat, Lalique, and recently Saint Gobain Desjonquères. Two Houbigant bottles highly sought by collectors are for "Subtilité" and "La Belle Saison". The Baccarat crystal Buddha holding "Subtilité" perfume came enshrined in a black moire box lined in red silk. The flacon for "La Belle Saison" created by Rene Lalique was moulded with a portrait of a woman's face surrounded by radiating flowers.

RICHARD HUDNUT

The Hudnut company was founded in New York City in 1880. Richard Hudnut was the first of many Americans to enter the perfume and cosmetic market in a major way. As the son of a New York druggist, he was familiar with the typical uninspired marketing of scent and perfume products in the late 19th century. After graduating from Princeton he traveled to Paris where he noted the extensive and tasteful use of cosmetics and perfumes by all classes of women, unlike their American counterparts. Hudnut realized that if these products were correctly presented to American women, a vast, virtually untapped market would open up. Flashy in his taste and preferring the style of Louis XV, Hudnut converted the family drugstore at Broadway and Ann Streets into an elegant showcase for beauty products. No expense was spared and the shop fittings included marble floors, mahogany counters, and cut crystal chandeliers. It became the most talked about drugstore in New York and attracted a large clientele. The wholesale end of the company eventually became so profitable that Hudnut closed his retail store. Richard Hudnut sold the thriving business and retired a very wealthy man in 1916.

Hudnut's first fragrance was "Violet Sec" toilet water which premiered about the time of the opening of his store. It was one of the most popular scents in the United States for over three decades. One of Hudnut's best selling lines, "Three Flowers", was introduced in 1915. In the 1920's the Hudnut company marketed several perfumes in bottles made in France by J. Viard (or J. Villard), including the deluxe flacon for "Fadette" and "Deauville". The Hudnut perfume "R.S.V.P." (respond if you please), introduced in 1936, came in an interesting flacon shaped like the envelope of a billet-doux with matching box.

145 Two flacons used by Forvil to hold various flower perfumes.

146 Rare amberina colored Rene Lalique flacon with a moulded design of a woman with butterfly wings held the perfume "La Phalène" by D'Heraud. A 1923 advertisement identified the bottle. Came with two numbered stoppers. (3-3/4"). Photo by Elizabeth A. McCarron.

148 Lanvin marketed "My Sin" in 1923 in a black sphere bottle designed by Armand Rateau. The artist Paul Iribe designed the stylized symbol of Mme. Lanvin and her daughter dressing for a party. The logo was trademarked in the U.S. in 1924. (3-1/4").

147 Houbigant debuted the perfume "Le Temps des Lilas" in America in 1922. The flacon was made in France by Rene Lalique. Numbered stopper. (3-3/8"). Photo by Elizabeth A. McCarron.

149 Regular box and bottle for "Le Jade" by Roger & Gallet. Box marked R. Lalique. (3-3/4"). Photo by Elizabeth A. McCarron.

150 Black leather case held a three bottle set with metal stopper covers by Rene Lalique for Coty. Numbered stoppers. Circa 1920's. (2-7/8").

151 Two rare Mahaaga moulded glass flacons shaped like ancient oil lamps with flame stoppers. Notice the fine detail on the handles with the moulded angel figure kneeling, holding a chalice. Stained color. (2-1/4").

152 Snail bottle, with a moulded glass shell-shaped stopper cover with green staining, has no marks or labels. (3-1/4").

153 Black glass "My Sin" by Lanvin flacon with a moulded flower decoration and gold enamelling. (3-3/8").

RICHARD JAECKEL (ARE-JAY)

The Jaeckel fur salon was opened in 1863 in New York to supply the most elegant, exclusive and costliest furs to the wealthy carriage trade. Jaeckel also carried a fashion line, hand picked in Paris. Created by Richard Jaeckel for his fur salon, the perfume "Are-Jay" was marketed in exclusive shops and department stores in 1938. The advertising stressed the affinity for furs the perfume had. Besides a rather plain crystal bottle in four sizes, a deluxe presentation could be purchased. The deluxe bottle was of beautiful cut crystal with a regal frosted crown stopper encased in a silk lined wine-red velvet jewel gift box.

LANCOME

Lancome was founded by the perfumer M. Armand Petitjean in France in 1935. Lancome was a family name. M. Petitjean was employed at one time by the house of Coty. The scent "Conquete" was the first perfume in the line introduced in France in 1935. Members of the British royal family patronized the firm including Queen Elizabeth II, the Duchess of Kent, and the Duchess of Windsor. Lancome perfumes were not marketed heavily in the U.S. until after World War II.

The Lancome perfume "Tropiques" was inspired by the tropical port of Bahia in Brazil. The rich medley of scents from the spices, woods, fruits, rum, and molasses on the docks stimulated the visiting perfumer M. Armand Petitjean. Upon his return to France, he immediately began to try to turn his experiences into a perfume. The search took him four years to complete.

The perfume "Magie" (Magic), presented in France in 1946, was introduced in the United States in 1952. The deluxe flacon was a twisted rectangle of heavy crystal by Baccarat sold in two sizes. It came in a white satin jewel case, sparkling with sequins and brilliant colors. "Sphere Magie", also introduced in 1952, was a Lalique star studded globe with a 14 karat gold plated dome. Lalique also designed the "Magie" baton de Magicien, a slender wand with stars presented in a suede sheath. Also in 1952, Lancome presented its twin set "Jumeles". Two Lalique half-ounce bottles holding "Magie" and "Tropiques" were tied together with satin ribbon and enclosed in a romantic oval bandbox.

In 1953 Lancome marketed an Oriental perfume "Tresor" in the United States. The deluxe presentation, which came in two sizes, was a diamond-cut flacon that flashed brilliance from every facet. A ribbon-tied, crystal teardrop purse flacon was also available. In 1954 Lancome presented "Lavander", a lavender water made from French lavender, lighter and sweeter than the English variety. The bottle, shaped like a decanter with a basket weave design, was by Lalique. It was sold in four sizes. In 1978 Lancome unveiled "Magie Noire" (Black Magic). Pierre Dinand designed the plastic wrapped glass bottle.

LANDER CO.

The American firm of Lander, which is still in operation, was founded in 1920 by 22-year-old Charles H. Oestreich and two partners. Oestreich devised many innovative ways of manufacturing and distributing good yet inexpensive cosmetics, toiletries and perfumes aimed at budget-conscious women. Lander was the first cosmetic manufacturing firm to base its prices on the cost and overhead of an item instead of what it could bring in the marketplace. The Lander Co. started marketing perfumes heavily in the 1930's and 1940's. Among the perfumes introduced were "Romantic Days" in 1939, "The Untamed Perfume" in 1943, and "Samezi-Soir" in 1950. Also in the 1940's and 1950's, Lander produced many low cost novelty perfumes. By the 1950's the Lander Co. owned and controlled over thirty brand names and four subsidiaries, including Lundborg Perfumers Inc. and McGregor Men's Toiletries, Inc.

154 Mary H. Mullen was granted U.S. patent 87,674 on August 30, 1932 for this clear and frosted flacon with flower stopper. Scent unknown. Bottle by Wheaton. Photo courtesy of The Museum of American Glass at Wheaton Village.

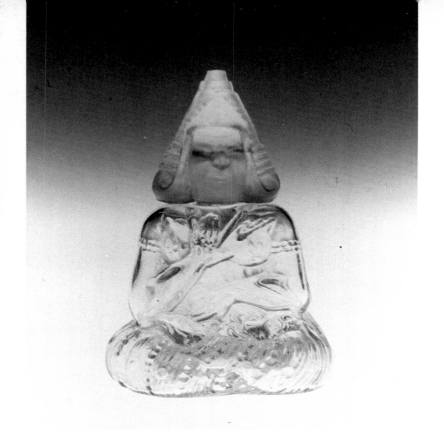

155 Oriental inspired bottles were very popular in the twenties. This clear and frosted bottle was used by the Vantine Co. for an unknown scent. Bottle made in France. Circa 1920's. (3-3/8"). Photo by Elizabeth A. McCarron.

157 Black opaque glass flacon with interesting gold enamelled detailing and stopper hel the perfume "Sensation" by Delyna. Bottl marked—Delyna Paris France. (1-7 8"). Phot by Elizabeth A. McCarron.

156 An original 1923 Coty perfume catalog identified this Rene Lalique flacon used for "Cyclamen" perfume. The clear bottle with grey staining is moulded with tiny figures with long insect-like wings. (5-5/8"). Photo by Elizabeth A. McCarron.

158 Named after a fashionable French resor of the 1920's, "Deauville" by Richard Hudnu was launched in the U.S. in 1924. The deluxe flacon by J. Villard was surmounted by coquettish little doll. Bottle made in France Numbered stopper. (4"). Photo by Elizabeth A. McCarron.

159 Forest perfumes introduced the perfume "Ming Toy" in 1923. The crystal bottle, shaped like a regal oriental beauty decorated with colored enamels, was made by Baccarat. Numbered stopper. (4-3/8"). Photo by Elizabeth A. McCarron.

160 Rooster shaped figural bottle held "Soirée" perfume by Nan Duskin. Bottle made in France. (10"). Photo by Elizabeth A. McCarron.

161 Unusual moulded decoration enhances this black glass flacon which held the perfume "Cir Cé". Polished bottom. Bottle marked— Made in France. (3"). Photo by Elizabeth A. McCarron.

162

162 & 163 Two illustrations from a 1929 Zanol
catalog. The brand name Zanol was used by
the American Products Co.

LANVIN

Jeanne Lanvin was a designer who helped found the La Maison de
Couture, the small Paris fashion group which, with a few other members,
set the fashion for the world. The daughter of a journalist, Jeanne Lanvin
was born in the late 1860's in Brittany. At an early age she began working as
a shop girl to help support her nine younger brothers and sisters. Lanvin
knew that her forte was dress design so she was apprenticed at thirteen to a
dressmaker. Lanvin became a milliner at the age of twenty-three. Her break
in the fashion business came when people noticed the dresses she made and
designed for her daughter Marie-Blanche. Soon clients flocked to her door
to buy dresses for themselves and their daughters.

Madame Lanvin started Lanvin Parfums in 1923 in Paris. The first
perfume by her chemist André Fraysse marketed was "My Sin" (Mon Peché)
in 1923. The famous black sphere bottle was designed by Armand Raïeau.
The deco artist Paul Iribe designed the stylized symbol of Mme. Lanvin and
her daughter Marie-Blanche dressing for a party. The logo was trademarked
in the United States in 1924, claiming use since 1923. Lanvin's best selling
perfume was "Arpege", the name derived from the musical term, arpeggio,
introduced in 1927.

LUCIEN LELONG

Lucien Lelong, one of the small band of great French designers who
secured the top markets of the world for Paris, was born in 1889 in Paris. His
father Arthur Lelong owned a textiles shop where Lelong learned the
properties of different dressmaking fabrics. He attended the Hautes Etudes
Commerciales in Paris from 1911 to 1913. At the age of twenty-four, in 1914,
Lelong designed his first collection of gowns. Just a few days before the
scheduled presentation, he was called to fight for France in World War I.
Lelong fought with the Army throughout the war and was awarded the
Croix de Guerre for bravery.

After Lelong was demobilized in 1919, he borrowed $2,500 from a friend
and opened a couture house on the Place de la Madeleine. Lelong's designs
were greeted with an almost overnight success. For a period of nearly three
decades he was considered to be the 'first gentleman of fashion' in Paris. He
also taught and employed such gifted designers as Christian Dior, Pierre
Balmain, and Hubert de Givenchy.

Lelong, a fierce French patriot, led the Resistance during the German
occupation in World War II that prevented the movement of the Paris
fashion houses from Paris to Berlin. Lelong fought throughout the war
edicts handed down by the Germans to hamper the fashion industry. He
also urged and encouraged the great couture houses to continue showing
collections despite little or no profit to keep as many people as possible
employed.

Lucien Lelong was a rather short, handsome man with straight forward
blue eyes and brown hair. He was married three times, first to Nelle Audey
in 1919, then to Princesse Nathalie Paley, and finally in 1954 to Madame
Dancovici. His hobbies included creating sculpture and collecting rare
Chinese porcelain and Russian glassware.

Lucien Lelong, believing perfume to be an essential part of a fashionable
woman's dress, established the Société des Parfums Lucien Lelong in 1924.
The first perfumes put on the French market were named "A", "B", "C",
and "N". The dry, light scent called "N" was said to have been named for
his second wife, the Princesse Nathalie Paley. The flacons for his scents,
which were widely copied, were many times designed by Lelong himself. In
1928 Lelong opened a brance in the United States in Chicago. All the bottles
and boxes had the Lucien Lelong *L* monogram on them.

In 1930 Rene Lalique designed two bottles for Lucien Lelong which were
patented in the U.S. in 1931. One of the bottles used for perfume "B" was
clear crystal with eight projecting sides. The other bottle used for several
scents was very thin frosted glass in a rectangular shape decorated with rows
of raised scallops finished in black enamel which fit into a smart black
enamel and silver metal container in the same shape as the bottle.

Lucien Lelong's square faceted crystal bottle in a mirrored box was introduced in 1933 for the perfume "Mon Image". The beautiful faceted crystal pyramid shaped bottle for "Opening Night" was introduced in the United States in 1934. This bottle was replaced in 1938 with a less dramatic flacon.

Lucien Lelong presented one of his best selling perfumes "Indiscret" in 1935. The flacon was designed to portray the trend of the mid-thirties in dress and interior decoration towards drapes. The perfume was originally marketed in six sizes ranging in price from $5.00 to $60.00 dollars. The feather design of both the bottles and package for "Les Plumes" was in keeping with the fashion for plumes as ornaments on hats in 1938. In 1940, packaged in standard jewelry tradition in a velvet lined box, Lucien Lelong presented a pair of perfume clips holding "Jabot" perfume shaped in glass like the feather bottles used in the "Les Plumes" presentation. The perfume "Jabot" was introduced in 1939 in a frosted crystal bow shaped bottle. Also in 1939 Lelong first introduced a valentine presentation with four chubby little heart shaped bottles sitting on white satin in a heart shaped box. The perfume "Tempest" introduced in 1947 came in a prismatic crystal bottle in a white embossed lace-paper box finished in gold binding. In 1951 Lucien Lelong issued a 200 bottle limited edition perfume called "Edition Limitee".

LENTHERIC

Lenthéric was founded by M. Guillaume Lentheric in France in 1885. M. Guillaume Lenthéric, one of France's premiere parfumers, was made a Chevalier de la Legion d'honneur in gratitude for his contributions to one of France's greatest industries. The scent "Au Fil de l'eau" was one of the earliest perfumes marketed in France. It was a lifetime favorite of the Queen of Spain.

Lenthéric perfumes were being sold in the United States by the twenties. John J. Murphy Co. of New York City was the distributor. In 1923 Lenthéric opened offices at 389 Fifth Avenue to handle the marketing of its product line. In 1928 Lenthéric opened a salon and new headquarters at the Savoy-Plaza, Fifth Avenue and Fifty Eighth St. The salon was lavishly decorated in gray, crystal, and silver, with a fountain opposite the entrance.

The perfume "Miracle" introduced in the United States in 1924, was inspired by a drama. A pantomime "The Miracle", staged by Max Reinhardt, was first performed in London in 1911. The play was the outstanding theatrical event of the season. The story was based on a Medieval legend of a young nun, Megildis, who escaped into the world for seven years from her convent. During that time the Virgin Mary took her place and performed her duties. Lenthéric's 'Miracle" was dedicated to the star of the show, Lady Diana Manners. The deluxe flacon for "Miracle" was made by Baccarat. This was a beautiful black crystal bottle dusted with gold. Owing to the special process used in making the bottle, each had a unique design caused by the dusting of gold. The bottle was changed in 1936 to a clear and frosted half column design made by Brosse.

In 1924 Lenthéric marketed the perfumes "Ambre Mousse" and "Coeur de Paris" in the U.S. in new containers. The blue and red canted crystal bottles had stopper covers of gold inlaid with enamel. The perfume "Lotus d'Or", also introduced in 1924, came in a bottle of embossed crystal. The box of gold and black was ornamented with lotus flowers.

In 1935 Lenthéric marketed two new perfumes in the United States, "Gardenia de Tahiti" and "Tweed". The flacon for "Gardenia de Tahiti" was like a triple-fluted Grecian column, classically simple and graceful with a base slightly tiered. One of Lenthéric's best-selling perfumes "Tweed" had a wooden stopper and came in a tweed covered box. Lenthéric also marketed in 1935 several special Christmas presentations. From the Lenthéric salons you could purchase different Lenthéric bouquet fragrances in beautiful crystal Orrefors bottles from Sweden. Also, a trio of perfumes boxed together, each in its own white satin lined cubicle, was offered. The round bottles of suspended bubble crystal had a crystal sphere stopper elongated for applying the perfume. "Miracle" came in blue, "Lotus d'Or" in rose, and "Asphodele" in clear.

163

164 Babani perfumes were sold exclusively in America by Elizabeth Arden. These flattened, round Babani bottles are signed Auzies. (2-5/8").

166 Moulded flowers enhance this black opaque glass flacon for "La Vierge Folle" by Poiret. The flacon was also used for "Mon Péche". (5-1/2").

165 Flattened round, black opaque glass bottle moulded with a design of 'paper-money' leaves enamelled in gold with matching stopper held the perfume "Feminette" by De Musset of Paris. Circa 1920's. (4-1/8").

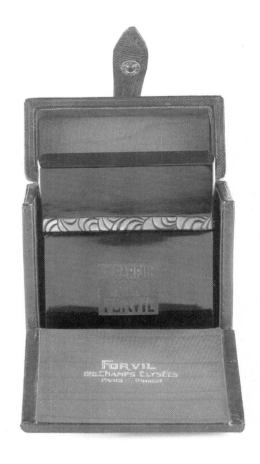

167 Square, clear and frosted, opaque black glass flacon was moulded with a simple geometric band and "Parfum NN Forvil". It came in a red leather case. Bottle marked—R. Lalique. Circa 1920's. (3-1/2").

72

168 Knight-inspired bottle for "Chevalier de la Nuit" by Ciro, introduced in Europe in 1923 and in the U.S. in 1925. The Knight bottle came in four sizes. (3-1/4").

169 Clear and frosted, opaque black glass flacon in an irregular hexagon shape was moulded with a lattice design. It was used by D'Orsay for various scents. Bottle marked—R. Lalique. (2-1/2").

170 The Frank M. Prindle Co. of New York imported the Violet perfume "Pourpre d'Automne" to the United States in 1924. The bottle, designed by Lucien Gaillard, is decorated with moulded and enamelled poinsettas. (3-1/2").

The oriental perfume "Shanghai" was fittingly presented in 1936 in a flacon inspired by an antique Chinese bronze urn. Square cut crystal handles on either side of the flacon accentuated its horizontal lines. The fragrance "A Bientôt" (goodby), introduced in 1938, was marketed in a slightly swirled bottle in a round box. Its name and "Lenthéric" were inscribed on its surface in gold.

Lenthéric marketed both "Pink Party", a scent aimed at teenage girls, and "Confetti" in 1940. The "Confetti" flacon was cylindrical with a glass bow on top and a petticoat ruffle fashioned of glass that flirted along the curve of the flacon. The package had three bright lacquered bows decorating it.

L'ORLE

Parfum L'Orle, pronounced Lor-Lay, was founded by A. T. Levy in 1934 in both Paris and London. The perfume "Cafe Society" was the first scent put on the market in 1934 in France. L'Orle opened an American office in 1935 on 6 East 39th Street in New York City. L'Orle fragrances were aimed at the large middle class market in the United States.

L'Orle's first presentation in America was in 1935. The company introduced a novel book-shaped package of perfumes of famous women of France of the seventeenth and eighteenth centuries. The perfume "Wine, Women, & Song", introduced in 1939, came in an interesting bottle packaged in a suede burgundy and gold box. Introduced in 1941, "Libido", an unusual fragrance, came in an elaborate mirror package.

In 1940 L'Orle marketed a series of colorful, porcelain type containers. The "Bud Vase" eau de toilette collection included six bud vases, each design a replica of a museum piece, executed in six different pastel colors. Each vase held three ounces and when finished the container could be reused as a decorative item in the home. The "Spirits of Perfume" collection was four L'Orle perfumes marketed in pastel porcelain-type cameo flask. Four men's fragrances were also sold in a spur shaped porcelain type flacon decorated with a polo scene.

LUBIN

M. Pierre Francois Lubin of Paris founded Parfumerie Lubin in 1793 in a shop under the sign "Aux Armes de France". A benevolent patron, Maria Paulina Bonaparte, a sister of Napoleon I married to Prince Camillo Borghese, allowed Lubin to use her name to promote his perfumes. George IV of England was so pleased with the artistry of Pierre Lubin in blending perfume that in 1821 he gave Lubin the "Patent of Perfumer to his Majesty the King of England". Lubin was the first European perfumer to market its products in the United States, that was in the 1840's.

A rare Lubin flacon was made for the perfume "Au Soleil". The grey tinted bottle has a life-like lizard encircling the bottle looking towards a fly on the stopper. Another beautiful Lubin flacon was for the perfume "Eva". The blue bottle has a nude woman sitting on a curled snake as the stopper. In 1921 the scent "Kismet" was presented in an unusual crystal elephant flacon by Baccarat with a turbaned rider as the stopper. Another Baccarat flacon was used for "L'Ocean Bleu" introduced in Europe in 1925 and in the U.S. in 1928. The bottle resembles two fish with heads and tails meeting.

F. MILLOT

Felix Millot established his small perfumerie business in an old quarter of Paris, Faubourg Saint Martin in 1839. For generations the firm remained in the hands of his descendents. For the 1900 Paris Exhibition the company commissioned the famous Hector Guimard to design the bottles to display its perfume. The first perfume marketed in the United States was "Crepe de Chine". It was blended by the grandsons of Felix Millot not too long after the turn of the century. The perfume, a mixture of jasmine, rose, and gardenia, was created to be like soft silk. In 1939 a companion perfume "Recital" was introduced in the U.S. It had been sold in France for some time previously.

MOLINARD

In the provincial French town of Grasse, the renowned perfume house of Molinard was founded in 1849. Monsieur Molinard opened a small shop in which he sold floral fragrances that he extracted from flowers and aromatic plants gathered fresh from the local Grasse fields. In 1894 a distillery was added to the expanding firm for the manufacture of perfumes. The fame of Molinard perfume and scents spread throughout Europe in the late nineteenth century, attracting an illustrious clientele including the Queen of England.

The House of Molinard in 1920 established its headquarters in Paris. To further enhance and display its perfume, Molinard commissioned both Baccarat and Rene Lalique to design and make beautiful containers for the company. In 1929 Lalique created a stunning frosted glass flacon highlighted with staining, moulded with a frieze of dancing nudes below stylized flowerheads for the Molinard perfume "Calendal". In 1930 Lalique designed the round, tubular glass flacon decorated with a satyr kissing a nude woman to hold the perfume "Le Baiser du Faune".

GERMAINE MONTEIL

Germaine Monteil was a famous Parisian couturiere. She also established a salon under her name in New York. In 1941 Germaine Monteil launched her first scent "Laughter" to both the French and American markets. The perfume name "Laughter" was changed to "Rigolade" in 1951. "Laughter" was a young and gay perfume which came in a severely simple flask. In 1947 "Nostalgia" was marketed in a simple cylindrical flacon. The perfume "Gigolo" was launched in 1951.

SOLON PALMER

An Englishman named Thomas Palmer settled in New England about 1635. One of his many descendants Solon Palmer, a Vermont professor of chemistry, moved to Cincinnati, attracted by the vast opportunities of the Middle West. Cincinnati, in the middle of the last century, was a city of great French fashions, fabulous wealth, and fine music. In 1847 Palmer laid the cornerstone of a perfume dynasty by blending three scents "Eau de Cologne", "Rose", and "English Lavender". The business was passed from father to son for four generations. All the Palmer scents and perfumes were created by a member of the Palmer family. Solon Palmer was one of the first perfume houses to use traveling salesmen to assure wide distribution of its product line.

Many bottles from the Victorian era may be found with charming embossed and decorated labels. A cute presentation for "Dress Parade" introduced in 1939 was a guard-house shaped box with the bottle stoppered like a plumed guard's helmet. "Centennial Bouquet" introduced in 1947 was in a book shaped box with a short history of Palmer's on the inside.

JEAN PATOU

The Jean Patou perfume house was founded in Paris in 1925 and in America in 1930. The firm was named after its founder, Jean Patou, who before his death was one of the leading couturiers in the world. Jean Patou, born in France in 1887, owned his own dressmaking and tailoring shop by 1910. He launched his first haute culture collection in 1919 at the age of thirty-two. Patou was the first designer to create casual, relaxed clothing for sports for women. He is also famous for his cubist sweaters which were inspired by the art of Braques and Picasso.

In 1925 Jean Patou followed the trend of the couturier going into the perfume business set by Paul Poiret and Chanel by introducing three perfumes, "Amour Amour", "Que sais-je?", and "Adieu Sagesse". Baccarat made the flacon for "Amour Amour" designed by the architectural and interior design branch of Jean Patou, Sue et Mare (Louise Süe and André Mare). In 1931 Patou's best-selling perfume, a blended floral essence with

174 Maison Violet of Paris created the perfume "Ambre Royal" in 1900. A new bottle for the perfume created by Lucien Gaillard was introduced in the U.S. in 1922. Stained decoration. (2-3/8").

171 The deluxe presentation for the perfume "Le Jade" by Roger & Gallet, introduced in the U.S. in 1923, was a spectacular green, René Lalique flacon in the form of a Chinese

172 The deluxe flacon for "Miracle" by Lenthéric was made in France by Baccarat. This beautiful black crystal bottle had a bakelite stopper cover. Owing to the special process used in making the bottle, each had a unique design caused by the dusting of gold. Acid mark—Made in France. U.S. introduction 1924. (4-1/2").

snuff bottle with a moulded design of entwined branches and a bird of paradise in full flight. (3-1/4").

173 Black opaque glass sailing ship bottle trimmed in gold for "Caravelle" by Marcel Guerlain of Paris, France. The Marcel Guerlain Company was founded in 1923. Circa 1924. (5").

175 A United States design patent was issued in 1924 to Jacques Worth of Paris, France for this "Dans La Nuit" cobalt blue bottle signed R. Lalique. (5-1/2").

176 Spherical flacon in clear glass with blue enamelling was designed by Rene Lalique for "Dans La Nuit" by Worth. Circa 1924. (5-1/2").

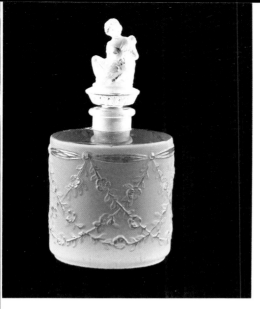

177 Beautiful frosted glass bottle with a moulded flower pattern and a figural stopper in the shape of a woman holding flowers was designed by J. Viard for "Fadette" by Richard Hudnut. Bottle marked—Bottle made in France. Numbered stoper. (4").

178 The Babbitt Co. of Philadelphia started using the name "Fleur de Nuit" for perfume in 1924. The bottle had a brass screw cap. (3-1/4").

179 Rectangular crystal flacon with a frosted knob stopper moulded with an entwined branch design held "Muguet des Bois" by Coty, introduced in the U.S. in 1923. Numbered stopper. (8-1/2").

180 Corday's signature perfume "Toujours Moi" was used for many years in Notre Dame and other famous cathedrals in Paris as an incense. Polished bottom. U.S. introduction 1924. (3-1/2").

181 Squatty, round, ribbed glass flacon with clear, petal-shaped panels and orange enamelling has an orange glass button stopper. The flacon held "IX" perfume by Delettrez. Bottle marked—J. Viard. Circa 1920's. (3").

182 Small 1/3 ounce bottle decorated with moulded fans, with a black glass fan-shaped stopper, came in a soft suede leather case with silver clasp. It held various Lentheric perfumes. Introduced in 1924, the bottle received a U.S. patent in 1926. (2-1/2").

overtones of rose and jasmine, called "Joy" was introduced. The clever merchandising slogan 'the world's most expensive perfume' for "Joy" was the inspiration of Elsa Maxwell. The Jean Patou flacon most sought by collectors is for "Normandie", created in 1935 to commemorate the launching of the famous ocean liner. The flacon came set in a silver metal, stylized replica of the ship.

PRINCE MATCHABELLI

Prince Matchabelli Parfums owed its existence to the Russian Revolution which cast up on these shores in the early 1920's the cultured, charming Russian Nobleman, Prince Georges V. Matchabelli. The Prince as a young man trained as a geologist, but he had learned to blend perfumes as a hobby. Upon his arrival in New York, he opened a small boutique on Madison Avenue called Rouge et Noir. The boutique carried antiques, Parisian novelties, Russian and Egyptian cigarettes, and blended perfumes to order. So successful were the "Individual Perfumes", that in 1926 Matchabelli started his perfume company. Among the first perfumes marketed were "Duchess of York", "Ave Maria", and "Princess Nina" named after the Prince's sister. The distinguished trademark of a crown and a bottle in the shape of a crown was an adaptation of the crown that appeared at the top of Prince Matchabelli's family coat-of-arms. The Prince patented the familiar bottle in 1927. A clear and frosted crown bottle for the perfumes "Ave Maria", "Catherine the Great", and "Duchess of York" first appeared on the American market in the late 1930's. In 1936 "Katherine the Great" perfume could also be bought in a white enameled crown bottle. An azure-blue crown for "Beloved" was introduced in 1950, a willow green crown for "Wind Song" in 1953, and a red tinted crown for "Added Attraction" in 1956.

In 1936 Prince Matchabelli offered a new sceptre bottle for toilet waters and talcum powders. The bottle was designed from the old sceptre of the Russian Imperial family, topped by the Matchabelli crown. The scent "Infanta" was presented in 1938 in a round crown bottle instead of the regular crown. Prince Matchabelli introduced a crown and star decorated, flattened, round flask to hold "Christmas Rose" cologne in 1940. The bottle was later used for other colognes. In 1947 "Summer Frost", a lime-colored cologne came in a special frosted glass version of the flask bottle. A gold crown miniature necklined in brilliants was sold in 1947 containing "Crown Jewel" perfume.

MAURICE RENTNER

American fashion designer Maurice Rentner was born in Warsaw, Poland. After the death of his wife, his father emigrated to the United States and opened a shirtwaist business. Rentner joined his father in America at age 11. At the age of seventeen he became a traveling salesman for another blouse firm. Disatisfied with the quality of the designs he was selling, he suggested changes to the necklines to the manufacturers. The suggestions were instrumented and the resulting styles sold more quickly.

Rentner soon became a sells representative for various wholesale dress firms. Again the designs disatisfied him and for a newspaper advertisement he created six satin day dresses. The advertisement received a large response, so Rentner decided to switch to the design side of the industry. In 1916 he opened his own dress firm. His designs reached the peak of their popularity during the 1940's.

Maurice Rentner introduced several perfumes to the market. The two most popular were "Twenty One" marketed in 1945 and "Eight Thirty" marketed in 1946.

ROGER & GALLET

The firm of Roger & Gallet was founded in Paris in 1862 by M. Armand Roger and Charles Gallet. In 1862 Roger and Gallet acquired the formula for the famous Farina Parisian Eau de Cologne. The containers used by Roger and Gallet were lush, chic, and had timeless great taste. The flacons were made by such great glasshouses as Lalique and Baccarat.

One of the earliest perfumes marketed by Roger and Gallet in America was "Fleurs d'Amour" (flowers of love). The square crystal bottle with cut glass top by Baccarat had a lovely embossed label showing cupid holding a bouquet in one hand and throwing flowers with the other. The longest selling perfume was "Violette de Popma", introduced in 1895.

The perfume "Le Jade", introduced in the U.S. in 1923, came in a spectacular green Lalique presentation flacon in the form of a Chinese snuff bottle with a moulded design of entwined branches and a bird of paradise in full flight. The oval Lalique bottle for "Pavots D'Argent" (silver poppies), introduced in the U.S. in 1927, was moulded in shallow relief on one side with two overlapping flowerheads with a moulded flowerhead stopper. Lalique also made the presentation flacons for the Roger & Gallet scents "Narkiss" and "Cigales". The perfume "Narkiss" came in a flattened heart shape flacon, moulded on each side with an open flower with brown enamelled center and the stopper was moulded with two bees. It came in a silk lined case with a matching open flower on the cover. The four-sided flacon for "Cigales" had a moulded cicada or locust at each shoulder. The flat, circular stopper was moulded as an open flowerhead.

In 1931 Roger & Gallet marketed "Feu Follet" (flame of folly) in the United States. The smart flat bottle, decorated with a row of diamonds up the center, had a box with similar decoration. The perfume "Fugue" presented in 1937 came in a lovely Baccarat flask of deeply cut crystal in a beautifully styled box of simple Duo design. During 1934 Roger and Gallet repackaged seven perfumes in buff containers trimmed in dark brown and labeled in gold. The bottle was a tall, square, crystal design, decorated with a row of five stylized roundels along the top. In 1940 Roger & Gallet presented "Blue Carnation" perfume in a handsome bottle which rested on a blue and gold base. The box was beautifully decorated with raised carnations of blue and pink.

NETTIE ROSENSTEIN

Nettie Rosenstein Perfumes was founded in 1946 in New York by the American designer Nettie Rosenstein. Born in Austria, Nettie, with her parents Joseph and Sarah Rosencrans, emigrated to this country in the 1890's. On arrival in the United States her parents opened a dry goods store on 118th Street where she was to learn about fabric. Sewing was a natural talent with Nettie and by the age of eleven she was making her own clothes.

In 1913 Nettie Rosencrans married Saul Rosenstein. She started a custom dressmaking business in her home in Harlem about 1916. The firm was moved to a more up-scale address on East 56th Street in 1921 where she employed 50 full-time seamstresses. She moved from custom designing to wholesaling when a buyer from I. Magnin in California became interested in her designs. Several times a year Nettie Rosenstein would travel to Paris for ideas she whould then adapt to her own collections. She popularized the 'little black dress' with the American woman. Among her clients were Dinah Shore, Norma Shearer, Hildegarde, and Mamie Eisenhower.

Nettie Rosenstein entered the perfume field in 1946 with a fragrance called "Odalisque", which was dramatically packaged in gold and white. Another best selling Rosenstein fragrance "Tianne" was introduced in 1948.

ROSINE

The twentieth century was to see the long-lasting marriage between high fashion and perfume take place. The couturier that started the trend of marketing fragrances to harmonize with his designs was Paul Poiret, a name almost synonymous with Art Deco. A design genius, Poiret studied under both Worth and Doucet. He opened up his own couture salon in 1903 at the age of twenty-four and soon his colorful, exotic, fluid designs became

183 Rochambeau Import and Export Co. of New York imported this hand-blown bunch of grapes, each small bottle with a different scent. Circa 1924. (5/8'').

184 Delettrez of Paris marketed the perfume ''Reveillon'' in Europe in the early 1920's and launched it in the U.S. in 1925. The Baccarat bottle is decorated with a black and gold enamelled tree design. (3-7/8'').

185 Opaque black glass bottle in a smart gold box with oversized tassel held the fragrance ''Byzance'' by Grenoville. Bottle by Verreries Brosse. European introduction 1925, U.S. introduction 1926. (2-1/2'').

186 Guerlain debuted the perfume ''A Travers Champs'' in the U.S. in 1924. The clear crystal Baccarat bottle was also used for the perfumes ''Guerlinade'' and ''Candide Effluve''. (5-1/4'').

187 Frosted glass bottle with a moulded shell design and a red glass stopper was patented by the Woodsworth Co. in 1925. (3-1/2'').

188 Rene Lalique created this beautiful bottle, moulded with a portrait of a woman's face surrounded by radiating flowers, for "La Belle Saison" by Houbigant. Circa 1924. (4").

189 Picture frame package for "La Belle Saison" by Houbigant. Circa 1924.

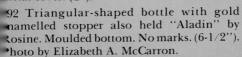

190 Black glass purse bottle for "Byzance" by Grenoville had a screw cap under the gold metal cover. (2").

192 Triangular-shaped bottle with gold enamelled stopper also held "Aladin" by Rosine. Moulded bottom. No marks. (6-1/2"). Photo by Elizabeth A. McCarron.

191 Beautiful opaque, jade green flacon for "Femme de Paris" by Ybry received a U.S. patent in 1925. The same bottle design was also used for "Dèsir du Coeur" in ruby and "Mon Ame" in amethyst. A less costly clear crystal bottle was added in 1934. Acid mark—made in France. (2-3/4").

the rage of fashion-conscious Paris. Poiret gradually became interested in every type of design from textiles to room decor and established a design firm called Atelier Martine named after one of his daughters.

In 1911 Poiret founded the company Parfums Rosine, named after his other small daughter, to produce perfume. Poiret created his perfumes with the assistance of Dr. Midy and M. Schaller, a perfumer. Rosine perfumes replaced the typical rose and lavender scents of the era with exotic, oriental-inspired perfumes. His perfumes were rich, mysterious blends using such ingredients as sandalwood, geraniums, begonias, spices, amber, and balsams. The intriguing, opulent packaging and bottles used by Rosine were designed for the most part by the Atelier Martine under Poiret's supervision, and made in Murano, Italy. The firms of Baccarat and Lalique also made bottles used by Rosine. Two unusual deluxe metal flacons by an unknown maker, highly sought by collectors, were used by Rosine for the perfumes "Aladin" and "Antinéa ou au fond de la mer".

Rosine perfumes made a short debut in America in 1913, but the beginning of the first world war soon stopped the flow of perfume from Paris. After the war the supply began again, but a real push to capture an American market for Rosine perfumes was not made until the mid-1920's when the company opened an office in New York at 20 West 37th Street.

HELENA RUBINSTEIN

Helena Rubinstein, one of eight children of a middle-class Jewish family, was born in 1882 in Krakow, Poland. In 1902, at the age of twenty, she traveled to Melbourne, Australia to visit relatives. She compared her beautiful creamy complexion to the sun- and heat-damaged skins of the Australian women and realized a cold cream she had been using since childhood helped protect her skin. Rubinstein sent a request to her mother for a supply of the cold cream and then opened a shop in Melbourne. The shop also sold other skin and hair products. The business was a tremendous and overnight success.

Placing her sister in charge of the Melbourne shop, Rubinstein at the age of twenty-two left Australia to launch her business in Europe with $100,000 capital the shop had generated. She first went to Vienna, Dresden, Berlin, Munich, and Paris to study with different dermatologists and increase her understanding of scientific skin care. In 1908 she converted Lord Salisbury's house in London into a beauty salon which soon attracted the most fashionable ladies of English society. Rubinstein was constantly adding new lotions, creams, cosmetics, and perfumes to the line made under her name. In 1912 she opened a salon in the center of fashion, Paris. In 1914 she came to the United States to expand her evergrowing business. In 1918 she began to wholesale her product line to department stores. She was among the first to employ women to act as her sales representatives.

A great, long-lasting rivalry existed between Helena Rubinstein and her competitor in the beauty business, Elizabeth Arden. Both Elizabeth Arden and Madame Rubinstein would swap employees, copy packaging, and borrow good advertising ideas. A bitter war over personnel was waged for years. Miss Arden, in 1938, lured away Madame Rubinstein's general manager with a salary offer of $50,000 a year and eleven members of his staff left with him. Madame was furious and wanted revenge. In 1934 Arden had divorced her husband and business manager, T. J. Lewis, legally enjoining him from entering the beauty business for five years. When the five years were up, in 1939, Madame hired him as the new manager of her firm.

Helena Rubinstein was a short, top-heavy woman with distinctive features and straight black hair which she wore gathered into a knot in the back. In 1908 she married an American chemist Edward J. Titus. They had two children, Roy Valentine and Horace Gustav. After twenty-five years of marriage she divorced Titus in 1937. A year later, Madame Rubinstein married a charming Georgian nobleman, some years younger than she, Prince Artichil Gourielli-Tchkonia.

The first perfumes marketed by Helena Rubinstein were "Mahatma" and "Tabac Russe" which were introduced in France. Helena Rubinstein introduced "Water Lily" perfume in 1934 in an opaque black glass cone-shaped bottle with a water-lily stopper. "Enchanté" cologne came in a bottle of similar design in clear glass with a frosted lily stopper. Designated by scenes etched on their bottles, the dramatic scents "Town" and "Country" were marketed in 1936. The colognes came in a candle shaped bottle. In 1937 the perfume "715", which took its name from the Rubinstein salon at 715 Fifth Avenue, came in a clear glass skyscraper bottle.

Named after a ballet of that name, "Gala Performance" came in a lovely glass ballerina bottle. In 1947, the same year Princess Elizabeth of England married Prince Phillip the Duke of Edinburgh, Helena Rubinstein introduced a French perfume called "Command Performance". The bottle looked like a squared, sawed-off, "Intoxication" by D'Orsay bottle. The bottle was packaged in a box of the same shape. Rubinstein, inspired by Gauguin's paintings of beautiful Tahitian women, introduced the perfume "Noa Noa" in 1954, imaginatively packaged in shades of amber and bamboo. The name "Noa Noa" means "so very fragrant" in Tahitian.

SCHIAPARELLI

Elsa Schiaparelli was an inventive, cultured designer who brought a refreshing sense of humour, daring, and Bohemian outlook to the fashion industry. Born into a prominent Roman family in 1890, she was educated in French, Swiss, and English schools. Interested in philosophy and poetry, she wrote "Arethusa" which was published when she was sixteen. When she was in England at the beginning of World War I, she was married to a Polish gentleman. After the war, Schiaparelli and her husband went to the United States where she worked as a movie script writer and translator. Her daughter Marisa, who was later to help in Schiaparelli's perfume business was born in New York.

With the breakup of her marriage, Schiaparelli went to Paris in the 1920's and acquired French citizenship. Her skill in designing and making her own clothes led Schiaparelli to designing sweaters which were made up by knitters in the Paris Armenian colony. By 1929 Schiaparelli had opened a business called "Pour le Sport" on the Rue de la Paix. By 1935 her success enabled her to move to larger premises—a 17th century building on Place Vendôme. At this address were sold many types of clothing for women—dresses, evening gowns, knitted wear, hats, lingerie, sportwear and accessories, as well as Schiaparelli jewelry, cosmetics and perfumes.

Schiaparelli's first perfume was called "Salut", created in 1934, but not marketed in the U.S. until later. The best known of her perfumes, "Shocking", was an instant success when introduced in 1937. The bottle of hand-etched Bohemian crystal was the joint design of Schiaparelli and a well-known surrealist artist Eleanor Fini. The bottle is said to have been inspired by the dressmaker's dummy that Schiaparelli had used when making clothes for Mae West. Elsa Schiaparelli filed for a U.S. patent on September 17, 1936 for the innovative flacon, several months before the perfume made its debut.

The bottles for all of Schiaparelli's perfumes have been truly creative and, therefore, highly collectible today. In 1939 "Sleeping", advertised as a night perfume, was introduced in a crystal candle in a holder flacon made by Baccarat. Also in 1939, her "Snuff" perfume for men was launched in a crystal pipe-shaped bottle. Salvador Dali, a personal friend of Schiaparelli, designed the gorgeous rayed sun stopper bottle in crystal made by Baccarat in 1945 for the Schiaparelli fragrance called "Roi Soleil". The bottle for "Zut" presented to the U.S. market in 1949 was shaped like the missing half of the "Shocking" torso, dressed only in a pair of painted-on panties. The bottle was so offensive to the typical American woman of the day that the perfume was only marketed in the U.S. for a few short years. Another unusual Schiaparelli bottle, that looked like a gilt-veined ivy leaf, was made for the fragrance "Succès Fou", introduced to the U.S. in 1953.

193 Houbigant used this gold-embellished, crystal, Louis XV flacon by Baccarat for both ''Quelques Fleurs'' and ''Parfum Ideal''. Numbered stopper. Circa 1925. (7-3/4'').

196 Unusual perfume presentation for ''Les Parfum XXIII'' by Delettrez is called by collectors 'String of Pearls'. Each graduated pearl-shaped bottle had a cork stopper with a kid leather cover. (Box 11-1/4'').

194 Clear and frosted glass flacon used for ''Rève De Noël'' by Veldez of Paris. Bottle marked—Linnerie France. (4-1/4'').

195 The perfume ''Shari'' by Langlois (United Drug Co.) came in a silk fabric-covered box. Circa 1925. (2-3/4'').

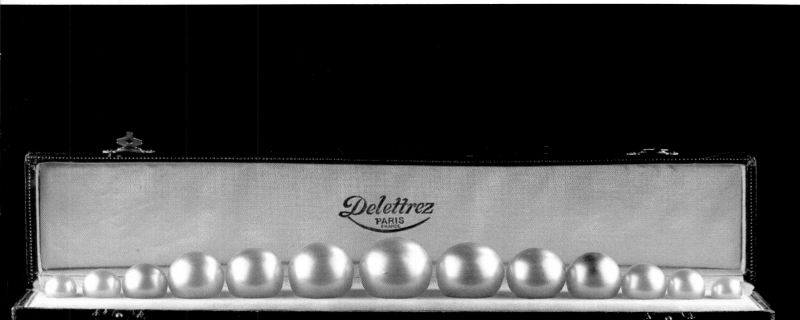

197 Moulded clear glass flacon decorated with gold has a Richard Hudnut label. Perfume unknown. No marks on bottle. (2-1/4'').

198 Small clear and frosted glass purse flaconette was marketed by the Harriet Hubbard Ayer Company. (2'').

199 The perfume ''Le Gourde du Poete'' was made and bottled in France in hand-blown gourd-shaped bottles. The Rochambeau Import and Export Co. imported the set to the U.S. Circa 1923. (1-1/2'').

200 Nude woman, metal, Art Deco holder with clear glass bottle was made in France for the Vantine Co. The holder was signed by the designer A. Ouveb. Circa 1920's. (7-1/2'').

201 The perfume ''Maskee'' by Ciro was sold in a clown shaped bottle in a black satin box with a whimsical figure of a clown in gold on it. European introduction 1923, American 1925. (8'').

SHULTON

William L. Schultz founded Shulton Inc. in New York in 1934. Schultz learned the business from working at the Lightfoot Schultz Co. The name Shulton was derived from Schultz and Son. The company first specialized in quality soap and cosmetics, but in 1937 perfumes were added to the line. The first fragrance marketed was "Early American Old Spice" inspired by an old potpourri recipe of rose petals and Far Eastern spices. The packaging was the inspiration of William Schultz and was the first comprehensive theme on early Americana used for toiletries. The bottles for the perfume and toilet-water were authentic reproductions of stiegel bottles. The design on them in colored enamels were inspired by "brides' boxes" in the Metropolitan Museum of Art. The packages had a wood finish and were decorated with gay little figures, flowers, and mottoes. The scent "Friendship's Garden" introduced in 1940 was inspired by the memorable gardens of Charleston. The bottle made by Wheaton came in a lovely triptych box.

George L. Schultz, the son of the founder, commissioned eight master perfumers to develop an unusual, truly new perfume for Shulton. The search resulted in "Escapade", introduced in 1954. Shulton developed an undulating, free-form shaped bottle, topped with a 23 karat gold-flecked cap. The bottle rested on a free-form dais that resembled unpolished white porcelain.

STUART PRODUCTS CO.

The Stuart Products Co. was started in St. Paul, Minnesota by William B. Cohen in 1935. The company specialized in inexpensive novelty perfumes and became one of the largest producers in this country. Stuart Products sold its perfume to variety stores, drug stores, and mail order firms.

The company's first big success was "Floral Quintuplets", designed by Robert B. Karoff in 1936. The set of five bottles, each with a cute hand-painted wooden screw top and ruffled collar retailed for about 39¢. The same bottles were used by Stuart for several different novelty items and can be found with Mexican hats and serapes, graduation caps and gowns, feather collars, or jockey caps and silks. Stuart Products also marketed several metal, miniature furniture novelties that held bottles of perfume. Many of the perfume items made by Stuart were sold under the name Karoff Creations of New York. Stuart Products Co. continued to manufacture imaginative, well-made, yet inexpensive, perfume novelties until 1946. In 1947 the name of the company was shortened to the Stuart Co., which was in operation throughout the 1950's.

SUZY

Suzy was a Parisian creator of millinery whose labels went into some of the most divine and fashionable hats of the 1930's and 1940's. Her first perfume "Ecarlate de Suzy" was introduced in the United States in 1940 and distributed by S. P. F. of America, Inc. The Baccarat crystal bottle was appropriately crowned with a Suzy hat as a stopper. The bottle rested firmly on a scarlet satin foundation in front of a small mirror which reflected its charm. Three sizes, ¼, ½, and 1 ounce, were marketed.

In 1943 Suzy marketed a replica of a hat stand used in her famous salon decorated in gay scarlet and gold. Three, tiny, clear hat boxes, each holding a miniature bottle of Suzy perfume, were perched on the stand. The perfume "Madrigal" trademarked in 1944 was packaged in a diamond-shaped box, studded with sparkling stones on a blue base.

TUSSY (LESQUENDIEU)

Tussy Cosmetiques, originally called Parfumerie Lesquendieu, was founded in Paris in 1882 by Joseph Lesquendieu. Tussy, the name of Lesquendieu's best selling lipstick, eventually gave its name to the company. Lehn and Fink Products Corporation purchased Tussy Cosme-

202 Two crackle finish bottles with pointed opaque glass tops were used for "Orange Blossom Fragrancia" by Raquel Inc. of New York. The perfume was marketed in 1927. The bottles were made by Wheaton. Photo courtesy of the Museum of American Glass at Wheaton Village.

203 Jean Patou, the famous French couturier, launched three perfumes, "Amour Amour", "Adieu Sagesse", and "Que sais-je?" in 1925 in this classic flacon. The flacon was designed by Sue et mare. (Dummy bottle 5").

205 Jet black, opaque glass flacon used for "Le Dandy" by D'Orsay. Numbered stopper. (3-1/2").

204 Imitating the popular "Xmas Bells" by Molinard, Dubois also used an opaque black glass bottle in a red box for "Xmas Chimes". (2-1/4").

206 Fabulous opaque black glass flacon decorated with red, white, and gold enameling with the original box. No labels. Maker unknown. (4-1/4").

207 Black opaque glass cube bottle with the stopper and rim moulded with lizards held the D'orsay perfume "Mystère". When D'Orsay trademarked the name in the U.S., it claimed the use since 1915. Bottle marked—R. Lalique. Numbered stopper. Bottle circa 1920's. (3-3/4'').

209 Sue et Mare designed the black, opaque glass, cubistic flacon for the masculine perfume "Dandy" by D'Orsay. Numbered stopper. (3-1/2'').

208 Black opaque glass bottle with simple stopper was also used for "Reve De Noël" by Veldez. No marks. (3-3/4'').

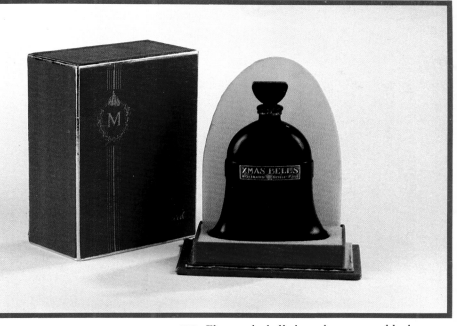

210 Flattened, bell-shaped, opaque black glass flacon with gold lettering was used by Molinard for the perfume "Xmas Bells" introduced in 1926. Acid mark—Made in France. (4-1/4'').

211 Renoir Parfums Ltd. of New York patented this mannequin bottle in 1947. The bottle was made by Wheaton. Photo courtesy of the Museum of American Glass at Wheaton Village.

tiques in 1928. "Rouge et Noir" was the first perfume marketed in France and was imported to America in 1928. In 1935 the "Rouge et Noir" perfume came in an imported black glass bottle and white plastic container which served as a decorative base.

A haunting perfume called "Safari" was presented in 1937. The attractive crystal wedge bottle was packaged in handsome boxes of white and gold finished with a tassel. In 1947 a quiet fragrance called "Terpsichore" came in a simple flacon in a leather jewel case. The perfume "Optimiste" was introduced in France in 1943 and the United States in 1948. "Optimiste" was a complex floral blend in a package decorated with clouds, stars, mandolins, Pierrot and Pierrette.

ALLEN B. WRISLEY

During the early 1860's two brothers Allen and George Wrisley, born in Gill, Massachusetts, worked their way west by slow stages to seek their fortune. A long stop in Ohio allowed Allen to study at Oberlin College where he earned his way by teaching in log cabin schools. The boom town of Chicago was their final stop. In 1862 the brothers invested their small savings in wooden kettles, rented an undistinguished building on the edge of the business quarter and started making soap. In the beginning they handled everything themselves. During the day they would make sales calls and deliver finished merchandise and at night they made the soap.

The brothers changed locations several times in response to their expanding business. In 1882 the brothers purchased two lots on South Fifth Avenue which were the beginning of a permanent home. Here they built a six story structure.

It was toilet soaps which were to bring fame and fortune to the Wrisley name. They started making hard milled toilet soap about 1880. The Wrisley Co. was among the first to manufacture smooth, hard, long-lasting bars which are still standard in the industry today.

The Allen B. Wrisley Co. added colognes and talcum powders to its product line about 1895. The colognes were not given much emphasis until the 1930's when aggressive advertising was put to use.

An interesting bottle was used for Wrisley's "Queens Guard" cologne introduced in 1936. The stopper resembled the head of a guard with helmet and the rest of the bottle gave the suggestion of a uniform. In 1938 Wrisley introduced two attractive ribbed bottles holding cologne and bubble bath topped with wooden stoppers. They came on a metal tray with wooden trim to match the bottle caps.

In 1939 Wrisley decided to follow the new trend in home decoration for early American furniture by presenting its colognes in bottles that would blend with the fashion. Wrisley commissioned the Fenton Art Glass Co. to make reproductions of a classic opalescent hobnail bottle blown in 1779. Five different colognes came in the bottle which sold for one dollar. Ads of the time stressed the re-use value of the bottle for vases, lamp bases or as a decorative home accessory.

The hobnail bottle was such a success that Wrisley also presented "White Flower" cologne in 1942 in an antique reproduction. The handsome milk glass bottle with embossed diamond-quilting was shaped like a Victorian barber bottle. In 1943 Wrisley presented "Frille" cologne in three different melon-ribbed opalescent bottles with neck frille made by Fenton Art Glass. These bottles were also used by the DeVilbiss Co. of Toledo, Ohio.

YARDLEY

Yardley of London was founded in 1770 by Thomas Yardley with a royal charter from King George III. Thomas Yardley was of the same family as an early governor of Virginia. The first scent marketed in the United States was "Lavender" which was first introduced in England about 1780. The firm was honored with an appointment of Perfumer and Fine Soap Maker to H.R.H. the Prince of Wales in 1921 and later, in 1932, was honored again by a similar appointment to Her Majesty, Queen Mary. (cont. on p. 94)

212 Clear and frosted glass flacon with a moulded design of young children held the perfume "Sourire Fleuri" by Isabey. U.S. introduction 1926. (5").

213 Frosted glass skirt-shaped flacon with a milk glass figural stopper has no labels or marks. Cork and glass stopper. (4-1/4"). Photo by Elizabeth A. McCarron.

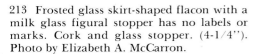

214 Black glass American made bottle held different floral odors by Cartier, distributed by Dermay Perfumers Inc. Cork and glass stopper (6-1/4").

215 A minor Parisian couture house, Martial et Armand had Rene Lalique design the flacon used for its perfumes "Un Rien", "Place Vendome", "Chypre", and "Ambre". U.S. introduction 1926. (7-1/2").

216 Clear flacon moulded into the design of a bunch of violets with blue staining and matching stopper held the perfume "La Violette de Gabilla" by Gabilla. This flacon was pictured in a Gabilla advertisement placed in a December 1926 *Femina* magazine. Bottle marked—R. Lalique. (3-1/4").

217 Deep orange, opaque glass bottle in a tasseled leather box held the perfume "Devinez" by Ybry. The perfume debuted in the U.S. in 1927. Acid mark—Made in France. (2-1/4").

218 Richard Hudnut presented the perfume "La Soirée" in the United States in 1926. The perfume came in a beautiful cut crystal flacon flashed with cobalt blue with a pressed glass stopper. Bottle marked—Made in France. Numbered stopper. (4").

219 Moulded glass bottle with a hieroglyphic-like design and a red glass coolie hat stopper complete with tassel held the perfume "1925" by Rosine. U.S. introduction 1926. (4-3/4"). Photo by Elizabeth A. McCarron.

In keeping with the origins of the company, Yardley adopted in 1913 the charming, romantic 'Flower Sellers' group as a trademark of all its lavender products. The group is from the painting by the famous F. Wheatley, published in 1793 as one of a series of color prints called the 'Cries of London'. This series of prints is now extremely scarce and valuable.

220 Square bottle with square flat top by Wheaton held Nettie Rosenstein's "Tianne" perfume introduced in 1948. Photo courtesy of The Museum of American Glass at Wheaton Village.

221 Shulton marketed "Friendship's Garden"
in 1940 in a lovely triptych box. Photo courtesy
of the Museum of American Glass at Wheaton
Village.

222 Lucien Gaillard, a contemporary of Rene Lalique, designed this striking, frosted glass flacon with a moulded butterfly woman design. It was used for the perfume "Femmes Ailées" by De Clamy of Paris. A December 1927 Vogue magazine article on perfumes identified the scent and maker. The bottle is a modern edition by Verreries Brosse.

223 Tall, frosted glass flacon held "Lily of the Valley" toilet water by Luxor. Circa 1926. (7-3/8").

224 The oriental perfume "Cappi" by Cheramy came in a bright colored, flowered box. Circa 1920's. (2-1/2").

225 Six-sided, opaque, pink glass flacon with silver star held the perfume "Astris" by L. T. Piver. The perfume was launched in the U.S. in 1927. Bottle by Baccarat. (4-1/2").

227 Black and gold flacon for Mury's "Notturno" came in a tasselled box. Bottle made in France by Baccarat. (3-7/8"). Photo by Elizabeth A. McCarron.

226 Jet black and gold Baccarat flacon for "Femme du Jour" by Corday. Numbered stopper. Circa 1926. (4"). Photo by Elizabeth A. McCarron.

228 Opaque black glass flacon with enamelled decoration was the deluxe package for "Kai Sang" by Corday. U.S. introduction 1924. (3").

229 Small frosted and clear glass bottle was used for Lucretia Vanderbilt perfume. It came in a blue and silver metal case.

230 Square crystal flacon with an arched top was made by Baccarat in 1927. No labels. (3-1/4").

231 Grey stained frosted glass flacon with four moulded arched sides decorated with a moulded design of tiny four petal flowers and matching stopper held "Lilas" by Gabilla. The bottle was shown in a 1926 French fashion magazine called *Femina*. Bottle marked—R. Lalique, made in France. (3-1/2").

232 Flacon used by Worth for the perfume "Vers le Jour". The bottle is moulded with a repeating triangular design with a matching stopper. Circa 1926. (4-1/4").

233 Thick cut crystal bottle with a pedestal base and green enamelled stopper held the perfume "Pois de Senteur de Chez Moi" by Caron, launched in 1927. A similar cut glass bottle is now being used to hold "Eau de Caron", introduced in 1980. Marked Baccarat, numbered stopper. (6").

234 Deluxe presentation for "Shari" by Langlois was a fountain-shaped flacon with gold trim. Bottle designed by J. Viard. Acid mark—made in France. (3-7/8").

235 Glass scent bottle decorated with moulded tulip heads over its surface and a tulip stopper by Rene Lalique for "Jaytho" by Jay-Thorpe. Jay-Thorpe was an exclusive New York fashion salon which catered to the carriage trade. Two sizes. (2-3/4").

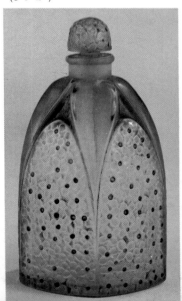

239 Modernistic crystal flacon with gilt trim was made by Baccarat for "Misti" by L.T. Piver. U.S. introdution 1927. (5-1/2").

237 The Lucretia Vanderbilt logo, consisting of a butterfly in a circle, was trademarked in 1927. The cobalt blue bottle was patented in 1928. The Lucretia Vanderbilt brand was marketed by McKesson & Robbins Inc. of Bridgeport, Connecticut. American-made bottle. (4-3/4").

238 Deluxe edition of "Blue Grass" by Elizabeth Arden decorated with gilding. (5-1/2").

236 The flattened round flacon, streaked with deep amber shading to yellow with a stopper moulded with a triangular design, was designed by Rene Lalique for the perfume 'Vers le Jour" by Worth. A U.S. trademark on the bottle claimed use of the design since 1926. 3").

240 Rectangular glass flacon with a moulded knotted rope design highlighted with black enamel was used by Forvil for the perfume "Les 5 Fleurs". Bottle marked—R. Lalique. Numbered stopper. Circa 1920's. (2-3/4").

241 Caron launched the perfume "Fête des Roses" in 1936. The gilded bottle designed by Félicie Bergaud was made by Baccarat. Numbered stopper. (5").

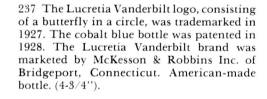

242 Hand-etched crystal presentation decanter used for many Lenthéric perfumes was patented in 1933. (7").

243 The familiar crown-shaped bottle was an adaptation of the crown that appeared at the top of Prince Matchabelli's family coat-of-arms. The bottle was patented in 1927. (3-1/4").

244 Faceted crystal bottle designed by Madame Vanpouille, co-owner of Caron perfume who designed many of the company's bottles and packages, for the perfume "Bellodgia" in 1927. Bottle marked Baccarat. Numbered stopper. (3-1/2").

245 Clear and frosted flacon moulded with a design of plumes with a plume-shaped stopper held the perfume "Si" by D'Herblay of Paris. Acid mark—made in France. (6-1/2").

246 Clear and frosted flacon by Verreries Brosse, introduced in 1936, held the perfume "Miracle" by Lenthéric. This bottle replaced the black and gold Baccarat flacon. (2-1/8").

247 "Cassandra" by Weil came in a bottle shaped like a slender Ionic column of hand-cut crystal with gold letter by Baccarat. Circa 1936. (3-1/2").

248 Round crackle glass bottle with a long neck and ball stopper was patented in 1933 by Lucien Lelong. It was used for many Lucien Lelong colognes. (7").

249 'Royalty evening cologne" came in a clear four-sided glass bottle. The screw top is a metal crown lined in red velvet. Bottle marked with a crown on the botton. (4-1/2").

252 Interesting presentation for "April Showers" by Cheramy had a small bottle of perfume dressed in a net skirt with an umbrella draped over the stopper. (5").

250 Silver trimmed opaque green glass bottle moulded with stars and a man-in-the-moon face, finished with a crescent moon stopper, held "Honeymoon" perfume by an unknown maker. Acid mark—France. Circa 1920's. (4-5/8").

251 Clear glass purse flacon with green bakelite screw-on cap with tassel held "April Showers" perfume by Cheramy. Circa 1930's. (2-1/4").

253 Square pressed glass bottle with a frosted glass stopper held the perfume "Gordon's" by Gordon Gordon. (3-3/4").

254 Bottle with a moulded waffle design on the sides and matching frosted stopper was made by Brosse to hold "April Showers" by Cheramy introduced to the U.S. in 1927. Photo courtesy Brosse USA, Inc.

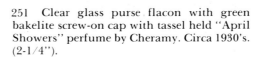

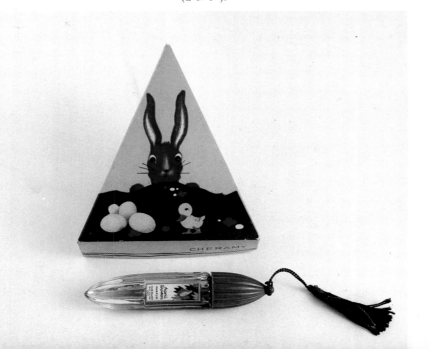

255 A crystal flacon designed and made by Rene Lalique held Parfums Lengyel's "Parfum Imperial". The Imperial Russian double eagle and the crown of Empress Catherine decorated the bottle. The package was covered with gold leaf. (2-1/2").

256 Lucien Lelong marketed "Impromptu" in 1937 in a clear and frosted sunburst flacon in a gold-emblazoned package. (5-1/2").

257 The designs in colored enamels for "Early American Old Spice" by Shulton bottles were inspired by 'brides' boxes' in the Metropolitan Museum of Art. Bottles by Wheaton. Circa 1937. (2").

258 Opaque green glass bottle with flower stopper was for an unknown scent. In recent years, Daniel Aubusson of Paris had the bottle copied in frosted glass for his perfume. Bottle marked—Made in France. Circa 1920's. (3-2/8").

259 D'Orsay's "Trophee" was introduced in France in 1935 and in the United States in 1936. The Baccarat flacon came in a bright yellow box. (1-3/4").

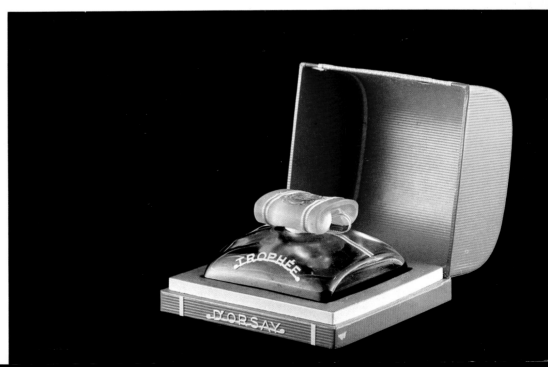

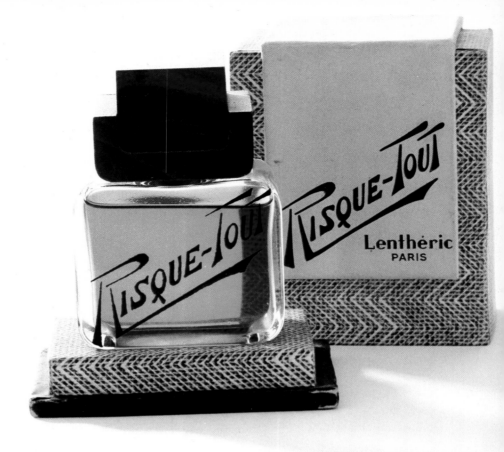

260 Lenthéric "Risque-Tout" perfume was presented in the United States as "Tweed" in 1935. Wooden stopper. (2-3/4").

261 Elizabeth Arden premiered "Blue Grass" in 1934; however, this bottle with two horses on the blue glass stopper cover wasn't introduced until 1936. The bottle was made in France by Verreries Brosse. (2-3/4").

262 Pressed glass talcum powder bottles used by Dubarry of England came in a smart Deco box. Circa 1920's. (Large bottle 5").

263 Houbigant travel set with the perfumes "Quelques Fleurs" and "Ideal" in a red leather case lined in white satin. Circa 1920's. (3").

264 Gueldy first introduced the perfume "Les Glycines" in the U.S. in the early 1920's. This clear crystal flacon was made by Baccarat about 1936. Numbered stopper. (3").

265 Frosted glass bottle decorated with gilt had a porcelain flapper girl head stopper. It contained "White Rose" perfume. Circa 20's. (3").

266 "Projets" (clear sailing) by Worth was introduced in 1936. The flacon by Rene Lalique has a moulded design of a sailboat. It was marketed in three sizes. (3-1/4'').

267 Coty's "Le Vertige" was introduced in 1936 in three sizes. The flacon was highly polished with facets cut into the glass surface. The original bottle was by Baccarat. Ground bottom—no marks. (4'').

269 Double circle design crystal flacon by Baccarat held the perfume "Toquade" by Silka. Circa 1926. (4''). Photo by Elizabeth A. McCarron.

270 A frosted glass bottle, a replica of an ancient Chinese scent bottle by Brosse held "Kobako" by Bourjois introduced in 1936. The bottle was encased in an Oriental red embossed plastic box. It came in four sizes. (3-1/4'').

268 Coty marketed this special refillable flacon in 1935 in a red leather case. This deluxe flacon was made of sterling silver and 14k gold, ornamented with two sapphires and one diamond. After the initial purchase, the flacon would be refilled with Coty perfume free of charge. (2-1/2'').

271 André Chenier marketed "Gardenia" perfume in a pressed glass bottle with a simple ball stopper. (1-1/2'').

272 Clear pressed glass bottle made in Czechoslovakia held the scent "Extrait Des Fleurs Chypre" by Soubise. Circa 1930's. (4-3/4").

273 Book shaped opaque black bottle with gilt trim held the perfume "Contes Choisis" by Marcel Guerlain. U.S. introduction 1927. (3-1/2").

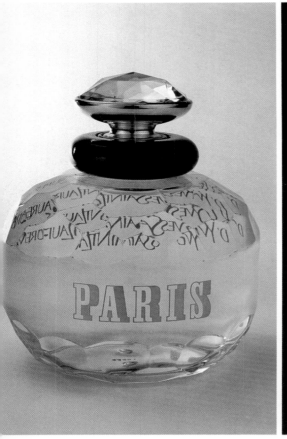

274 Yves Saint Laurent launched the perfume "Paris" in 1983 in this faceted bottle with jewel-like stopper. (7").

275 Heavy pressed glass bottle was used by Bienaime for the scent "Fleurs d'Ete". (4-1/2").

276 Inspired by a triumphal arch, this stylized clear crystal flacon made by Baccarat held "Voyage A Paris" by Corday, created in 1933 and introduced to America in 1935. Numbered stopper. (5").

277 The toilet water called "Duska" by Langlois (United Drug Co.) came in a brick red Deco bottle with black glass stopper. Circa 1930's. Bottle marked—France. (3-1/2").

279 Lenthéric's "Shanghai" perfume introduced in 1936 was fittingly presented in a flacon inspired by an antique Chinese bronze urn. In 1939 the design was simplified. Numbered stopper. (2").

278 Lionceau applied for a U.S. patent for this flacon on November 8, 1927. The bottle can be found in different opaque colors for various Lionceau scents. An advertisement of the era states that the bottle was designed by Lalique. Bottle marked—Made in France. (3-1/4"). Photo by Elizabeth A. McCarron.

280 Grenoville of Paris introduced this four bottle miniature set called "Les Quatre" in 1935. The round box was made of hard plastic and metal. (Bottle 2").

283 Introduced in the United States in 1935, "Dykil" by Lenthéric of Paris came in a smart pink box. It can also be found with a gray metal stopper cover. (2-1/4").

281 Parfumerie De Raymond triplex package held three dram bottles of perfume. The metal-edged, velvet, and satin-lined box of red leather could be reused as a jewel case. The complete package retailed at $3.00. Circa 1934. (Bottle 1-1/2").

284 Presented in 1934, Coty's "A Suma" came in a spherical, frosted glass flacon encircled by raised flowers. It was mounted on a black plastic pedestal which stood on four red plastic feet. The octagonal case had a lacquer-like finish. The deluxe edition came in a case of red Morocco leather with gold-tone metal fittings and ivory satin lining. (2-1/2").

282 Lucien Lelong presented this four miniature bottle "Penthouse" set in 1934. The box resembled a skyscraper. (2-1/2" box, 1-1/2" bottle).

285 Clear glass bottle with an accordian pleat design was used by Florel of Paris to hold "Duke of Kent" perfume. (3").

286 Lengyel's "Essence Imperiale Russe" was originally made in St. Petersburg, Russia in 1733. This exquisite cut crystal decanter with its collar of Hermine Fur was sold in two sizes in a beautiful red velvet coffret. This deluxe presentation was marketed as a special Christmas package in 1935 in the United States. (8-3/4").

289 In 1936 Prince Matchabelli offered a new sceptre bottle for toilet waters. The bottle was designed from the old sceptre of the Russian Imperial family, topped by the Matchabelli crown. (4-1/2").

290 Pressed glass bottle ornamented with a design of radiating branches held "Narcisse" perfume by Vernet. Circa 1930's. (3-1/2").

291 Pressed glass bottle shaped like a basket of flowers had a celluloid butterfly screw-on top. Maker and scent unknown. (3-1/4").

287 Duchess of Paris (Jolind) used this urn-shaped opaque white glass bottle for perfume. Circa mid-1930's. (2").

288 Prismatic clear glass bottle with a black plastic screw cap was used by the W. T. Rawleigh Co. of Freeport, Illinois. (2-1/8").

292 The perfume "Romance of the South Seas" came in a pressed glass bottle with a pair of birds perched on the sides. Circa 1930's. (3-1/2'').

293 Barbara Gould "Bridge Set" held four different perfumes. A contract bridge score pad was also included in the box. Circa 1934.

294 The perfume "Midnight Hour" by Deltah came in this clear glass bottle with frosted stopper. Circa 1934. (2-5/8'').

295 Renaud marketed this small vial of "Gardenia" perfume in its green leather box in 1933 in the United States.

296 Dressmaker's flacon designed by Elsa Schiaparelli for "Shocking" perfume, introduced in 1937. This surreal bottle was originally of hand-etched Bohemian crystal with glass flowers typifying the escaping fragrance. It was boxed in shocking pink satin. (5'').

297 Red opaque glass bottle with a moulded Japanese scene and screw top was made in Czechoslovakia. No labels. Circa 1930's. (3'').

298 Charbert used this drum inspired flacon for several of its perfumes beginning in the 1930's.

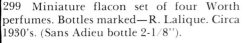

303 Indented octagon bottle used by Lanchere to hold six different floral colognes came in a marble and gold telescope box. Circa 1937. (5-1/2'').

304 Lucien Lelong Perfumes was established in France in 1924. The first perfumes put on the market were "A", "B", "C", and "N". In 1928 Lelong launched all four of his perfumes in the U.S. (3-1/2'').

299 Miniature flacon set of four Worth perfumes. Bottles marked—R. Lalique. Circa 1930's. (Sans Adieu bottle 2-1/8'').

300 Parfums Le Galion introduced "Sortilege" to the United States in 1937 in three sizes.

301 This corrugated bell bottle came in an ivory and gold gift case. The bottle was used to hold six different floral colognes by Lanchere. Circa 1937. (6-3/4'').

302 D'Orsay's "Belle de Jour" perfume came in an unusual milky white glass sculptured bottle by Brosse. The box was shiny black with a ribbon engraved on it. (3-1/2'').

305 Mary Dunhill used this corrugated bottle to hold several of the company's colognes. Circa late 1930's. (6-1/2'').

306 In 1930 Jean Patou presented a perfume cocktail bar with three new scents—"Dry", "Sweet", and "Bitter Sweet"—for mixing one's own perfume. Polished bottom. Bottle marked—Jean Patou France. (4"). Photo by Elizabeth A. McCarron.

309 Guerlain presentation for an unknown scent came in a red, white, and blue box. The flacon, trimmed in blue painted metal had a cobalt stopper with overlay panels. Bottle marked—Made in France. (4"). Photo by Elizabeth A. McCarron.

310 Smart black enamel and silver metal container held a bottle of similar design by Rene Lalique for the Lucien Lelong perfumes "A", "B", "C", "N", and "J". The package was patented in 1930. (4-1/2").

307 Large, square, cobalt blue glass bottle with frosted glass stopper for "Evening in Paris" by Bourjois. No marks. (4").

308 Opaque yellow glass flacon with a screw cap was used by Renaud for a floral perfume. Bottle marked—Made in France. (4").

311 Frosted glass, four-sided bottle moulded with a flower design was used by Arys. Bottle marked—Arys, Made in France, with a chalice mark with LM & AL on each side. (3"). Photo by Elizabeth A. McCarron.

312 Black opaque glass bottle used by Helena Rubinstein for "Water Lily" perfume, first marketed in 1934. (3").

313 Elizabeth Arden's "Night and Day" perfume came in a smart, simple clear bottle with an unusual many-faceted pink stopper cover. Bottle made in France by Brosse. (3-1/2"). Photo by Elizabeth A. McCarron.

314 The perfume "Djedi" by Guerlain was debuted in America in 1927. The perfume was created to commemorate one hundred years of Guerlain artistry. Metal piece on stopper. Bottle marked—Baccarat. (3-1/2"). Photo by Elizabeth A. McCarron.

315 Simple, cylindrical, opaque green, glass bottle held the perfume "Peking Moonlight" by Oriental. (3").

316 Striking turquoise blue bottle made by Brosse held "Springtime in Paris" by Bourjois, introduced in 1931. (1.9 oz.).

317 Tester racks were used in stores so that customers could sample a variety of a company's perfume. This tester was used by Lanvin.

319 Lucien Lelong's striking crystal pyramid bottle for "Opening Night", introduced in 1934, received a U.S. patent in 1935. (3").

318 Five piece "Co-Ed" toilette set including perfume came in a satin lined box. The labels were decorated with pink Deco inspired flowers.

320 Corday's eau de cologne bottle came in four colors—green for "Brut", amber for "Sec", blue for "Lilas", and rose for "Lavande" The bottles were first marketed in the U.S. in 1934. (6-1/2").

323 Tester racks were used in stores so that customers could sample a variety of a company's perfume. This tester was used by Houbigant.

321 Green opaque glass bottle in a gold box with large black tassel held "Sweet Pea" by Renaud. The bottle can also be found in other opaque colors, each used for a different Renaud perfume. U.S. introduction 1930. (4-5/8").

322 The Myrurgia perfume "Maderas De Oriente" (Woods of the Orient) had a splinter of a rare wood in every bottle. The bottle came in a bullet-shaped wooden box adorned with a large black tassel. Polished bottom. U.S. introduction 1929. (4-3/8").

324 Marly launched the perfume "Adagio" in the U.S. in 1932. The deluxe crystal oval flacon was trimmed in gold and came in a white satin-lined leather case. Numbered stopper.

328 D'Orsay presented the perfume "Milord" in the United States in 1933 in a smart chubby little bottle. A picture of Alfred D'Orsay is etched in the top. Acid mark—made in France on the bottom. (1-3/4").

329 Four-sided crystal flacon with an unusual moulded geometric motif trimmed in gold held the perfume "Pinx" by De Seghers. Acid mark—A. Jollivet, made in France. U.S. introduction 1932. (3-3/4").

325 Clear glass flacon with pointed stopper, moulded with a design of pinnated leaves, was designed by Rene Lalique for Arys. (3-1/2").

326 This flacon moulded with the design of French aviator's wings held the perfume "Vol de Nuit" by Guerlain. Metal top. U.S. introduction 1933. Bottle by Baccarat. (2-3/4").

327 Rene Lalique designed these ball-shaped bottles with moulded rings of petite flowers for Arys.

330 Tester racks were used in stores so that customers could sample a variety of a company's perfume. This tester was used by Houbigant.

331 Odd figural bottle has black enamel in the design lines. No marks or labels. Circa 1930's. (5").

332 Lucien Lelong presented the radiant perfume "Mon Image" in 1933 in a crystal bottle in a package of flashing mirrors. (2-3/4").

333 Clear octagonal bottle with a moulded flower design picked out in brown staining held "Mimsy" by De Raymond. Bottle marked—A. Jollivet. U.S. introduction 1930. (2-1/4").

334 The perfume "Surrender" by Ciro came in a jewel-faceted crystal bottle nestled in a Deco-inspired brown velvet and wood box. Marked—Baccarat. Circa 1931. (4-3/4").

335 Square, brick-red, opaque glass bottle with opaque black stopper held the perfume "Tabac Doux" by Marie Magdeline of Paris. (5-1/2").

336 Blue glass flacon and stopper of reeded cylindrical form held "Je Reviens" by Worth. Bottle by Rene Lalique. Circa 1931. (5-1/4").

337 Another flacon used for the perfume "Je Reviens" by Worth. Bottle marked—Made in France. (6").

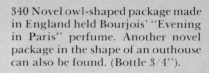

340 Novel owl-shaped package made in England held Bourjois' "Evening in Paris" perfume. Another novel package in the shape of an outhouse can also be found. (Bottle 3/4").

339 Two cobalt blue purse bottles used by Bourjois for "Evening in Paris", first introduced in America in 1929. Round bottle marked Austria, long bottle unmarked. (2", 3").

338 Cobalt blue bottle used by Marques de Elorza for the perfume "Argentina". U.S. introduction 1929. Acid mark—made in France. (4-1/4").

341 Presented in 1933, the perfume name "Heure Intime" meant intimate hour. The perfume was by Vigny and the bottle was made by Brosse. It came in 3 sizes, plus a purse flacon. Bottle made in France.

345 A U.S. patent was filed on November 21, 1929 for this clear, ribbed glass bottle with amberina stopper. It held various perfumes by Guimet of Paris imported by Storfer Laboratories.

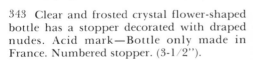

344 Beautiful fan-shaped bottle by Baccarat held Elizabeth Arden's "Cyclamen" perfume. Circa 1938. (6").

342 Square glass bottle with an opaque green glass top was used by De Raymond for "Demain" eau de toilette introduced in the U.S. in 1930. The bottle was also used for "Sweet Magnolia" by De Seghers, introduced in 1932. (4").

343 Clear and frosted crystal flower-shaped bottle has a stopper decorated with draped nudes. Acid mark—Bottle only made in France. Numbered stopper. (3-1/2").

346 Ybry bottle used in different sizes for various colognes and perfumes beginning in 1930. The one in the picture holds "Old Fashioned Garden". (6-1/8").

347 Lubin's "Ouvrez Moi" (open me) came in a little bottle of opaque black glass which resembled a lady's handbag. Every detail of a handbag was carefully carried out, right to the tiny silk cord which served as a handle. U.S. introduction 1937. (3").

348 The head on this milk glass flacon in the shape of a woman's bust lifts off to reveal an inner glass stopper. The flacon held "Coup de Chapeau" by Gilbert Orcel. Bottle by Brosse. (4-1/2").

349 Clear glass cylindrical flacon with moulded wisteria trailing from the shoulder came in a cylindrical brass case. It can be found in two sizes. Marked—R. Lalique. (3").

350 Beautiful amber glass flacon executed by Rene Lalique is moulded with a design of four turtles. Made for Morabito "No. 7" perfume, it came in three sizes. Bottle marked—R. Lalique. (5-1/2").

351 Launched in 1930 by Molinard, this clear and frosted tubular glass flacon decorated with a satyr kissing a nude woman held the perfume "Le Baiser du Faune". Bottle marked—R. Lalique. (6").

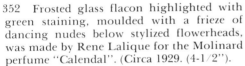

356 Short, squatty cobalt blue bottle with a frosted stopper moulded with flowers held "Evening in Paris" sachet. (2-1/4").

352 Frosted glass flacon highlighted with green staining, moulded with a frieze of dancing nudes below stylized flowerheads, was made by Rene Lalique for the Molinard perfume "Calendal". (Circa 1929. (4-1/2").

353-355 The perfume houses competed in the teens and twenties to make their salons as inviting and romantic as possible to the customer. The Richard Hudnut Salon in Paris, shown in the three photographs, was lavishly decorated with crystal, silver, marble, and mirrors. The murals were by the famous French lacquerist, Jean Dunant. (Illustrations 1928).

357 Miniature perfume pump dispenser made of brass, called a "Flirtgun", resembles an insecticide sprayer. Circa 1920's. (1-1/2").

358 Fashion advisors of the twenties recommended that the up-to-date woman carry her perfume with her at all times. Many interesting purse bottles and atomizers can be found from the era to add to a collection. This small, orange, bakelite purse atomizer was marketed by the Bo-Kay Co. Circa 1920's. (2'').

360 Opaque black bottle by Baccarat with a gold paper label for "Liu" by Guerlain came in a matching black and gold wooden coffret. The perfume was name after a character in Puccini's opera. Circa 1929. (2-1/4'').

359 Flacon made in Czechoslovakia with red glass stopper and red painted trim held the perfume "Dimanche" (Sunday) by Condé. It came in a box of black and gold with a shocking pink interior. Polished bottom. Numbered stopper. Marked—Made in Czechoslovakia. Circa 1930's. (3-3/4''). Photo by Elizabeth A. McCarron.

361 Cobalt blue bottle with a clear glass fan-shaped stopper was also used for "Evening in Paris" perfume. (4-1/4'').

362 Cute porcelain bottles in bright colors were made in Germany to hold "Canadian Beauty Revue Parfum" and "Canadian Club", a men's cologne. They can be found in sets of four. Circa 1920's. (Flapper girl 2-1/2", bellboy 3-1/4").

363 The Stuart Products Co. introduced "Castanettes" in 1937. The three flaconettes of perfume represented three Mexican senoritas colorfully costumed with zarapes and sombreros. (2-5/8").

364 Mould blown, dog and cat figural perfume bottles, made in Germany, were used to hold various floral scents. Circa 1920's. (2-1/2").

365 Figural perfume bottles made of luster-finished porcelain were made in Japan. The winking cat and chicken were used by Lioret and the rabbit by Delinet. The name Delinet was trademarked in 1927. (3-1/4").

366 Frosted glass bottle shaped like a dog with his eyes closed and tongue hanging out was called "Bonzo" by Potter & Moore of London. Bottle marked—Potter & Moore England. (3"). Photo by Elizabeth A. McCarron.

368 Two pressed glass bottles with hand painted wooden stoppers were marketed by Karoff (Stuart Products Co.). The second bottle introduced in 1938 was called "Picanette". It represented a southern mammy in a colorful silk dress. (4").

367 Cute begging dog bottle has a label that reads "OOLOO for Luck - Potter & Moore London". The name "Ooloo" is moulded above the tail, and printed in gold on the bottom is 'German Make'. Metal screw top. (3-1/8"). Photo by Elizabeth A. McCarron.

369 Beautifully detailed, opalescent glass, fish-shaped bottle screws on the black glass base which forms the stopper. Scent unknown. Acid mark—A. Jollivet, made in France. (4-1/2").

370 Rene Lalique filed for a U.S. patent in 1928 for the flacon which held the perfume "Le Parfum Des Anges". The flacon was moulded in the shape of a bell decorated with a design of two angels supporting a bell with a clover-shaped stopper. The perfume was made to celebrate the opening of the Oviatt building in Los Angeles. (3-1/4").

371 Pinaud's interpretation of the favorite heroine of 1937, Scarlett O'Hara. The doll-like figure in plastic came in several colors. It was filled with various floral colognes or skin perfumes. (7").

372 A gardenia perfume by Lenthéric of Paris called "Asphodèle" was introduced in the U.S. in 1928. The bottle had a triangular shaped metal and glass stopper. (5-1/2").

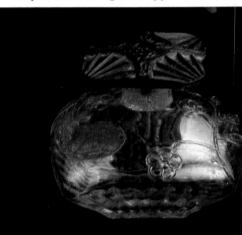

373 Clear glass flacon decorated with a moulded flowering vine pattern with matching black stopper held "Narcisse" by Vana Cie. Bottle marked— . Circa 1928. (2-1/2").

374 Red opaque glass flacon with a gold enamelled swirl design held "Mascarade" by L. T. Piver. Two sizes. Acid mark—France U.S. introduction 1928. (3-3/4").

375 La Lete perfumers used this pink satin glass box for "Blue Bird" powder. Circa 1929. (2-1/4").

376 and 377 Veolay of Paris (Violet) first started using the perfume name "Niobe" in 1915. This deluxe flacon with moulded birds on the sides by Rene Lalique was shown in a 1928 U.S. advertisement. (4-1/4").

382 Clear and frosted bottle used by Guimet for several different scents was imported to the U.S. by Storfer Laboratories, Inc. of New York. Circa 1928. (3-3/4").

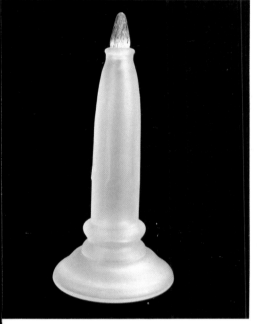

380 Inspired by the helmet of an officer in the Chevalier Garde, crowned by the double eagle, this clear and frosted flacon held Chevalier Garde perfumes: "Fleur de Perse", "Roi de Rome", or "H.R.H.". U.S. introduction 1937. (2-7/8").

378 Spencer Perfume Co. Inc. of South Bend, Indiana used this frosted glass candle bottle patented in 1928. Glass and cork stopper. (6-1/2").

379 Stunning flacon with a moulded scene showing a bride being led down the aisle by cupid held the perfume "Marche Nuptiale" by Marqués de Elorza of Paris. U.S. introduction 1929. Embossed mark—Made in France. (4-1/4").

381 The container for Lucien Lelong's "Indiscret" cologne is an interesting bottle made to look like carved ivory with a tracery of design in high relief. The material used feels like plaster and most have turned brown over the years. Circa 1937. (8-1/4").

383 Lovely crystal flacon with a golden lotus for a stopper held "Colony" by Jean Patou. The box is of woven jute. U.S. introduction 1937. (5").

384 Clear crystal eight-sided bottle has a frosted stopper with a moulded leaf design. It was used by Coty for "L'Aimant", introduced in 1928. Numbered stopper. (6-1/2").

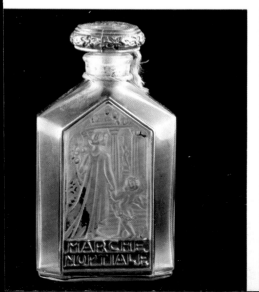

388 Octagonal bottle, also with a moulded geometric design decorated in gold enamelling, was for an unknown scent. Acid marked—A. Jollivet, Bottle made in France. (4-7/8"). Photo by Elizabeth A. McCarron.

385 The inspiration for Ciro's "Danger" bottle was a Baccarat vase displayed at the French Exposition of 1936. "Danger" was introduced in the United States in 1938. The large bottle in the picture is by Baccarat and the small bottle by Brosse. (4", 3-1/8").

386 Seven basic Roger and Gallet extracts were sold in this crystal clear flacon beginning in 1934. (4-1/4").

387 Lenthéric launched "Anticipation" in the United States in 1937. A taller form of the perfume bottle was used for the cologne called "Bouquet".

389 Yardley presented its formal evening perfume "Fragrance" to the United States in 1934 in a flower decorated box. Enameled mark-England. (2-3/4").

390 A Spanish senorita decorates the label for "Valencia" by Marques de Elorza. Bottle marked—made in France. U.S. introduction 1929. (3-3/4"). Photo by Elizabeth A. McCarron.

391 Guerlain's "Vega", named for the constellation, was placed on the American market in 1937. The attractive Baccarat bottle came in a box of rich ruby red. (3").

392 Cylindrical, green flacon with a pine cone stopper consisting of stepped glass disks held "Sans Adieu" by Worth. U.S. introduction 1929. Marked—R. Lalique. (5-3/4").

393 Saville of London presented "Mischief" perfume to England in 1935 and in the United States in 1937. The black opaque glass bottle snaps into a moulded plastic top hat. It was packaged in a miniature hat box. A hinged larger top hat with three perfume bottles was also marketed. (Hat 2-1/4").

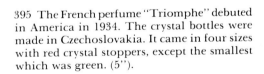
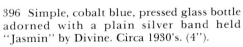

395 The French perfume "Triomphe" debuted in America in 1934. The crystal bottles were made in Czechoslovakia. It came in four sizes with red crystal stoppers, except the smallest which was green. (5").

394 Amber colored crystal bottle by Brosse held "Kismaju" by Le Clairac of Paris. Circa 1934. (5-1/8").

396 Simple, cobalt blue, pressed glass bottle adorned with a plain silver band held "Jasmin" by Divine. Circa 1930's. (4").

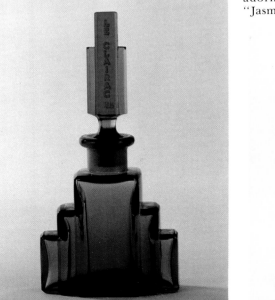

397 In 1937 Prince Matchabelli presented a perfume called "Infanta". It came in a new type of Matchabelli crown, round instead of oval, and rested on a cushion of royal-blue velvet. (1-2/8").

398 Bourjois presented "Mais Oui" (but yes) to the American market in 1938. (2-3/4").

399 Revillon's "Carnet de Bal" came in a diverting bottle, which reversed proved to be a brandy glass. It was introduced in Europe in 1937 and in America in 1938. (2").

400 Clear, Deco bottle for "Yu" by Harriet Hubbard Ayer was introduced in the United States in 1938. (5-1/2").

401 Pressed glass bottle with a sunburst design held "Impromptu" cologne by Lucien Lelong, introduced in the U.S. in 1938. The bottle received a patent in 1939.

402 Worth presented three flower fragrances, "Lilas", "Oeillet" (carnation), and "Gardenia" in 1939 in a beautiful R. Lalique bottle with an all-over moulded floral design. It was marketed in two sizes. (3-1/4").

403 Egyptian figures and hieroglyphics decorate this pressed glass dime-store novelty bottle. (2-1/8").

408 Four sided clear glass bottle decorated with swags was used for the perfume "Wine, Women, & Song" by L'Orle. Circa 1939. (4-1/2").

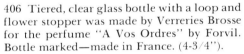

406 Tiered, clear glass bottle with a loop and flower stopper was made by Verreries Brosse for the perfume "A Vos Ordres" by Forvil. Bottle marked—made in France. (4-3/4").

409 Gold ribbed glass bottle held the perfume "Tail Spin" by Lucien Lelong. The bottle was patented in 1938. (3-1/2").

410 Corday debuted "Tzigane" eau de toilette in the U.S. in 1939 in this three ounce flask with frosted stopper. (6-1/2").

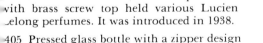

404 Unusual miniature feather shaped bottle with brass screw top held various Lucien Lelong perfumes. It was introduced in 1938.

405 Pressed glass bottle with a zipper design had a metal cap that slid open. The bottle was for "Cordon Noir" by Coty. Circa 1939. (4-1/2").

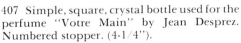

407 Simple, square, crystal bottle used for the perfume "Votre Main" by Jean Desprez. Numbered stopper. (4-1/4").

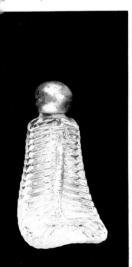

411 Babs Creations introduced "Yesteryear" perfume in 1939 to sell for $1.00. The Victorian style figural bottle came encased in a glass dome. (5-1/2").

413 Frosted glass mannequin bottle held t[...] perfume "847" by the Chicago dressmake[...] Eisenberg et Sons. Ads claimed the name ha[...] numerological fashion power. Circa 193[...] (3-1/2").

412 The famous Parisian fashion house of Revillon launched the perfume "Egoist" in France in 1935 and in the United States in 1938. (3").

414 A gilt sun decorates the flacon designed by Felicie Bergaud for the perfume "Aldona" by Caron. Numbered stopper. (4-1 2").

415 This aristocratic double eagle bottle held the perfume 'Nikki'' by Orloff. It came in a silk-lined velvet case and retailed at $10. Circa 1939. (4-3 4").

416 Famous American dress designer Hattie Carnegie started using this unique portrait bottle that held various scents in 1938. The bottle was made by Wheaton.

417 Saravel used this gold-capped crystal cube to hold the perfumes "Morocco" and "Sirocco". The bottle was patented in 1939. The perfume came enshrined in a blue and gray pavilion box. (1-1/2").

418 Three dime store novelty perfumes that retailed for 10¢. Some bottles were used by several different companies. Circa late 1930's and early 1940's. (4", 3-1 4", 4").

419 A violin shaped bottle by Brosse and violin shaped shocking pink box held the perfume "Zigane" by Corday. U.S. introduction 1949. (4-1/2").

420 Mary Chess Robinson took the designs of her chesspiece bottles from an antique chess set. Beginning in the late 1930's, Mary Chess perfumes were sold in them. The bottles were made by Wheaton.

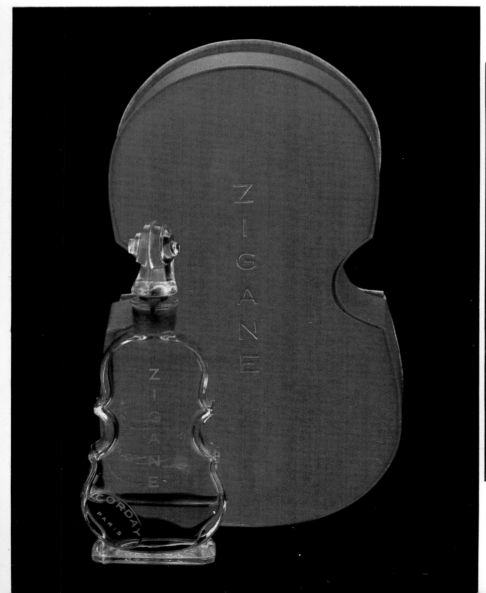

421 Cologne bottle for "Sleeping" by Schiaparelli. (7-1/2").

422 Blue opalescent hobnail bottle with the original wood and cork stopper made by Fenton Art Glass exclusively for Wrisley to hold various floral colognes. The bottle also came in white opalescent glass. The original selling price was $1.00. Circa 1939-1940. (6").

424 Miniature glass barrel, equipped with polished brass spigot and mounted on a polished brass stand held three different floral odors by Karoff (Stuart Products Co.). Circa 1939. (3-1/2" long).

425 Pressed glass flower basket bottle with painted flowers and matching stopper held "Fleurs de Jericho" by Benoit of Paris. Bottle marked—France. (4-1/4").

423 Gabilla used this bottle for various scents starting in the late 1930's.

429 Bradshaw of Boston packaged "Woodbine" perfume and toilet water in maple finish wood containers made in New England. The old fashioned girl shown held one dram of perfume. Circa 1940. (3-1/4").

430 The parfumeur Jean Desprez of Paris launched the perfume "Etourdissant" in 1939. The Deco style box housed a simple Baccarat crystal bottle. (3-3/4").

426 Famous New York hat designer Lily Daché launched two perfumes in 1941, "Dashing" in a poodle shaped bottle and "Drifting". The surreal "Drifting" bottle was shaped like a woman's breasts spouting from green leaves with a bright pink feather-topped stopper. American made bottle. (5").

427 In 1940 Helena Rubinstein presented "Gala Performance" perfume, christened after a ballet of that name. The bottle, shaped like a dancer, came in a stage-shaped box. Polished bottom. (5-7/8").

428 Karoff (Stuart Products Co.) introduced "Celestial Dream" perfume in 1940. The lovely nude figurine was made of transparent lucite in blue, smoke, or old rose. The bottle was mounted in a gilded brass or chromium finish. It retailed at one dollar. (6").

431 "Barette" by Stuart Products Co. was a miniature bar consisting of three bottles of perfume with brass stoppers representing a champagne goblet, bottle and cocktail shaker. Circa 1939. (4-1/2").

432 Modern flacon made by Brosse to hold the perfume "Nostalgia" by Germaine Monteil. European introduction 1941, U.S. introduction 1947. Photo courtesy Brosse USA Inc.

433 Lenthéric marketed "A Bientot" (goodbye) in the United States in 1938. (2-1/2").

434 American fashion designer Hattie Carnegie introduced her first perfume "Hattie Carnegie" in a black glass bottle reminiscent of an inkwell. Acid mark—Made in France. Gilding worn off stopper. (3-1/4").

435 Rene Lalique designed the multi-tiered bottle that held "Imprudence" by Worth. It was marketed in a box of midnight blue edged in gold. The perfume was marketed in three sizes. (3").

436 Guerlain's perfume "Coque d'Or" (bow of gold) came in a striking bow shaped bottle by Baccarat. It can be found in six sizes, three in gold and three in blue. Circa 1938. (2", 3-3/4").

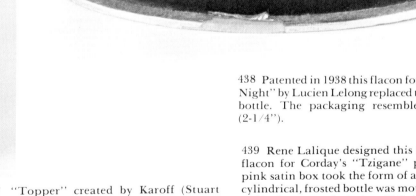

437 "Topper" created by Karoff (Stuart Products Co.) was a unique little perfume and sachet ensemble. A miniature champagne bottle perfume, two white silk gloves filled with sachet, a black walking stick, and a boutonniere were presented in a black felt top hat. Circa 1938. (4"). Photo by Elizabeth A. McCarron.

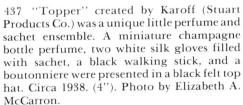

438 Patented in 1938 this flacon for "Opening Night" by Lucien Lelong replaced the pyramid bottle. The packaging resembled a stage. (2-1/4").

439 Rene Lalique designed this modernistic flacon for Corday's "Tzigane" perfume. Its pink satin box took the form of a violin. The cylindrical, frosted bottle was moulded with a stylized, geometric design. U.S. introduction 1938. (4-1/2").

441 The Paris perfumeur Jean Desprez presented the perfume "Votre Main" in 1939. This deluxe presentation, made of fine white porcelain shaped like a hand, has a pink rose porcelain stopper. No marks. (7-1/8"). Photo by Elizabeth A. McCarron.

440 Karoff (Stuart Products Co.) introduced "Par-fumes" in 1939. Each bottle represented a gold club with polished brass golf club head. They came in a miniature replica of a golf bag made of Scotch plaid silk with a hobnailed polished brass collar and base. The set retailed for $1.00. Included in the picture is a perfume lapel pin with screw top probably from the same era. (3" and 6").

442 Baccarat bottle for "It's You" by Elizabeth Arden was introduced in 1939. The bottle came as shown or had a golden torch in an opaque white hand. (7-1/2").

444 Schiaparelli marketed "Sleeping" in France in 1939 and in America in 1940. The charming Baccarat crystal candlestick bottle came in a box in the form of a cone-shaped snuffer in blue and gold. (6-1/2", 8").

443 Corday's first post-war perfume was called "Frenzy", handsomely packaged in a black and gold round box. It came in four sizes. Numbered stopper. Bottle made in France. Circa 1945. (3-3/4"). Photo by Elizabeth A. McCarron.

447 Flacon designed like a bow of a ship with a compass rose top held "Cap A La Vie" by Mury. The bottle was made by Brosse. Circa 1940. (4-1/4").

445 The eau de toilette "Gay Whirl" by Babs Creations debuted in 1940. A plastic ballerina stopper was poised atop a carpeted glass staircase bottle. (6-3/4").

446 Clear squatty bottle has a flower-shaped frosted stopper with a small artificial orange and orange blossom tied to its neck. The bottle held "Orange Blossom" perfume by Or-Blos of Jacksonville, Florida.

448 Clear glass bottle decorated with gold held the Lucien Lelong cologne "Jabot". The bottle was marketed in the U.S. in 1940 and received a patent in 1941.

449 Interesting clear glass oval flacon moulded with a scroll-work design was made by Brosse for Bruyere. (3").

450 This cylindrical flacon with a glass bow on top and a petticoat ruffle fashioned of glass which flirts along the curve of the flacon held "Confetti" by Lenthéric. Introduced to the United States in 1940. (6").

453 Kathryn (Kay Daumit) of Chicago introduced "Double Dare" in 1942. The bottle had a red bakelite screw cap and was also used for the perfume "Forever Amber". (5-1/4").

454 Brass container with lock and key held two perfumes by Cardinal of New York. Circa late 1930's, early 1940's. (4" across).

451 The Cleevelandt Corporation presented this miniature gilt harp holding "D'Amour" perfume in 1940. It came on a little red plush and wood stand and retailed for $1.00. (6").

452 Prince Matchabelli marketed "Christmas Rose" cologne in this crown and star decorated flattened flask and later used it for other colognes. Circa 1940.

455 Violin-shaped perfume bottle has realistic details. Bottle marked—Milano, Italy. (6").

460 Cocktail set with metal tray held perfume by Lauré of New York. Similar sets were marketed by Dainty Dabs and Charaise. Circa late 1930's, 1940's. (2-1/2").

458 Wrisley used this handsome milk-white bottle with gold trim to hold its "White Flower" cologne. Circa 1942. (6-1/2").

461 In a bottle shaped like a piece of twisted rope, Lucien Lelong presented "Sirôcco" to the U.S. market in 1942.

456 Pinaud launched the perfume "Lilianelle" in 1945 in a bottle decorated with white enameled polka-dots. The scent came in three sizes.

457 A handsome frosted and clear glass flacon by Brosse held the perfume "Fulfillment" by Delettrez introduced in the U.S. in 1941. The flacon can also be found with a flattened, square stopper.

459 In a champagne bottle look-a-like, Caron introduced "Royal Bain De Champagne" in 1941. (6-1/2").

462 Madame Suzy, a Parisian milliner, introduced her first perfume "Ecarlate de Suzy" (scarlet of Suzy) in France in 1939. The Baccarat crystal bottle, appropriately stoppered with a Suzy hat was marketed in the U.S. in 1940. The bottle came on a red satin foundation in front of a small mirror. It was sold in three sizes. Numbered stopper. (4-4/8").

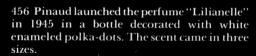

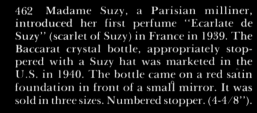

463 Round crackle finish bottle with a wooden screw top held "Spellbound" toilet water by Lynette. Circa 1943. (4").

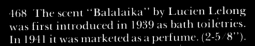

464 Small brass purse bottle shaped like an army gasoline can was called "My Jerrycan" by Marc Faël of Paris. Circa 1940's. (2").

465 "Spring Rain" cologne by Charles of the Ritz came in a 4 oz. parasol bottle with a wooden handle stopper and base. The bottle was patented in 1941.

466 Sherk first introduced the perfume "Renaissance" in 1921. The box and bottle shown is a design used starting in 1943. (4-3/4").

467 Pressed glass bottle shaped like a tassel held Wrisley's "Gold Tassel" cologne and talc introduced in 1942. (6-1/2").

468 The scent "Balalaika" by Lucien Lelong was first introduced in 1939 as bath toiletries. In 1941 it was marketed as a perfume. (2-5/8").

469 Ann Haviland introduced "Perhaps" in 1939. This bottle was shown in ads starting in 1941. (8-1/2").

470 Wooden sleigh presentation held four small bottles of Coty perfume. Circa 1940's. (Sleigh 9-1/2'', bottles 1-3/4'').

471 Schiaparelli introduced her first man's fragrance in 1940. Called "Snuff", it came in a pipe-shaped container in a cigar box package. (5-1/2'').

472 In a pink and white box, the bottle of "Chantilly" by Houbigant sits demurely framed by a lacy ruffle. U.S. introduction 1941.

144

474 Three bottle set of "Prince Douka" by Marquay of Paris. The bottles have frosted glass head-shaped stoppers wearing jeweled turbans and dressed in satin caps. The name "Prince Douka" was trademarked in the United States in 1951. (3").

473 Ciro's "New Horizons", introduced in 1941, came in a clean, simple bottle with a graceful curve that suggested the horizon. The stopper was a Deco inspired eagle. Bottle marked made in France. (3-1/8").

475 Verreries Brosse created this clear glass flacon shaped like a butterfly for Forvil. (3").

479 Dana introduced the oriental perfume "Tabu" in Europe in 1932. It wasn't until 1941 that it reached the American market in a box and bottle of simple, classic design. (2-3/4").

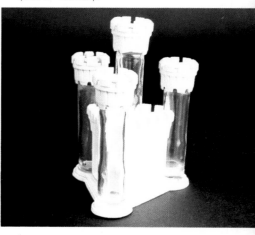

480 Brass perfume bar with lock and key held three small bottles of assorted Weil perfumes. (Bar 3" across).

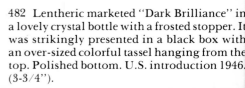

476 "Requete" by Worth made its bow in the United States in 1946. The flacon of flask form had scalloped edges, enameled in deep blue. Marked: Lalique France. (6-1/2").

477 Roger & Gallet presented the perfume "Aveu" in 1945. (3-1/4").

478 Mary Dunhill's "Scentinel" was a tightly stoppered inner glass perfume vial in a slim case. It came in sterling silver or gold plated. It came filled with Mary Dunhill perfume or could be purchased unfilled. U.S. introduction 1937. (2").

481 Miniature medieval castle called "Le Castel" was introduced and patented in 1940. It held four different Lucien Lelong perfumes. The bottles were made by Wheaton. (3-3/4").

482 Lentheric marketed "Dark Brilliance" in a lovely crystal bottle with a frosted stopper. It was strikingly presented in a black box with an over-sized colorful tassel hanging from the top. Polished bottom. U.S. introduction 1946. (3-3/4").

483 Windsor House of Hollywood, California debuted its "Opera Night" presentation in 1941. Two perfumes "Romeo and Juliet" came in a glass and plastic opera glasses container. Retail price $1.00. (3-3/8").

484 Schiaparelli launched the perfume "Le Roy Soleil" in the United States in 1946. The beautiful Baccarat crystal bottle designed by Salvador Dali was topped by a sunburst stopper. The bottle rested in splendor on white satin in a gold shell-like coffret.

485 Miniature lamp bottles used by various perfume manufacturers were popular dime store items in the 1940's and 1950's. The shades were made of plastic, glass, or metal.

487 Adrian, a well-known American designer, launched two perfumes, "Saint" and "Sinner", in 1944. The design of the bottles followed the column design prominently featured in Adrian salons in Beverly Hills. Bottle by Wheaton. (5-1/4").

486 Prince Obolenski of New York marketed the perfume "Credo" in 1937. The crown shaped stopper cover was of metal. Polished bottom. (5-1/4").

488 Charles of the Ritz debuted the perfume "Directoire" in 1948 in an urn shaped bottle packaged in gold and white. Numbered stopper. Acid mark—France. (3-1/2").

489 Three tiered bottle held "Memoirs Cologne" by Dorothy Perkins. Circa 1944. (5-1/2").

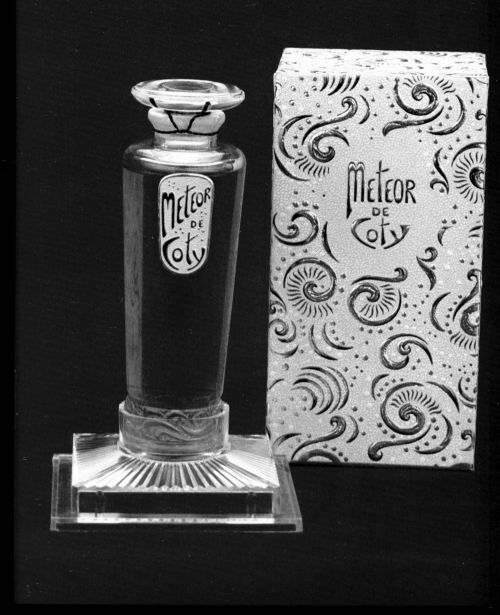

492 Coty marketed the floral perfume "Meteor" in four sizes in 1951. The bottle was made in France. (4").

490 Renoir perfumes of Paris, France used this clear glass flask with silver strips for many of its perfumes. It received a U.S. patent in 1945.

491 Clear glass bottle decorated with zig-zag pleats and a flower stopper was used by Guermantes of Paris for the perfume "Swingtime". (3").

493 The package for Charbert's "Grand Prix" was a miniature lady's riding boot made of leather. Circa 1938. (3-1/4").

494 Commemorative World War II victory bottle with eagle stopper. No labels. Circa 1945. (3-1/4").

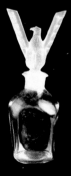

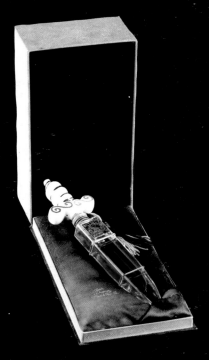

498 Curved metal scimitar with perfume in the glass hilt was made for Placcato Oro. The presentation was bought at the Doge's Palace in Italy as a souvenir. Circa 1980's. (10'').

495 Alexa founded by Martin de Markoff was an abbreviation of his mother's name, Alexandra de Markoff. The first fragrance in the Alexa line was "Enigma", introduced in 1944 in a dramatic opaque black glass bottle. (5-1/2'').

496 The great perfume house of Guerlain for its 120th anniversary presented the perfume "Fleur de Feu" in 1949.

497 Schiaparelli's contribution to Christmas 1940 was "Shocking Scamp", a lapel pin. The pin was in the form of a fencer which held a dram bottle of "Shocking" perfume behind its golden bars. The head was the stopper-applicator. (2-5/8''). Photo by Elizabeth A. McCarron.

499 Sword-shaped, clear crystal flacon with an embellished porcelain hilt stopper came in a box lined in black satin. The flacon held the perfume "Escarmouche" by Jean Deprez. (8'').

500 Clear glass bottle wth a brass plated pedestal and screw cap, with a band hung with bells around the middle was a special promotion for Coty. Circa 1940's. (3'').

502 Serene, silver colored Budda bottle held the perfume "Saree" by Rodin of Paris. The bottle was patented in the United States in 1946. The head stopper is all metal and the bottle is glass encased in metal. (7-3/8"). Photo by Elizabeth A. McCarron.

501 Candle-shaped bottle with a red flame screw-on top was used by the Colonial Dames Co. of California for "Candlelight" cologne. Bottle made in the U.S.A. Circa 1940's.

503 Helene Pessl marketed a complete line of children's toiletries, including perfume for little girls. Circa 1940's.

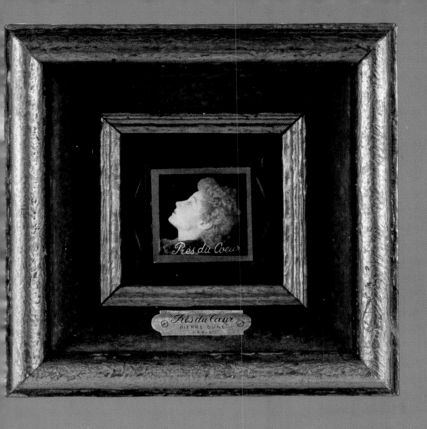

504 & 505 Fanciful portrait bottle held the perfume "Très du Coeur" by Pierre Dune. The bottle came showcased in a frame of wood and composition. The bottle was trademarked in the United States in 1946. Numbered stopper. Bottle made in France.

506 Rack of amber plastic held four bottles of perfume by Bouton. Circa 1940's. (4-3/4").

509 The House For Men Inc. introduced the "His" elite series in 1947 as a supplement to the standard "His" line. The torso bottle with a sculptured stopper of the "His" trademark in ivory plastic was designed by Mrs. Glen Claypool. Shaving lotion, cologne and talcum came in the bottle. Bottle by Wheaton. (6-1/4").

507 "Naughty 90's" by Milart of Miami, Florida came in a torso bottle wearing a corset trimmed in lace. Circa 1940's. (4-1/2").

510 Clear, screw top bottle for a lotion called "Saigon" by a company called Lalique.

511 Coty launched "Muse" in 1946 in a crystal bottle of classic outline with frosted stopper by Baccarat. It was packaged in a white satin lined box covered in handsome white and gold with an all-over stylized design in gold, blue, and crimson. Numbered stopper. (4").

508 Hattie Carnegie had her unique feminine head bottle by Wheaton washed in twenty-two karat gold to hold perfume "49" in 1944. (4").

512 Tussy debuted the perfume "Tahmina" in the United States in 1947. The silver box was decorated with Indian hunters and animals. (4-3/4'').

513 Rhoduis Perfumes of San Antonio, Texas packaged four perfumes, each in a different bottle, boxed separately in this set. (2'').

514 Gold washed bottle was made in France for the perfume "Gamine" by Fragonard. Numbered stopper. (3'').

515 Jean Patou launched his perfume "L'Heure Attendue" in France in 1946 and in the United States in 1948. A rising sun decorated the bottle and box. Acid mark— France. (3-1/2'').

516 Laverne of New York marketed three tiny bottles of perfume held by a metal tray inside a round painted glass container. The glass container can be found in several finishes and was used by other companies. Circa 1940's. (3'').

517 Four-sided clear glass bottle enhanced with a pattern of undulating ridges was patented in 1949 by Elizabeth Arden. It contained "Memoire Cherie" perfume. (7").

518 A clear lucite shoe holds a small bottle of Coty "Paris" perfume. Circa 1940's. (2-1/2").

519 "Crepe de Chine" perfume was first deputed in America in 1929 by F. Millot. In 1946 a new series of bottles and boxes, designed and made in France, were marketed.

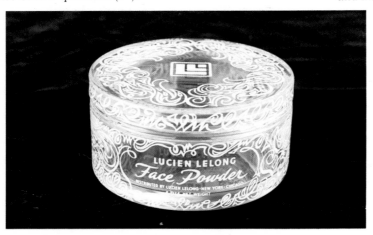

520 Glass powder box patented in 1944 by Lucien Lelong. (2").

521 Lancome's four bottle perfume set made in France included "Tendres Nuits", "La Vallee Bleue", "Fleches", and "Gardenia". The box had a free entry U.S. armed forces gift certificate tucked inside. Circa 1940's. (2-1/4").

522 The Lancome perfume "Magie", presented in France in 1946, wasn't introduced in the United States until 1952. The deluxe flacon, sold in two sizes, was a twisted rectangle of heavy crystal by Baccarat. It came in a white satin jewel case, sparkling with sequins and brilliant colors. (5-1/2").

523 Oblong bottle set in a transparent package decorated with clumps of flowers made by hot needles held "Taglio" by Lucien Lelong, introduced in 1945.

524 "Tempest" perfume by Lucien Lelong came in a prismatic crystal bottle nested in a white embossed lace paper box with gold trim. U.S. introduction 1947. (3-1/2").

525 "Divine" by D'Orsay was bottled in a graceful crystal spiral, spiraling up to the matching crystal stopper. U.S. introduction 1947. (6").

526 Wallner and Mayer, Inc. were U.S. agents for Delavelle of London in the late 1940's. They distributed four figural bottles, a snowman, Father Xmas, scottie dog, and bellhop, containing various scents. Circa 1948. (3-1/8", 3").

527 Black glass container held Elizabeth Arden's "Kohl", a modern version of an ancient eye cosmetic. The fine powder was applied with a tiny wand around the eyes. Circa 1950's. (2-3/4").

528 Three bottle Corday gift set included "Possession", "Tzigane", and "Fame" in a beautiful presentation box. Circa late 1940's, early 1950's. (3").

529 Carousel container of metal, cardboard, and plastic held three bottles of perfume by Novell. Circa 1940's.

530 Prince Matchabelli marketed small bottles of "Stradivari" and "Duchess of York" in a petite black hat box, flaunting two crown stick pins for Christmas 1947. (Bottles 1-1/4'').

531 Three moulded glass figural perfum[e] bottles embossed "Holland" with paper tag[s] reading 'S. Kleinkramer Bergen op Zoo[m] Holland'. The dog bottle was granted a U.S[.] patent in 1947. Circa late 1940's. (2-1/2'', 2[-]1/4'', 2-3/4'').

532 Familiar wooden household objects held tiny bottles of perfume by Binnie. Circa 1940's. (2-1/2'', 1-3/4'', 1-1/2'').

534 Black satin sachet pillow decorated with white and pink flowers held a petite bottle of "Enigma" by Alexa. Circa mid-1940's.

533 A gold puffed heart embellished the box for Zofaly's "Passion" perfume. The bottle was made in France. "Passion" was introduced in Europe in 1946 and in the United States in 1947. (3-1/4'').

535 Lancôme presented ''Fleches'', ''Tropiques'', and ''Cuir'' to the American market in 1946 in this beautiful frosted flacon. The bird decorated package had a drop front. (4-3/4'').

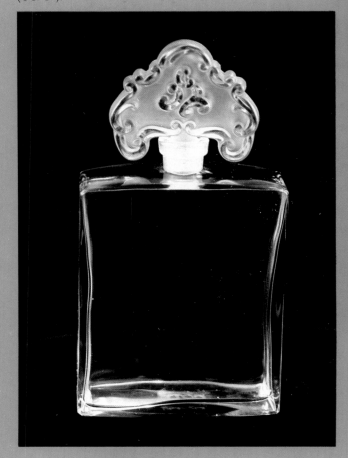

536 A 1948 advertisement identified this bottle as ''Paris'' by Coty. Numbered stopper. (2-7/8'').

537 Interesting presentation used by Charles of the Ritz for ''Directoire'' toilet water. Circa late 1940's. (6-3/4'').

538 Elizabeth Arden launched the perfume "My Love" in 1949 in a classic bottle with a frosted glass feather stopper. (4-1/2").

539 Beautiful cut glass tiered bottle used by Eyvan for many of its perfumes beginning in the late 1940's.

540 Jacques Heim filed for a U.S. patent in 1947 for this unusual bottle and metal holder for "Alambic" perfume. (6").

543 Raphael of Paris launched the perfume "Réplique" in the United States in 1946. Bottle marked—LG, made in France. (2-7/8")

541 Schiaparelli's "Shocking Radiance" were beauty oils for the skin perfumed with "Shocking" perfume. The oils were packaged in square cut crystal bottles. The labels on both the bottles and the boxes by Salvadore Dali. U.S. introduction 1943. (5").

542 The perfume "Blue Waltz" (Joubert) was first introduced in the late 1920's. This three, heart-shaped, bottle set included perfume, cologne, and sachet. Circa 1950's.

544 Parfum Moneau of New York introduced "Discovery" in 1942. The clear glass bottle had a frosted glass stopper shaped like a globe. It came in a box decorated with antique maps. Photo by Elizabeth A. McCarron. (4-3/4").

545 Gold washed glass bottle held the Lucien Lelong perfume "Orgueil", introduced in Europe in 1946 and in the U.S. in 1947. (4-3/4").

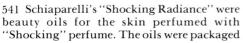

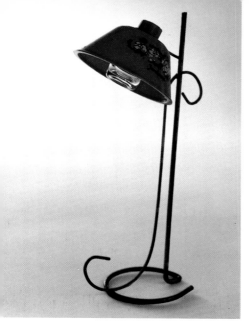

546 Miniature floor lamp of metal held a small bottle of gardenia perfume. Manufacturer unknown. Circa 1940's. (6'').

547 Clear crystal flacon designed by Madame Bergaud and made by Baccarat held the Caron perfume "Or et Noir". Numbered stopper. Circa 1949. (5'').

548 Cylinder shaped bottle with interesting twisted cord design made by Brosse to hold "Repartee" by Lentheric. U.S. introduction 1949. Photo courtesy Brosse USA, Inc.

549 A moulded leaf pattern decorates this bottle of "Cachet" by Lucien Lelong introduced to the U.S. in 1949. (5-1/8'').

550 Baccarat made the crystal barrel shaped flacon used by Caron to hold the perfume "With Pleasure" introduced in the United States in 1949. Numbered stopper. (3-1/4'').

551 Beautiful, clear crystal, urn shaped flaco
cased with red was made by Baccarat fo
Christian Dior. The flacon came nestled in
red velvet coffret lined with red satin. Th
flacon, which also came in blue and whit
was used for the perfumes "Miss Dior" an
"Diorama". Circa 1949. (6-3 4").

553 The special Corday presentation calle
"Rue de la Paix" was a metal Parisian stre
lamp which held three perfumes. The ceram
ashtray base looked like a cobbled street. U.
introduction 1952. (8-1/4").

552 Renoir Parfums first American presentation was "Chi Chi" in 1942. The bottle was
heart shaped with a ruffle pedestal forming a
firm base. The frosted glass stopper was in the
shape of the feathered end of an arrow. The
bottle was set on a pleated satin ruffle in a red
and white pyramid box. "Chi Chi" came in
three sizes. (4").

554 Car-shaped bottle with a screw-on top held the perfume "Milky" by Muguet of Paris. Paper tag—bottle made in France. (3-1/4" long).

555 Spray bottle with embossed portraits held "On Dit" by Elizabeth Arden. (4-3/7").

556 Frosted glass bottle shaped like the Eiffel Tower with screw-on top held the perfume "Ffilues de Paris". (3-3/8").

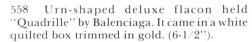

557 The perfume "6½" by Kislav of Paris was named after a glove size. The clear glass bottle had an opaque black glass stopper. (3-1/8").

558 Urn-shaped deluxe flacon held "Quadrille" by Balenciaga. It came in a white quilted box trimmed in gold. (6-1/2").

559 Brilliant crystal diamond-cut flacon was the deluxe offering for "Tresor" by Lancome. It was handsomely set like a jewel in a box covered with amaranth satin. Two sizes. U.S. introduction 1953. (4-1/2").

560 Odd-shaped clear glass bottle held the fragrance "Acclaim" by Ciro. The perfume debuted in the U.S. in 1950 in three sizes in a wedge shaped box. (4-1/4").

561 Many department stores have, over the past decades, marketed perfumes under their own label. This plain cylindrical bottle with ribbon label held "Number Nine" perfume by Bergdorf Goodman. (2-1/2").

562 For Christmas 1951, "Shocking" by Schiaparelli could be purchased in a gold color metal flacon studded with simulated rubies. It came in a protective case of blue calf. Screw top. (2-1/2").

565 Chunky, square, clear glass bottle trimmed with a blue velvet bow was made by Pouchet et du Courval for the perfume "Gambit" by John Robert Powers. Bottle marked—H P. (2-1/2").

566 Clear glass bottle with a white screw-on top held "Cocaina" by Parera. Circa 1950's. (3").

567 Realistic metal birdcage patented by Coty in 1951 held a small bottle of perfume. (Cage 4-1/2").

563 Long, narrow, clear glass bottle with a silver trimmed base and silver screw-on top was used by Molyneux. Acid mark—France. (6").

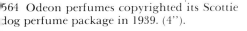

564 Odeon perfumes copyrighted its Scottie dog perfume package in 1939. (4").

568 Simonetta, a postwar Italian couturies, launched the perfume "Incanto" in America in 1955. The perfume came in opaque black, round, crown-shaped bottles with cut glass stoppers, packaged like a Roman column. (2", 3").

570 Unusual presentation for the perfume "Griffonnage" by Jacques Griffe of Paris included a melon-ribbed, clear, inkwell bottle with a metal stopper topped by a long feather in a package decorated with black and red ink splatters. Circa 1949.

571 A 1947 advertisement identified this striking black mask decorated bottle as "Savoir Faire" by Dorothy Gray. The octagonal box also sported the masks. (4"). Photo by Elizabeth A. McCarron.

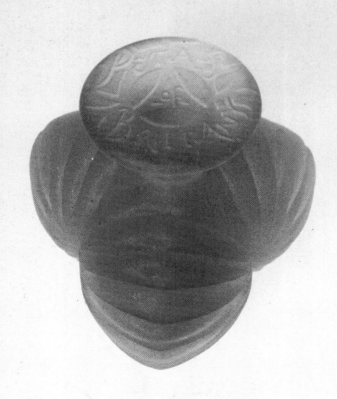

569 Odd frosted glass flacon held the perfume "Petals of Brittany", maker unknown. No marks. (3"). Photo by Elizabeth A. McCarron.

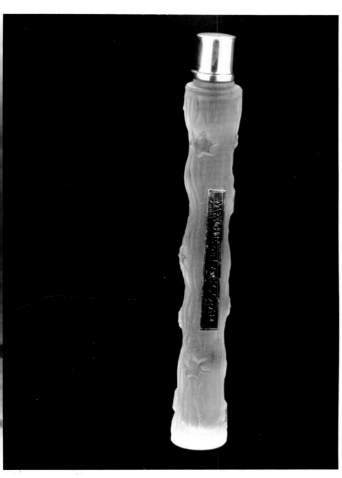

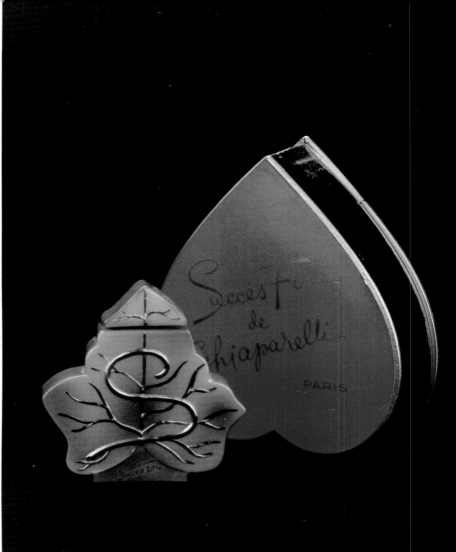

572 Lalique designed the "Magie" baton de magicien, a slender wand studded with stars presented in a suede sheath. U.S. introduction 1952. (5'').

574 Green, ceramic-like, ivy leaf-shaped bottle with gilt veining held "Succès Fou" by Schiaparelli. The shocking pink box was heart shaped. The bottles made in France came in three sizes. (3'').

573 Pierre Dune presented "Evocation de Violette" in a replica of the 16th century apothecary bottle. Lancry de Paris also used a similar bottle for several perfumes. Circa 1940's. (3-3/8'').

575 'Suspicion" eau de toilette by Sardeau of New York came in a zebra-shaped bottle of the thinnest glass, hand-blown and painted. U.S. introduction 1951. (4-1/2'').

579 "Sphere Magie", a Lalique star studded globe with a 14 karat gold-plated dome, was also introduced in the United States in 1952. (1-1/2").

580 Jacques Griffe designed a white moiré box that opened like a lotus flower for the 1954 American debute of his perfume "Mistigri". European introduction 1950. Enameled mark—made in France. (6-1/2").

576 Twisted glass candle bottle holding "Spice" perfume by Lander came in a glass boot. Circa 1950's. (3-1/2").

577 Fabergé debuted the perfume "Act IV" in 1952. The bottle shown was also used for other Fabergé scents. (3-1/4").

578 Helena Rubinstein, inspired by Gauguin's paintings of beautiful Tahitian women, introduced the perfume "Noa Noa" in 1954. The perfume was imaginatively packaged in shades of amber and bamboo. (One ounce size.)

581 Square frosted glass bottle with black opaque glass stopper held the perfume "Lady Knize", introduced in America in 1954. (2").

582 Deluxe presentation for the marquay perfume "L'Elu" came in a coral pink velvet drawstring bag lined in white satin.

583 Cristobal Balenciaga, a Spanish-born designer of haute couture, created the perfume "Quadrille" in 1952. The perfume was launched in America in 1956. The flacon shown was used for several Balenciaga perfumes beginning in the late 1940's. (3").

584 Long, narrow, triangular shaped crystal bottle in a matching box held "Fantastique" by D'Orsay. U.S. introduction 1953. Acid mark—France. (7").

585 Christian Dior launched the perfume "Diorissimo" in 1956 in the Baccarat crystal urn used for other Dior perfumes since 1948. (4-3/4").

587 Jacques Fath, a brilliant Parisian couturier of the 1940's, launched the perfume "Canasta" around 1950 in Europe, and in 1953 in the U.S. The flacon came in a shocking pink velvet cylindrical package. (4-1/2").

586 Artificial flowers decorated the frosted glass stopper for "Jolie Bouquet" perfume by Lucien Lelong. One ounce bottle. U.S. introduction 1953.

588 Beautifully sculptured, hand-blown portrait bottle made in France was used by Elizabeth Arden for the perfume "On Dit" and "Mémoire Cherie". The bottle was patented in 1952. (7").

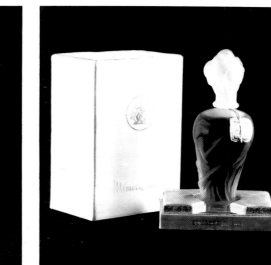

589 Miniature Lalique bottles of Nina Ricci's perfumes were packaged together in a satin-lined gift box. The set was introduced in America in 1953.

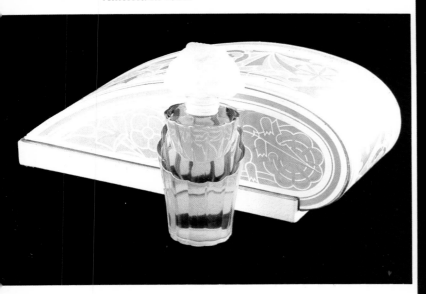

590 Flacon with a frosted triple flower stopper held "Plus Tard" by Figine, packaged in a white, green, and gold wheel-cover shaped box. Bottle made in France.

591 French couturier Pierre Cardin applied for a trademark for his perfume "Suite Seize" in 1959. Bottle made in France. (3-1/2").

592 The history of the perfume "Ecusson" goes back to the sixteenth century. It wasn't until the early fifties that the French firm of Jean D'Albert marketed "Ecusson" in the United States. (7-3/4").

593 Artificial flowers were used on a screw-on top for "Blue Organdy" perfume by Arthur Philippi of New York. Circa 1950's. (3-1/2").

595 A deluxe crystal presentation flacon by Baccarat with a gilt flower stopper arrived in America in 1956 holding the perfume "Diorissimo" by Christian Dior. (8").

594 Beautiful, square flask, engraved with a design of leaves and flowers, was a special presentation for the perfume "Nuit de Longchamp" by Lubin. Circa late 1950's. (7-1/4").

596 American dress designer Nettie Rosenstein launched the perfume "Fleurs d'Elle" in 1961. The bottle was made in Italy and came in a round white satin box. (1-3/4").

597 Bright red and white box held the clear glass bottle for "Charme Slave" by de Florel of Paris. (2-3/8").

598 "Little Miss" cologne by the Lander Co. came in a clear glass bottle shaped to resemble an old-fashioned hoop skirt with a cork and porcelain doll head stopper. The porcelain heads came in assorted designs. Circa 1957 and 1958. (3-1/2").

599 Influential French perfumer Jean Desprez debuted his most successful perfume "Bal à Versailles" in 1962. A painting by Fragonard decorates the label. Bottles made in France.

600 Mary Chess's sparkling "Souvenir d'un Soir" was housed in a frosted crystal replica of the Plaza fountain. (4-1/2").

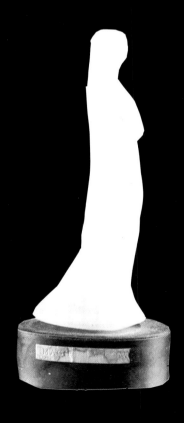

Clear glass flacon adorned with a green vet ribbon held "Chant D'Aromes" by uerlain, introduced in 1962. Acid mark— ttle made in France. (5").

602 Twisted glass candle bottle with red plastic flame-shaped screw-on cap came in a glass candle holder. The bottle held "Heaven" perfume by Lander. Circa 1950's. (4-1/2").

603 Wonderful lady figural bottle of sabino-type, pale, pink glass with a screw-on covered base was a special edition presentation for "Magie" by Lancome. (4-5/8").

604 In 1963 the firm of Baccarat made this beautiful metal trimmed crystal flacon to hold "Diorling" by Christian Dior. (7-1/8"). Photo by Elizabeth A. McCarron.

605 Caron launched the perfume "Poivre" in the United States in 1954. The bottle came on a black base and had a brass screw-on top. It debuted in two sizes.

606 Caron purse bottle similar to the "Poivre" bottle with the same brass screw-on cap. (3-1/2").

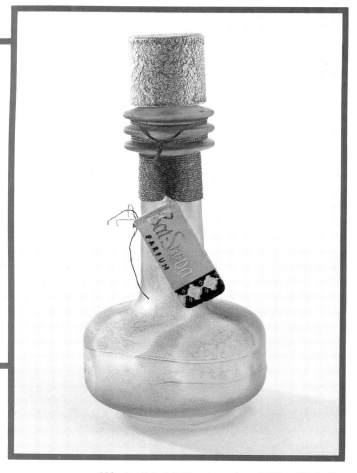

07 Fine crystal bottle decorated with 24 carat old and a rib-shaped stopper held the perfume Adam's Rib" by Lentheric. U.S. introduction 954. (2-3/4").

08 Wooden box held three bottles of obinson's "Extra Scotch Maid" perfume. irca 1940's. (3-1/4").

609 Judith Muller introduced "Bat-Sheba" perfume in the United States in 1967. The art glass bottle can be found in different color combinations. Bottle marked—Bottle made in Israel. (3").

611 Square, dense glass bottle with an opaqu black stopper held the perfume "Mis Balmain" by Balmain launched in 1967.

610 Named after the American designer Norman Norell, the perfume "Norell" by Revlon was launched in 1968. (6-1/2" Dummy bottle).

612 Clear glass flacon with a plastic top was used by French Masters. (4-1/8"). Photo by Elizabeth A. McCarron.

3 A flacon used by the French perfumer an Desprez for "Bal á Versailles" perfume.

614 Sevres porcelain bottle designed by Léon Leyritz for Jean Desprez's "Bal A Versailles" was made in 1969. The gold and silver stopper is missing. (5-1/2").

616 Frosted glass dagger flacon with an opaque black glass hilt-shaped stopper was marketed by Zofaly of Paris, France. Circa 1940's. (8-1/2").

615 The famous movie star Brigitte Bardot launched the perfumes of Brigitte Bardot in 1959. The bottle made in France is marked— Viva Maria Custom. (4").

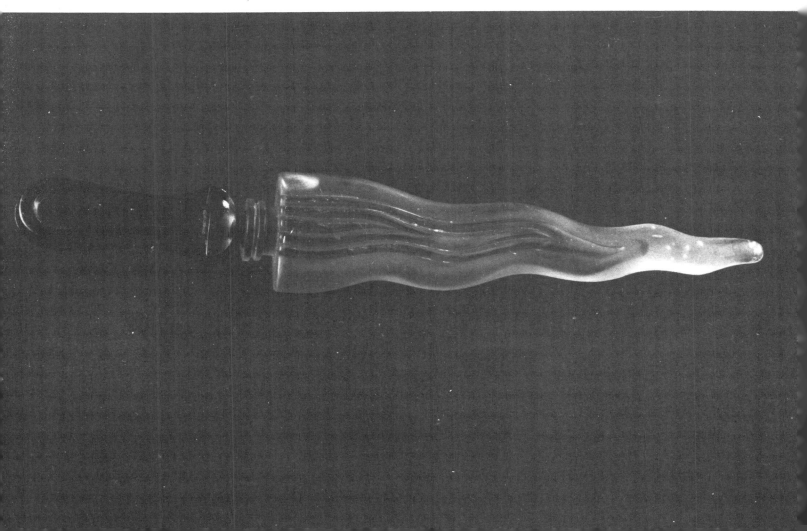

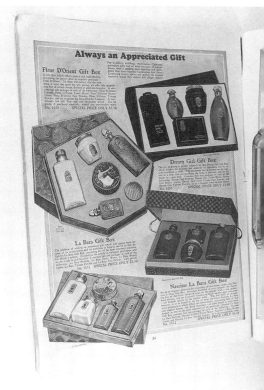

617-619 Zanol, a brand name used by the American Products Co. of Cincinnati, Ohio, included five pages of perfumes and toilet waters in a January 1929 catalog.

Bottle Care and Collecting Tips

* Denatured alcohol, fingernail polish remover, or lime-away toilet bowl cleaner (made by enconomics laboratory of St. Paul) are the best cleaning agents to use inside a perfume or cologne bottle to remove hardened perfume residue and stubborn stains. The next best cleaning agents are denture cleaners, isopropyl alcohol (rubbing alcohol), and warm water and soap.
* A small metal funnel (an ideal type is the kind made to transfer perfume into a purse bottle) or a glass eye dropper should be used to fill a bottle with the cleaning agent when the original labels are still intact. Cleaning solutions can remove or damage the labels, so be careful!
* To remove stoppers that are stuck or frozen, run warm water around the neck of the bottle to soften the perfume resins, then gently apply pressure to the stopper.
* Do not scrub, especially with abrasive cleaners, perfume bottles decorated with enamelling or gilding as the ornamentation can be rubbed off or chipped easily.
* Perfume bottles decorated with hand staining or painting should be cleaned with care. Check that the decoration is color fast before you submerge the bottle in water or a cleaning solution.
* To help prevent accidental chipping or breakage of bottles, use a rubber or plastic mat in the sink when cleaning bottles.
* Hand ground stoppers were ground to an exact fit for its particular bottle. A hand ground stopper will prove to be impossible of a straight-pull removal when firmly inserted, yet will come clear quite easily when it is twisted and pulled from its matching bottle. The hand ground stoppers made in France will quite often have a number or mark scratched on the stopper dowel, the bottom of the bottle, or both.
* If a bottle with perfume has an unbroken seal, it adds to the value of the bottle if the seal is left intact. If the seal is broken and part of the contents is gone, the bottle collector should consider pouring out any remaining perfume and thoroughly cleaning the bottle before adding it to a collection. The often cloying or rancid fragrance of an old perfume is unpleasant and, if left standing in a bottle for a lengthy period of years, can sometimes harm the surface, biting into it or leaving behind a scummy unsightly residue.
* Original labels and boxes add to the resale value of a bottle. If the original box is not in good enough condition to display with the bottle, consider stowing it away instead of throwing it away.
* It was not unusual for a bottle design to be used for several perfumes or by different perfume firms with only the labels or decorated finish to indicate which perfume it held.
* In the life of a perfume, the same bottle design will many times have been made by more than one glass company. An example of this is the Ciro "Danger" bottle which was produced by both Baccarat and Verreries

Brosse. It is common practice among perfumers today to spread the manufacturing of their bottles among several glass companies.

* The misty bloom on the inner surface of a bottle can often be removed with liquid laundry bleach. Pour the bleach into the bottle and let stand for a few hours. The bloom can also be treated professionally with acid to repolish the interior. Do not attempt this method yourself.

* A bottle with an iridescent, whitish, or scaly surface or interior cannot be fixed. This condition is the result of underground burial or exposure to dampness for a long period of time which causes a permanent chemical change in the glass to occur.

* A bottle with minor chips in the glass or a broken dapper can be ground smooth by a glass grinder. The repair of a broken bottle, however, is a complicated art and should only be attempted by a knowledgeable person in the field.

* Direct sunlight over a period of time can change the chemical composition of a clear glass bottle occasionally, causing the bottle to turn an amethyst, amber, or grey color. Lighted display cabinets are an excellent way to both protect and show off a perfume bottle collection.

* When choosing the place in your home to display your bottle collection, avoid areas with fluctuating temperature extremes. A steady temperature and humidity is the best because a rapid change in air temperature can crack or shatter a bottle.

* When storing or transporting perfume bottles it is better and safer to use several small boxes instead of a few large boxes. A large box can be extremely awkward and heavy to handle when fully packed. It is also a good idea to reinforce the bottom of the boxes with a heavy strapping tape. Wrap each bottle and stopper individually with bubble wrap, tissue paper, newspaper, or other protective material.

* A large majority of the perfume and cologne bottles made were in clear or frosted glass, so the colored glass bottles are usually more valuable and harder to find.

* Keep an inventory of your collection. It should include a photograph for each bottle with description, present condition, repairs made, current value, date and place purchased, and the amount paid. A duplicate copy should be kept in a separate place for safety.

* To find worn, faint, or faded acid-etched marks on the bottom of a bottle, try rubbing the bottom briskly on a bath towel or a piece of denim until warm to the touch. This will bring the acid to the surface for a few seconds. Breath immediately on the surface to frost the mark. You may have to try several times, holding the bottle at different angles to a strong light to find a mark.

Ads and Patents

1. A 1902 Victorian Christmas ad for Lundborg perfumes.

2. A 1903 ad for the perfume "Violettes Celestes" by Delettrez of Paris.

3. A 1903 ad for the perfume "Aglaia" by Delettrez shows a cut glass bottle typical of the era.

4. This 1913 ad for Dralle's "Illusion" stated that it was the most costly perfume in America. The perfume came in a cut glass bottle in a polished wooden case.

5. A 1913 ad for a miniature bottle of "Flower Drops" perfume by Paul Rieger of San Francisco.

6. This 1913 ad for "Geraldine Farrar" perfume by Rigaud stated that the perfume was for sale in high class toilet goods departments.

Lilas de Rigaud

The Perfume of Old-Fashioned Gardens and Tender Memories

. A 1914 ad for "Lilas de Rigaud" by Rigaud f Paris.

Parfums D'Orsay

The very soul of the flower re-incarnated

8. A 1914 D'Orsay ad featuring the perfumes "Les Roses D'Orsay", "Bouquet D'Orsay", and "Chevalier D'Orsay" in bottles by Baccarat.

9. A 1914 catalog illustration for "Nelly" by D'Orsay. The bottle was by Baccarat.

HOUBIGANT PERFUMES
SUPREME SYMPHONY OF THE MOST EXQUISITE ODORS

10. A 1914 catalog illustration for "L'Ambre" by D'Orsay. The bottle was by Baccarat.

13. Cute 1915 ad featuring a girl and her dog was for "Peg O' My Heart" perfume by D'Ormo.

11. A 1915 Houbigant ad featuring the perfumes "Quelques Violettes", "Quelques Fleurs" and "Coeur De Jeannette".

14. A 1915 ad for the perfume "Lilas" by Arly.

12. A 1914 catalog illustration for "L'Aveu" by D'Orsay. The bottle was by Baccarat.

15. A 1916 ad for "Cloth-of-Gold" toilet requisites by Lazell.

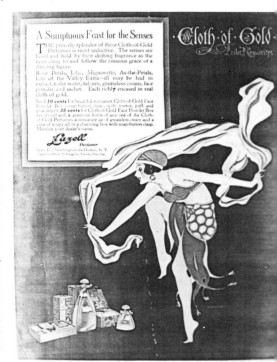

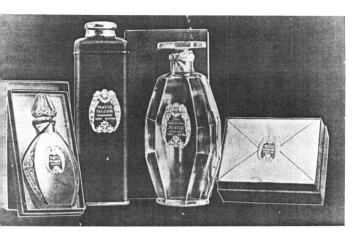

16. A 1916 ad featuring "Mavis" products by Vivaudou.

17. This 1916 ad featured a frosted glass bottle of "La Bohême" perfume by Arly.

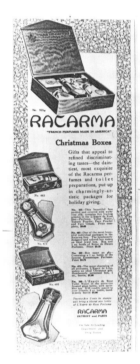

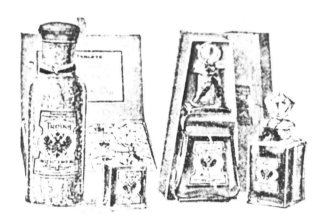

18. A 1916 ad for "Mary Garden" perfume by Rigaud.

19. A 1916 ad for Christmas boxes featuring Racarma of Detroit and Paris perfumes.

20. A catalog illustration from 1916 showing Troika sachet, extract, and toilet water.

21. A 1917 ad showing various products by Page of New York.

22. Cut glass bottle used for "Halcyon Rose" perfume by the Hanson-Jenks Company of New York, shown in a 1918 ad.

23. A 1918 ad for "Jardin de Marie" and "Jardin de Lilas" by the American Toilet Goods Co. of Boston.

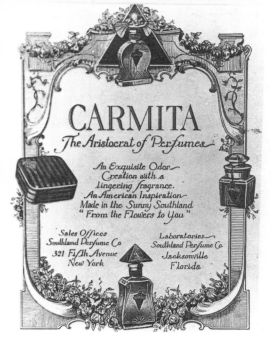

24. A 1918 ad for "Carmita" perfume by the Southland Perfume Co. of Jacksonville, Florida.

25. Picture from a 1919 ad featuring "Jonteel" perfume, distributed by the Rexall Drug Stores.

26. A 1919 ad for "Mavis" perfume by Vivaudou.

27. A 1920 ad for "Frivole" perfume by Luyties.

28. Egyptian influenced 1920 ad for "Un Air Embaumé" by Rigaud.

29. Bottle shown for "Le Chypre" by De Luzy of Paris in a 1919 ad.

30. Baccarat bottle for "Bluet" was shown in a 1920 Grenoville ad.

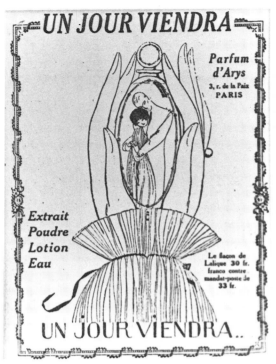

31. Bottle shown for "Pourpre Antique" by De Luzy of Paris in a 1919 ad.

32. A 1919 French ad for "Un Jour Viendra" by Arys of Paris.

33. A 1920 French ad for perfumes made by Fontanis. The bottle was made by Baccarat.

34. A 1920 French ad for perfumes by Oriza L. LeGrand.

35. A 1920 French ad introduced the new perfume "Jou-Jou" by Jones of Paris.

36. A 1920 French ad for the perfume "Maida" by Jones of Paris.

37. Beautiful bottle for "Altys" perfume with bees moulded on the stopper was featured in a 1920 Violet ad.

38. A 1920 ad for "Violet" toilet water by the Hanson-Jenks Co. of New York.

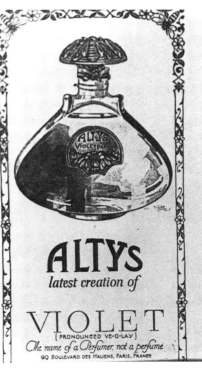

GLORIEUX

MOCQ, BURNIER & CIE.

A perfume of rare charm and appeal. The best that French Art can give to satisfy a discriminating taste. In the marble package.

Extract Toilet Water
Sachet Face Powder

SINCLAIR & BOLTE
(Inc.)
50 East 41st Street
NEW YORK
Sole American Distributors

39. A 1920 ad for "Glorieux" perfume by Mocq. Burnier, & Cie.

40. French ad from 1921 showing various Monna Vanna perfumes.

41. A 1921 French ad for "Jérusalem" perfume by Godet.

Nº 1028. Ambre de Delhi concentré, flacon et écrin de grand luxe spécial pour cigarettes. Le flacon : 95 fr.

42. Sketch from a 1921 French ad for "Ambre de Delhi" perfume by Babani.

A Lubin Creation Worthy of the Name

43. Part of a 1921 ad for "Douce France" perfume by Lubin.

45. D'Ormo of New Haven, Connecticut ran this catalog ad for "La Victoire" perfume in 1921.

44. A 1921 ad by Julius Schmid Inc., announcing their appointment as distributors for Gueldy of Paris perfumes. The bottle shown was by Baccarat.

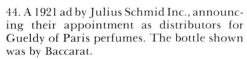

JULIUS SCHMID, Inc.

Announce their appointment as Sole Distributors in the United States for

Les Parfums Gueldy
PARIS

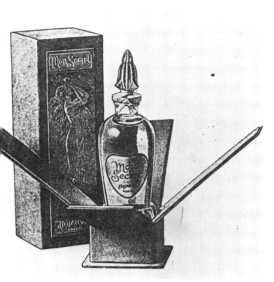

6. Sketch from a 1921 ad for "Mon Secret" perfume by Hugarvis of Paris.

47. D'Ormo of New Haven, Connecticut ran this catalog ad for "Dainty Maid" toilet products in 1921.

48. Picture from a 1921 ad for "Un Peu d'Ambre" perfume by Houbigant. The bottle was made by Baccarat.

49. Bottle with a moulded flower design for "Mon Succès" perfume by Rocca was shown in a 1921 ad.

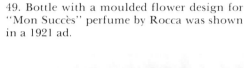

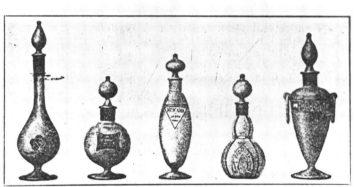

50. Picture from a 1921 ad showing the perfumes "Rose du Chemin", "Buisson Fleuri", "Muscadin", "Kadoura", and "Myrodata" by Jaspy.

51. Patent drawing filed in 1921 for a bottle used by the Erasmic Co. of Warrington, England.

Exquisite Perfumes

Creations of
GIVIEMME
MILAN - ITALY

SUBDOLA

CONTESSA AZZURRA

DIMMI DI SI MALIA

LA ROSA

Packed in exclusive and artistic containers

Giviemme
119 So. 4th Street
PHILADELPHIA, PA.

52. Sketch from a 1921 ad for Henri Muraour et Cie. Showing bottles made by Baccarat for its perfumes.

53. A 1922 ad for perfumes by Giviemme of Milan, Italy, featuring "Subdola" perfume.

54. A 1922 ad for perfumes by Giviemme of Milan, Italy, featuring "Nina Sorridi" perfume.

55. Gabilla ran this ad for its perfumes in a 1922 French magazine.

56. Picture from a 1922 ad for "Le Triomphe" perfume by Gueldy.

57. A 1922 French ad for "Taïmyr" perfume by Brocard.

58. Picture from a 1922 ad for "Mystikum". Perfume by Scherk.

60. A 1922 French ad showing a variety of Babani perfumes.

59. A 1922 Gueldy ad featuring bottles designed by Baccarat and the Cristallerie d'Art de Choisy le Roi.

Les Parfums de Volnay

RENÉ DUVAL
PARIS

Volnay is without any possible discussion the finest and most delicate perfume ever presented to the American public. The following odors have no rival and their names mean class and distinction to the extreme.

Yapana
Maoni
Cap d'Or
Chypre
Gri Gri
Jardinée
Fleurs Vives
Firefly
Ambre Indien

Jasmin du Cap
Rose Brumaire
Oeillet Kleber
Lilas de Lorraine
Mimeomai
Mousse Ambrée
Chypre Ambré
Napée

Most of Volnay's containers have been designed by the celebrated French artist and jeweller R. Lalique. Every one is a real "Objet d'Art."

PARFUMS DE VOLNAY, Inc.
565 FIFTH AVENUE   NEW YORK

Volnay's "de Luxe" catalogue mailed upon request

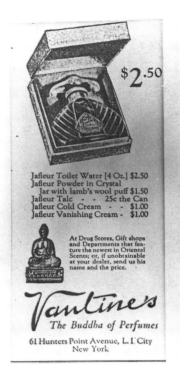

$2.50

Jafleur Toilet Water [4 Oz.] $2.50
Jafleur Powder in Crystal
  Jar with lamb's wool puff $1.50
Jafleur Talc - - 25c the Can
Jafleur Cold Cream - $1.00
Jafleur Vanishing Cream - $1.00

At Drug Stores, Gift shops and Departments that feature the newest in Oriental Scents; or, if unobtainable at your dealer, send us his name and the price.

Vantines
The Buddha of Perfumes

61 Hunters Point Avenue, L. I. City
New York

61. A 1922 Volnay ad that states that most of the Volnay containers were designed by R. Lalique.

62. A 1922 ad showing "Jafleur" toilet water by Vantine.

63. Three Egyptian style crystal bottles by Baccarat were shown in this 1923 Ramsès ad.

64. A 1923 French ad for various Babani perfumes.

65. A 1923 French ad for "Belle-Jolie" perfume by Lérys.

66. Various Luyna of Paris perfumes were shown in this 1923 ad.

67. A 1923 ad showing bottles for "Fox Trot" and "L'Amour Dans le Coeur" perfume by Arys.

68. A 1923 ad for "La Phalène D'Heraud" perfume by d'Heraud, featuring a beautiful Lalique bottle.

69. Picture of a Lalique bottle used for "Semis Des Fleurs" by D'Heraud was shown in a 1923 ad.

70. An ad from 1923 for "Vasthi" perfume by Gueldy showed a bottle with a moulded rose motif.

71. Drawing used in a 1923 ad for "Vivante" perfume by Lournay.

72. Part of a 1923 ad for "Secret des Fleurs" by Marie Earle.

73. A 1923 ad for "Adam et Eve" perfume by Marcel Raffy.

74. Drawing of a Lucien Gaillard bottle in a 1923 ad for "Les Sylvies" perfume by Violet.

75. Mullens No. 4711 used this drawing of a "L'Offrande" eau de toilette bottle in a 1923 ad.

76. Drawing used in a 1923 ad for "American Beauty Rose Perfume" by Mullens No. 4711.

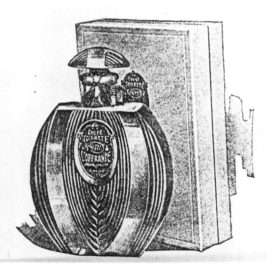

81. Frosted glass bottle with metal seal for "Narcissus" perfume by Carlova, Inc. of New York, shown in a 1923 ad.

77-80. Four presentations for "Mai-Ton" perfume by Spencer of South Bend, Indiana, shown in a 1923 catalog.

82. "Narcissus" eau de toilette by Carlova, shown in a 1923 ad.

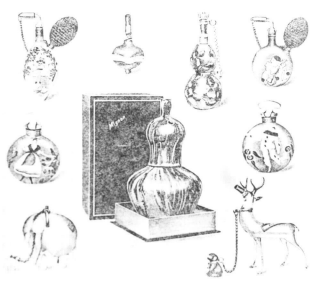

3. Petite atomizers and novelty perfumes by Mignon, featured in a 1923 ad.

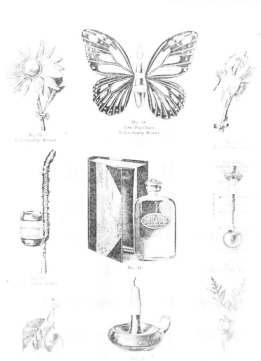

84. Page of novelty perfumes from a 1923 Rochambeau catalog.

85. A 1924 French ad for "Sketch" perfume by Violet.

86. A 1924 ad for "Quand Les Fleurs Rêvent" by Boué-Soeurs of Paris.

87. Baccarat made the bottles shown in this 1924 Gabilla ad.

88. A 1924 French ad for "Volt" perfume by L.T. Piver.

89. A 1924 ad for Degener of New York perfumes.

91. This 1924 John Blocki of Chicago ad stated that real flowers were put in the bottles

90. Two novelty bottles are shown in this 1924 Elesbé ad.

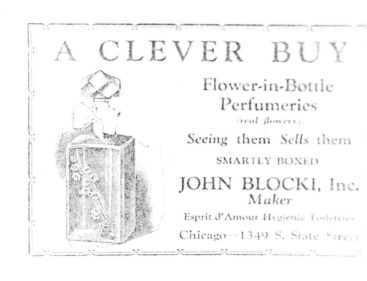

92. Illustration from a 1924 ad for "Lybis" by Luxor.

94. A 1924 French ad for Isabey perfumes.

95. Picture of a flacon with coffret from a 1924 Isabey ad.

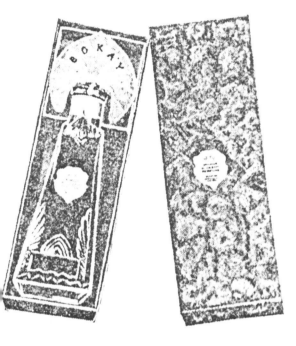

96. Picture of a bottle decorated with a long double tassel holding "Halo" perfume by Loret was in a 1924 ad.

97. Illustration of "Hallo Coco!" perfume from a 1924 Jovoy ad.

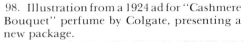

93. Two pictures from a 1924 ad for "Orange Blossom" perfume by Bo-Kay.

98. Illustration from a 1924 ad for "Cashmere Bouquet" perfume by Colgate, presenting a new package.

99. A 1924 ad for three perfumes by Corday of Paris.

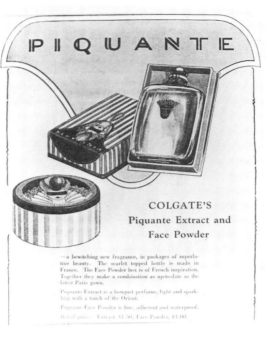

100. A 1924 ad for "Piquante" perfume and face powder by Colgate.

101. Jazz era French ad from 1924 for "Mon Parfum" by Bourjois.

102. A 1924 ad for "Ameria" toilet articles by Leigh.

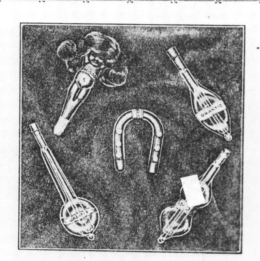

103. Illustration from a 1924 ad for perfume novelties imported by Debans of New York.

104. Illustration of a perfume novelty from a 1924 Holman ad.

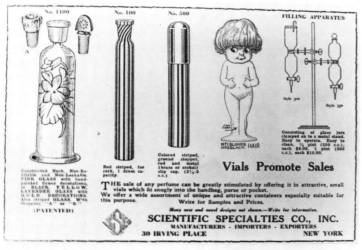

105. A 1924 wholesale ad for fillable perfume vials.

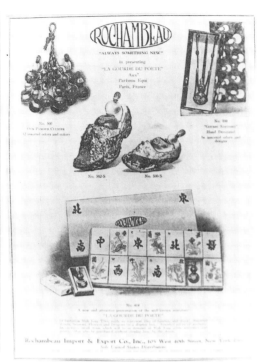

110. Patent drawing for "Ting Shang" perfume by Rendes of Paris filed in 1924.

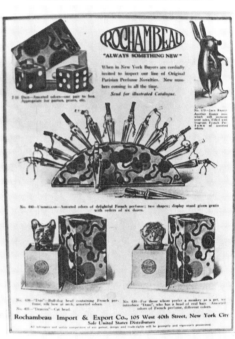

106-109. Four ads used by Rochambeau of New York in 1924 for perfume novelties.

111. Patent drawing for a perfume bottle filed in 1924 by Charles L. Marcus.

113. The bottle for "La Perle" by Isabey, shown in this 1925 French ad, had a pearl-like finish.

112. Patent drawing for a candle-shaped perfume bottle filed in 1924 by Joseph A. Fields.

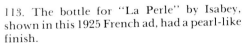

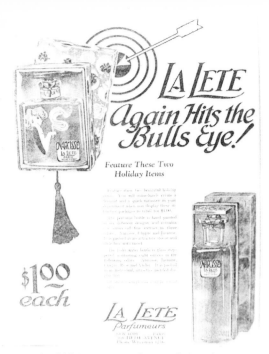

114. A 1925 La Lete perfume ad showing two different bottles for "Narcisse" perfume.

115. A 1925 ad for "Perlerette" perfume by Volnay. The iridescent bottle came on a black velvet base.

116. A 1925 ad for "Giardino Antico" perfume by Giviemme of Milan, Italy.

117. Illustration from a 1925 Betty Fayes (Viviny Perfumers) ad.

118. A picture taken from a 1925 French ad for "Parfum Tendre" by Rigaud.

119. A 1925 French ad for "Narcisse Bleu" by Mury.

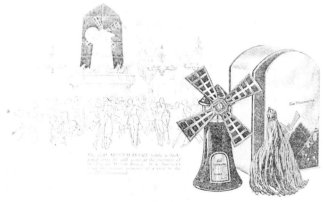

120. A 1925 ad for "Gai Montmartre" perfume by Deroc of Paris in a windmill bottle.

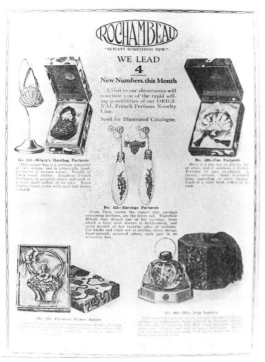

121. A 1925 Rochambeau novelty perfume ad. Note the perfume earrings that held "Jasmine" perfume.

122. A 1925 French ad for "Valle Des Rois" perfume by L.T. Piver. The bottle was made by Baccarat.

123. A 1925 French ad for Lenthéric perfumes.

124. Illustration of "Jardins Celestes" perfume from a 1925 Renaud ad.

125. A 1925 ad for "Day Dream" perfume and cosmetics by Stearns.

126. The black and gold crystal bottle for "Sous Le Gui" (Under the Mistletoe) was prominent in this 1925 French Jean de Parys ad.

127. Illustration from a 1925 Wilma Company of New York ad for "Desir De Toi" perfume. The ad stated that "Desir De Toi" was made, bottled, and packed in France.

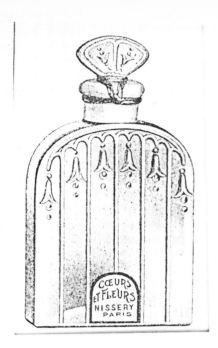

128. Sketch from a 1925 Nissery of Paris ad. The flacon was used to hold twelve different perfumes.

129. Illustration from a 1925 ad for "Djer-Kiss" perfume by Kerkoff.

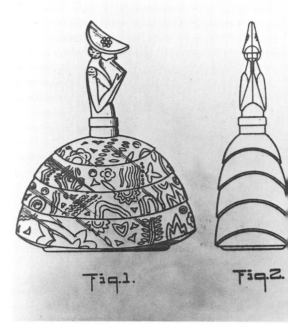

130. Patent drawing filed in 1925 for the bottle used for "Tre-Jur" perfume by Tre-Jur. The frosted glass bottle was made in France.

131. Illustration of L'Ambre Des Pagodes" perfume taken from a 1926 French Lydès ad.

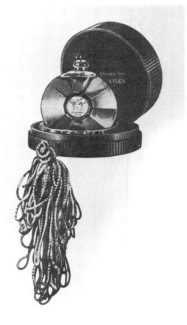

132. Illustration of "Daimant Noir" perfume taken from a 1926 Lydès ad.

133. Illustration of "Bleu De Chine" perfume by Isabey taken from a 1926 French ad.

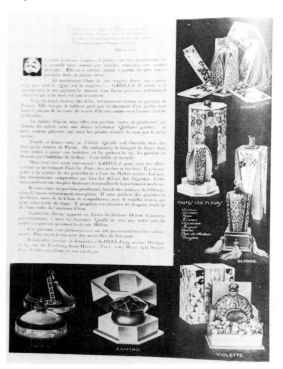

134. A French 1926 Gabilla ad showing various perfumes in bottles by Baccarat and Lalique. The bottle for "Chin Li" came in three colors, red, jade and mandarin; the Baccarat bottle for "Xantho" came in two colors, ruby and jet. The bottles by Lalique were decorated with various moulded flower motifs.

135. A 1926 ad for "Bouquet Antique" perfume by Ciro.

198

137. A 1926 Christmas ad for various "Blue Rose" by Lanchére products.

136. A 1926 French ad featuring "Happy Days" perfume by Lérys of Paris.

LES PARFUMS DE VIOLET

GRAND PRIX
EXPOSITION INTERNATIONALE
DES ARTS DÉCORATIFS
PARIS 1925

138. A 1926 French ad showing several Violet perfumes.

139. A 1926 French ad for "Le Collier de Perles" by Ysiane.

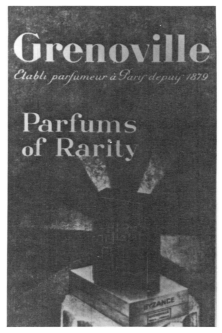

Grenoville
Établi parfumeur à Paris depuis 1879

Parfums of Rarity

140. A 1926 ad for "Byzance" perfume by Grenoville. The square black bottle was made by Baccarat.

MADOUKA

141. A 1926 ad for "Madouka" perfume by J.A. Marceau of Paris.

142. A 1926 French ad for "5 Fleurs" by Forvil. The bottle with a moulded rope design was by Lalique.

Le Secret De La Perle

143. A 1926 French ad for "Coeur Enchainé" by Honoré Payan.

144. A 1926 ad for "Chaine D'Or" perfume by Grenoville.

145. A 1926 ad for "Le Secret De La Perle" perfume by Pleville. The ball-shaped flacon was an iridescent blue color.

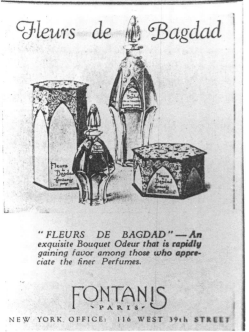

Fruit Defendu (Forbidden Fruit)

One of the finest of the PARFUMS ROSINE

146. A 1926 Bonwit Teller & Co. ad showing the five sizes that Martial et Armand perfumes came in. The bottles were designed by R. Lalique.

148. A 1926 ad for the perfume "Fruit Defendu" by Rosine.

147. A 1926 ad for "Fleurs de Bagdad" perfume by Fontanis of Paris.

150. A 1926 ad for "Amaryllis" perfume by Lubin.

149. A 1926 French ad for the perfume "Désir Du Coeur" by Ybry.

151. A 1926 French ad featuring the perfume Au Fil De L'Eau'' by Lenthéric.

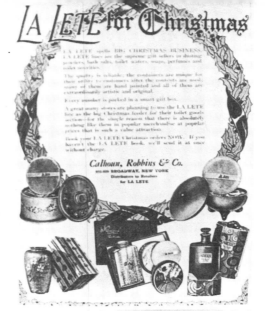

152. A 1926 Christmas wholesale ad promoting La Lete toilet items.

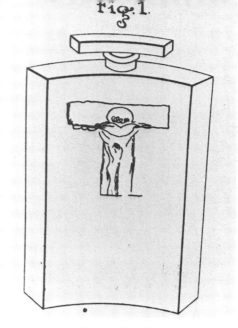

153. Patent drawing filed in 1926 for a perfume bottle assigned to the Park & Tilford Co.

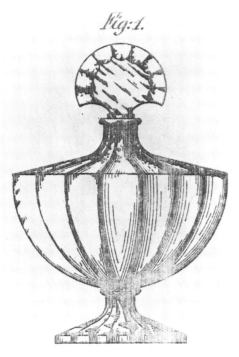

154. Patent drawing filed by Raymond Guerlain in 1926 for the classic ''Shalimar'' bottle.

155. A 1927 French ad for four different Rigaud perfumes.

156. A 1927 French ad for the perfume ''Fétiche'' by L. T. Piver.

157. Illustration of ''Flamme De Gloire'' perfume by Pleville from a 1927 ad. The bottle was made by Baccarat.

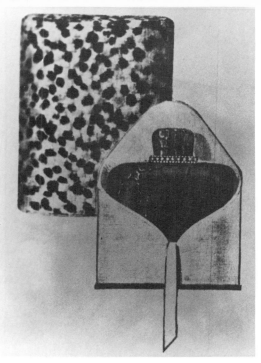

158. Picture from a 1927 ad for "Erotique" perfume by Terri of New York City.

159. Illustration of "Chu Chin Chow" perfume by Bryenne from a 1927 French ad.

160. A sketch of a bottle from a 1927 French ad for Eliane perfumes.

161. Drawing of the bottle for "Saturnale" eau de cologne from a 1927 Ysiane ad.

165. Patent drawing filed in 1927 for the perfume bottle used by D'Orsay to hold "La Flambée" perfume. The bottle was made by Baccarat.

162. A 1927 French ad for the perfume "Peut-Etre" by Jacqueline.

163. A 1927 ad for "Le Fleuve Bleu" perfume by Lionceau.

164. A 1927 French ad for the perfume "Ambre De Delhi" by Babani.

166. A 1927 ad for "Patricia" perfume by Mury. The flacon was made by Baccarat.

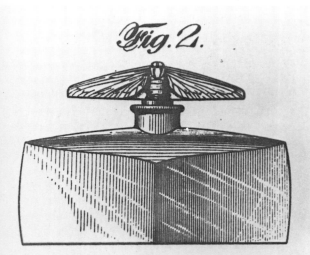

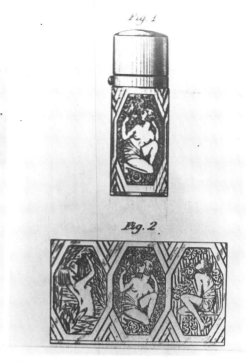

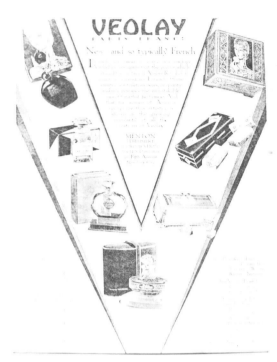

167. Patent drawing filed in 1927 for a toilet water bottle used by Le Gui of Paris.

168. Patent drawing filed in 1927 for a Corday travel atomizer. The frosted glass bottle had a 18 kt. gold-plated top and sold for $7.50.

169. A 1928 ad for a variety of Veolay (Violet) products. Note the deluxe package for "Niobe" perfume designed by R. Lalique, originally sold for eighteen dollars.

No. 523

1 ounce of real perfume, richly put up to retail at 59c

170. Illustration used by Bouton (George W. Button Corp.) in a 1928 wholesale ad. The bottle held the perfumes "Pearl D'Or" and "Sweet Pea".

171. Illustration from a 1928 ad for the perfume "Les Pois De Senteur" by Guimet.

172. Picture of a "Maharadjah" perfume bottle from a 1928 Rosine ad.

173. A 1928 French ad for the perfume "Pour Moi Seule" by G. Lemoine of Paris.

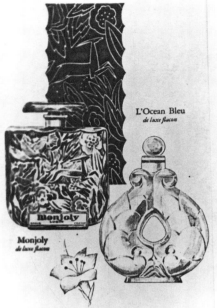

176. Illustration from a 1928 ad for "Masque Rouge" perfume by Marcel Guerlain. Marcel Guerlain was not connected with the famous Guerlain perfume house.

174. A French ad from 1928 for "Dyne" perfume by Plassard.

175. A 1928 Lubin ad featuring the perfumes "Monjoly" and "L'Ocean Bleu". The flacon for "L'Ocean Bleu" was made by Baccarat.

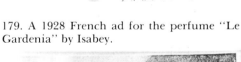

177. A 1928 French ad for perfumes, cremes, and powders by Coryse.

178. A 1928 ad introducing the perfume "Mon Talisman" by Gabilla to the United States. The white and gold flacon was made by Baccarat.

179. A 1928 French ad for the perfume "Le Gardenia" by Isabey.

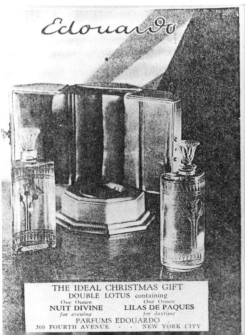

180. A French ad from 1928 promoting the perfume "No. 9" by Cadolle.

181. A 1928 Christmas ad for Edouardo perfumes. The bottle was made by Baccarat.

82. A 1928 French ad for the perfume "Sim Viva" by Studia of Paris.

183. A 1928 French ad for Ganna Walska perfumes.

184. A 1928 French ad for the Clamy perfume "A Tires d'Ailes".

186. Illustration from a 1928 ad for "Lucidité" perfume by Lérys of Paris. The crystal flacon was banded with black and gold with a gold stopper.

5. Illustration from a 1928 ad for the perfume Saigon" by Babani.

187. Perfume bottle patent drawing filed in 1928 by Irving W. Bean.

8. Illustration of a French-made three ounce ttle from a 1929 catalog. The bottle held the uimet perfumes "Tout Paris", "Multieurs", "Sweet Pea", "Jasmin" and hypre".

189. Perfume bottle patent drawing filed in 1928 by I. Barouh of Paris, France.

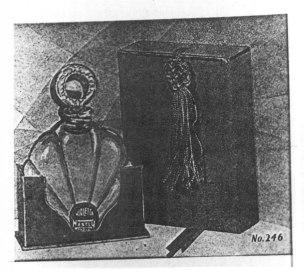

190. Illustration of a French-made two ounce bottle with aquamarine glass stopper from a 1929 catalog. The bottle held the Nestly perfumes "Chypre", "Numero 7", "Gardenia", "Jasmin", "Violetta", and "Sweet Pea".

191. Picture of a "Blue Waltz" bottle by Joubert shown in a 1929 ad. The blue glass bottle came in a blue and silver box.

192. A 1929 wholesale ad for four Joubert holiday perfume sets.

193. Illustration from a 1929 ad for Raffy perfumes. The perfume "Voici Paris" had a jade green stopper and the perfume "Le Rubis" had a red stopper.

194. A 1929 ad for the perfume "Sweet Peas" by De Raymond. The bottle shown was also used for other perfumes.

195. A 1929 ad for four different perfumes by Marqués de Elorza.

196. A 1929 French ad for the perfume "Vers la Joie" by Rigaud.

197. "Mirage" perfume by Gueldy. French ad from 1929.

198. Illustration from a 1929 ad for "L'Amazone" perfume by d'Ouchy. The bottle was made in France.

199. A 1929 French ad for the perfume "Gao" by L. T. Piver. The bottle was made by Baccarat.

200. A 1929 French ad for "Jardin Secret" perfume by Lubin.

201. A 1929 ad for the Lionceau perfume "Poème Arabe".

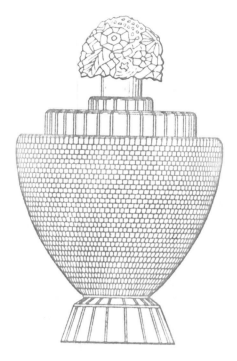

202. Patent drawing of a perfume bottle filed in 1929 assigned to Marcel Guerlain, Inc.

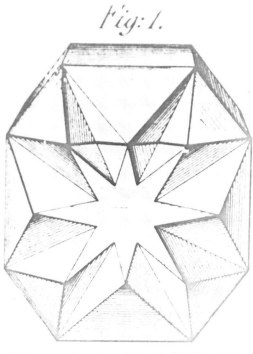

203. Patent drawing of a bottle filed in 1929 by L. Peszynska of Paris, France.

204. A 1930 ad for the perfume "Shanghai" by Raffy of Paris.

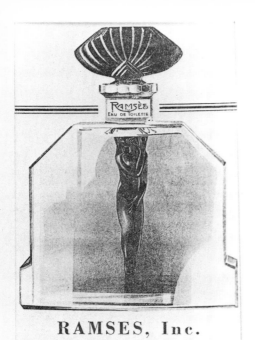

RAMSES, Inc.

Bridgeport, Connecticut

New York Showrooms: 339 Fifth Ave., Corner 33rd St.

205. Illustration from a 1930 ad for "Ramsès" eau de toilette by Ramses Inc. The bottle has a rare figural nude dapper and originally retailed for one dollar.

206. A 1930 French ad for the perfume "Maïdou" by Rallet.

207. A 1930 ad for "Secret de Satan perfume by Raffy. The flacon was of red crystal.

Fig. 2.

208. Patent drawing filed in 1929 of a perfume bottle used by McKesson & Robbins, Inc.

209. A 1930 ad for the d'Ouchy perfume "Chypre".

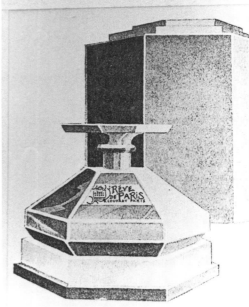

PARFUM
RÊVE de PARIS

210. Illustration from a 1930 ad for the perfume "Reve de Paris" by Coudray.

211. Illustration from a 1930 ad for the perfume "Charme de France" by Coudray.

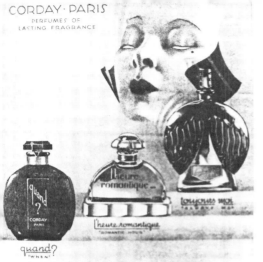

CORDAY

CHARME DE FRANCE COUDRAY PARIS

PARFUM

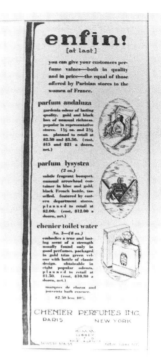

212. A 1930 ad for three perfumes by Corday. The ''l'heure Romantique'' bottle was made by Baccarat.

213. Illustration from a 1930 ad for the perfume ''Tendresse'' by Marly.

214. A 1931 ad featuring three Chenier perfumes.

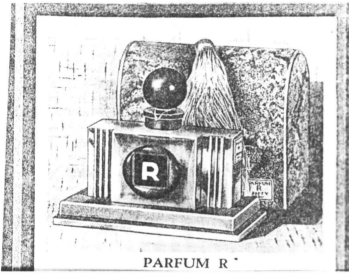

PARFUM R

215. Illustration from a 1930 ad for ''Parfum R'' by Raffy.

216. Illustration from a 1390 ad for ''Tulipe'' perfume by Raffy of Paris.

217. Illustration from a 1931 ad for ''Parfum R'' by Lucien Lelong. The eight point crystal flacon was by R. Lalique.

218. Perfume bottle patent drawing filed in 1931 by Robert Betts.

219. A 1932 ad for the Lucien Lelong perfume ''Whisper''.

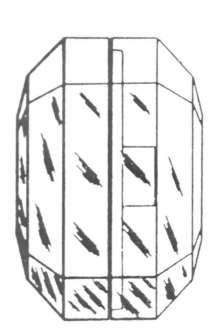

220. Illustration for a 1932 wholesale ad for Wrisley holiday items.

221. A 1932 ad for "Sweet Magnolia" perfume by De Seghers.

222. Illustration of a beautiful Baccarat bottle imported to the U.S. in 1932 by Parfums Francais Inc. of New York.

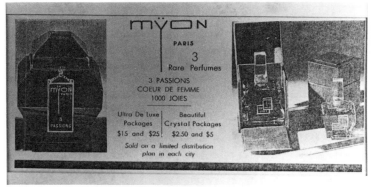

223. A 1933 ad for three Mÿon perfumes. The deluxe flacon was opaque green crystal by Baccarat with a gold metal stopper cover.

224. Illustration from a 1933 ad of the beautiful cut crystal flacons used for the perfume "Arcadi" by Ballarde of Paris.

227. A 1934 ad for the Lucien Lelong perfume "Opening Night".

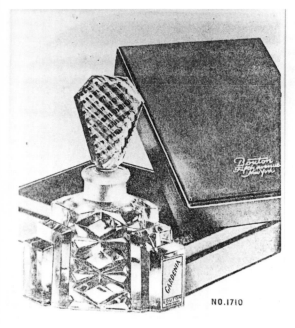

226. A 1934 ad introducing the Mÿon perfume "Exaltation" to the U.S. The flacon made by Baccarat came in three sizes.

225. Illustration from a 1933 Bouton ad. The bottle, with a ground glass stopper, was used for five different Bouton scents and sold for one dollar.

Exquisite!

Nuit d'Extase
(NIGHT OF ECSTASY)
by
Dermay

228. A 1934 ad for "Nuit d'Extase" perfume by Dermay of New York. The wooden bottle had a highly polished walnut grain finish.

"Emotion"
Created especially for Jean Harlow — a langorous perfume reminiscent of oriental romance.

"Mysterie Gardenia"
As dainty as the valuable blossoms itself. A perfume of lingering subtlety.

"Orchidée Perdue"
The real perfume of the famous Legend of the Lost Orchid.

231. Part of a 1935 ad for three perfumes by Prince de Chany of Paris.

234. A 1935 ad for "Byzance" perfume by Grenoville.

BYZANCE
Dynamique

229. A 1934 illustration of a Jeurelle parfum sphere which was used for six flower fragrances.

"The Sweetest Story Ever Told"
IN-FLOWERY-LANGUAGE
FLOWER-IN-THE-BOTTLE
PERFUME

COLOGNE
with the fresh plucked flowers immersed in their own essence—an added attraction to the bottle.

☆

Rose, Lilac, Violet, Sweet Pea, Orange Blossom, Lily of the Valley, Esprit D'Amour.

☆

Toilet Waters Colognes
4-Ounce, $7.20 Doz.

Perfumes
½-Ounce, $3.60 Doz.

☆

TOILET WATER

☆

A
JOHN BLOCKI, INC.
Product of Exquisite Charm

Only the True Flower and Its Natural Oils Utilized
No Synthetics

☆

ORDER NOW
Sample Assortment
2 Dozen, $10.80

Visit Our Display at Gift Shows

Penn Hotel, N. Y.
Room 412A

Statler Hotel, Boston
Room 518

☆

DE ROSE STUDIO, 225 5th Av., N.Y.C.

232. A 1935 De Rose Studio ad for "Flower-in-the-Bottle" perfume by John Blocki.

235. A 1935 French ad promoting the perfumes of Lancôme.

lequel...

des Parfums de
LANCÔME

EVEIL

BIENAIME

230. A 1935 French ad for the perfume "Eveil" by Bienaime.

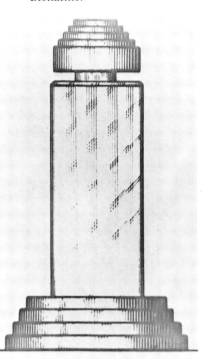

233. Patent drawing filed in 1935 for a perfume bottle assigned to Millot of Paris.

236. A 1935 ad for the Delettrez perfume "Inalda". The flacons were made by R. Lalique.

237. Illustration from a 1935 ad for the perfume Joie de Vivre" by Ybry.

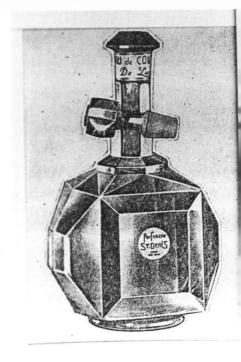

238. A 1935 illustration of a eau de cologne bottle used for several scents by St. Denis.

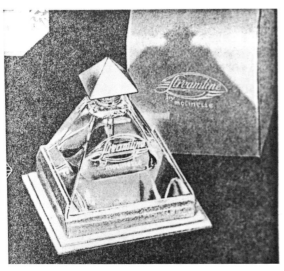

239. Illustration from a 1935 ad for "Streamline" perfume by Molinelle of London.

240. A 1936 ad for the perfume "Libretto" by Jeurelle. The perfume came in a clear crystal bottle.

241. Illustration from a 1936 ad for "Essence Imperiale Russe" by Lengyel.

242. Patent drawing filed in 1936 for a bottle used by Joubert Inc. for several scents.

243. Illustration from a 1936 ad for the Vigny perfume "Echo Troublant".

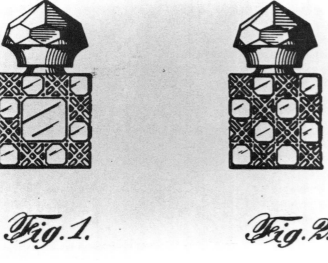

244. A 1936 ad for the perfume "Deviltry" by De Raymond. The striking mephistopheles figural stopper was made of red glass.

245. A 1936 French ad for the perfume "Sans Atout" by Lanselle.

246. A 1936 ad for "Forbidden Love" perfume by Le Clairac of Paris. The cut crystal bottle came in a beautiful pale peach color.

247. A 1936 ad for the perfume "Kismaju" by Le Clairac. The bottle was made by Brosse.

250. Illustration from a 1937 ad for the perfume "Fidelwood" by the House of Fragrance in Bermuda.

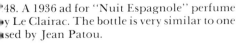

248. A 1936 ad for "Nuit Espagnole" perfume by Le Clairac. The bottle is very similar to one used by Jean Patou.

249. A 1936 ad for three perfumes by Bienaime.

251. Illustration from a 1938 ad for the Lentheric perfume "Anticipation".

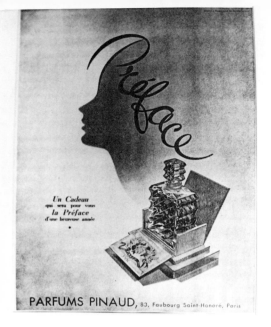

252. A 1937 French ad for the perfume "Prèface" by Pinaud.

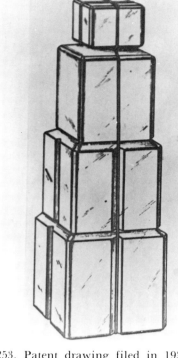

253. Patent drawing filed in 1937 for the perfume bottle used for "715" by Helena Rubinstein.

254. A 1937 ad for the "Pagliacci" perfume set by Dermay. The set of three clown-dressed bottles sold for one dollar.

255. A 1937 ad for the Kathleen Mary Quinlan of New York perfume "Organdy".

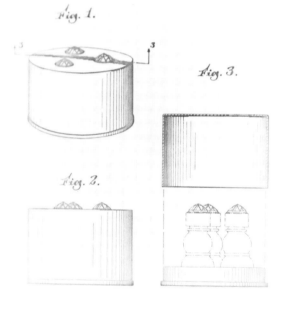

256. Patent drawing for perfume bottles and display unit was filed by Leo Mann in 1937.

258. A 1938 ad for a purse size flacon called an "Eaglet" by Chevalier Garde. The small bottle held various Chevalier Garde perfumes.

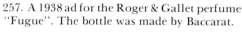

257. A 1938 ad for the Roger & Gallet perfume "Fugue". The bottle was made by Baccarat.

259. A 1938 ad for the perfume "Sans Nom" by Hedwig Orlik. The hand-cut crystal flacon came in a chartreuse silk box.

260. Illustration for "Warwick Lavender" cologne from a 1938 Dermay ad.

261. Illustration from a 1938 ad for the perfume "Safari" by Tussy.

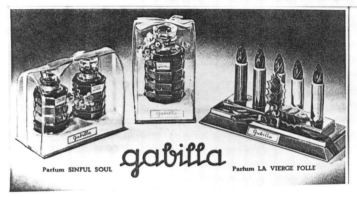

Parfum SINFUL SOUL   gabilla   Parfum LA VIERGE FOLLE

262. Patent drawing of a perfume bottle filed by Frank E. Ansell in 1938.

263. A 1939 ad for perfumes made by Gabilla. The candle-like vials contained five different Gabilla scents.

264. A 1939 ad for the Lucien Lelong perfume "Care Free".

265. A 1939 ad for "H.R.H." perfume by Chevalier Garde. The perfume was dedicated to Her Royal Highness, the Duchess of Kent.

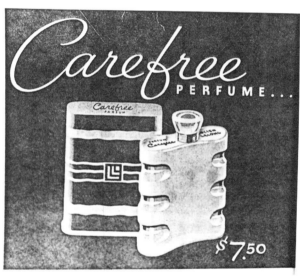

Carefree PERFUME...

$7.50

266. Illustration from a 1939 ad for "Dress Parade" by Solon Palmer.

267. A 1939 United Toilet Goods Corp. ad illustration for "18th Century" toilet articles.

268. Sketch from a 1939 Houbigant ad. The bottle and box were used for both "Le Parfum Ideal" and "Quelques Fleurs".

269. A 1939 ad illustration for De Heriot colognes. The cut glass, six ounce bottle held four different De Heriot colognes.

270. A 1939 ad for perfumes and toilet waters by Henri Bendel of New York.

272. Illustration from a 1940 A. A. Vantine of New York ad. The hand made opalescent glass cologne bottle with a fern design held four different Vantine scents. The original selling price was one dollar.

271. Patent drawing filed in 1939 for the bottle used by Helena Rubinstein for "Slumber Song".

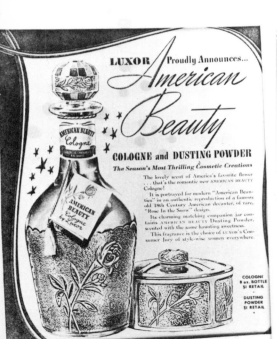

273. Illustration from a 1940 ad for Ybry cologne. The bottle shown held five assorted Ybry scents.

274. A 1940 ad for perfumes made by Lili of Bermuda.

275. A 1940 ad for "American Beauty" cologne by Luxor of Chicago. The bottle was a reproduction of an old 18th century decanter.

276. A 1940 ad for "Woodbine" toilet articles by the John Bradshaw Co. of Boston. The products came in maple finish wood containers made by New England craftsmen.

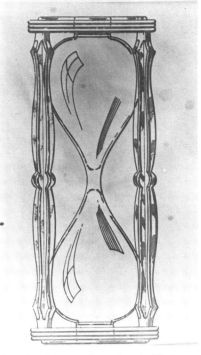

277. A 1940 ad for "Pineapple" cologne by the Irving W. Rice Co.

278. Illustration from a 1940 ad for "Flutter" perfume by Dorothy Gray. The heart-shaped bottle came in a transparent box with a lacy design.

279. Patent drawing for a perfume bottle filed in 1940 by W. R. Hauptman.

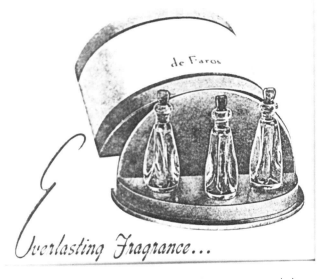

280. Illustration from a 1940 ad for "Suivez Moi" by Varva. The pearl-like bottle was mounted in a rhinestone setting on a velvet base.

281-283. Patent drawings filed in 1940 for porcelain-like perfume containers used by L'Orle.

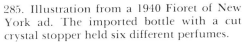

284. A 1940 ad for a petite flacon set containing the perfumes "Bretton Woods", "Lido", and "Lilac" by de Faros of New York.

285. Illustration from a 1940 Fioret of New York ad. The imported bottle with a cut crystal stopper held six different perfumes.

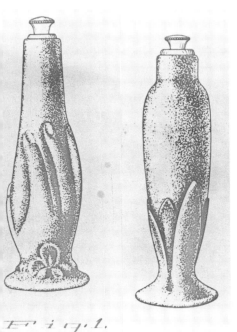

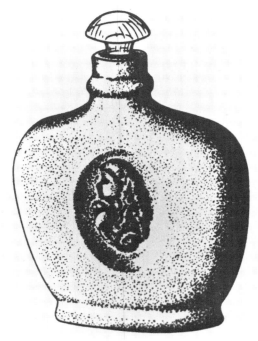

286. A 1941 ad for a three-piece perfume set called "Bells of Peace" by Cecile d'Avril. Each miniature bell-shaped bottle contained a different perfume.

287. A 1941 ad sketch for the perfume "Tout De Suite" by Suzanne.

288. Illustration from a 1941 ad for "Bombshell" perfume by Cecile d'Avril.

289. A 1941 ad for a "Pink Coral" gift set by Wrisley.

290. A 1942 ad for three Suzy perfumes.

291. A 1942 ad for the perfume "Elusive" by Babani.

292. A 1942 ad for "Lady in the Dark" perfume by Dorothy Gray.

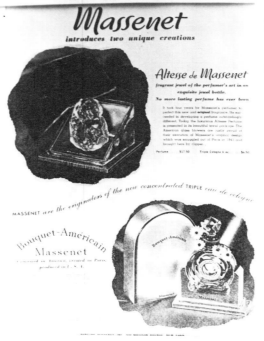

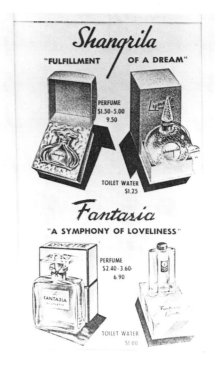

293. A 1942 ad for "Fire Magic" perfume by Jaquet. The hand-blown crystal teardrop bottle came in a pink satin box.

294. A 1942 ad for two Massenet perfumes. The bottles were made in the United States.

295. A 1943 ad for two Lynette of New York scents.

296. A 1943 ad for the perfume "Escape" by Mary Dunhill. The bottle was a copy of an antique poison bottle.

297. A 1943 ad for "Renaissance" perfume by Scherk.

298. A 1943 ad for the perfumes "Dashing" and "Drifting" by Lily Daché. The flacons were made in the United States.

299. A 1943 ad for "Canteen" eau de cologne and after-shaving lotion by Karoff. The container was a blue or khaki stone-like jug.

300. A 1943 ad for the perfume "Conquest" by Dorothy Perkins.

301. Daring ad published in 1944 for the perfume "On Leave" by Kay Daumit showed a couple kissing.

302. Another embracing couple appeared in this 1944 ad for Lynette perfumes.

303. A 1944 ad for the perfume and cologne "Trifling" by Lenel.

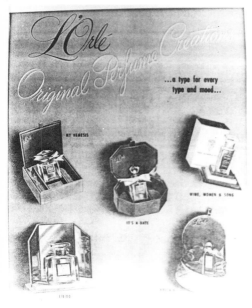

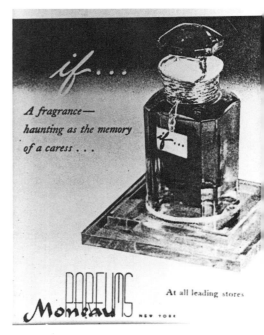

304. A 1944 ad featuring an assortment of perfumes by L'Orle.

305. A 1944 ad for "Fancy Free" day and night perfumes by Teboe of New York.

306. A 1944 ad for the perfume "If..." by Moneau of New York.

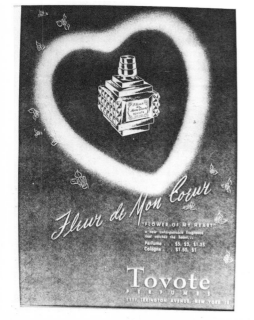

307. A 1944 ad for the Tovote perfume "Fleur de Mon Coeur".

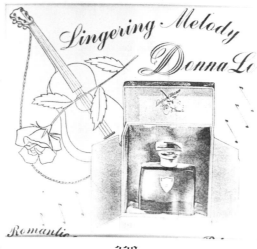

308. Sketch from a 1944 ad for the perfume "Lingering Melody" by Donna Lo.

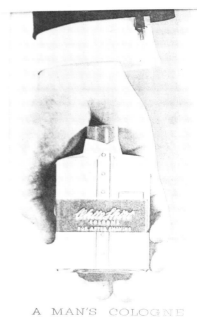

A MAN'S COLOGNE

309. Part of a 1944 ad for Old South toiletries.

310. Illustration from a 1945 ad for the perfume "Twenty One" by Maurice Rentner, an American fashion designer.

311. A 1945 ad for the man's cologne "White Shirt" by Kay Daumit.

PAGODA and PAGAN by RAVEL

312. A 1945 ad for the perfumes "Pagoda" and "Pagan" by Ravel.

313. A 1945 ad for the perfume "Credo" by Prince Obolenski of New York.

314. A 1945 ad for the perfumes "Acacia" and "Fleur Danoise" by Georg Jensen.

315. A 1945 ad for the perfume "Zezan" by Tuvaché of New York. The bottle cover was a copy of the Benin head of an African princess.

316. Illustration from a 1946 ad for the gift edition of the perfume "Forever Amber" by Kay Daumit of Chicago. The book was gold plated with a black sueded case.

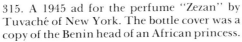

221

317. A 1945 ad for the perfumes "Seduction" and "Seventh Heaven" by Bergél.

318. A 1945 ad for Lysanda fragrance.

319. Illustration from a 1946 ad for "Calypso" by Rancour of Paris.

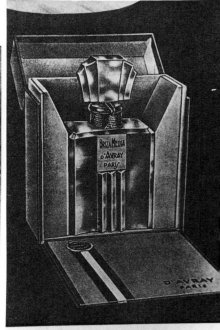

320. A 1945 ad for "Black Magic" perfume by Bombi.

321. Illustration from a 1946 ad for the perfume "Golden Arrow" by the American hat designer John Frederics. The bottle was made by Wheaton.

322. Sketch from a 1946 ad for the D'Avray perfume "Briza Media".

323. Patent drawing of a perfume bottle filed in 1946 by Leonid De Lescinskis.

324. Illustration from a 1946 ad for the perfume "Strange Music" by Farel Destin.

325. A 1946 ad for the Roger & Gallet perfume "Innuendo".

326. A wonderful ad from 1946 for the perfume "No Regrets" by Gaston de Paris of New York.

327. A 1946 ad for "Mountain Heather" cologne by Daggett & Ramsdell.

328. A 1946 ad for the South American perfume "Tuya" by Para Ti. The perfume bottle was made by Wheaton.

329. A surreal ad from 1946 for the perfume "Aorist" by Hugh Genske of New York.

330. A 1946 ad for the Jean D'Hennery perfume "Kim".

331. A 1946 ad for the perfumes "Et Cetera" and "Vice Versa" by Victoria Ltd.

332. A 1946 ad for perfumes by Lancry of Paris. The hand-made flacon was a copy of a 16th century apothecary bottle.

333. A 1946 ad for the perfume "Green Eyes" by Esmé of Paris.

334. A 1946 ad for the fragrance "By Appointment" by Yona Labs, Inc. of Chicago.

335. An attractive ad featuring six perfumes Corday.

336. A 1946 ad for "Dress Parade" perfume Solon Palmer.

337. Patent drawing of a perfume bottle fil in 1946 by Georges Baud of Paris, France.

338. A 1947 ad for the perfumes "Danseu Etoile" and "Estampe" by Degas.

339. A 1947 ad for perfume "Forever Ambe by Kathryn (Kay Daumit).

340. A 1947 ad for the scent "Going My Way" by Elmo of Philadelphia.

341. Illustration from a 1949 ad for the perfume "Something Blue" by Gourielli.

342. Patent drawing of a perfume bottle filed in 1947 and assigned to Bombi Perfumer Inc. New York.

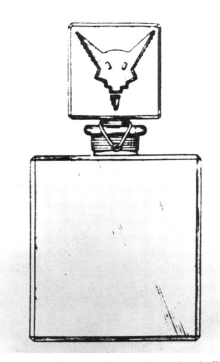

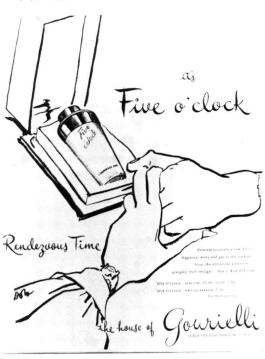

343. Patent drawing for a perfume bottle filed in 1947 by Jacques Heim of Paris, France.

344. A 1948 ad for the perfume "Star Fire" by Old South Perfumers of New York.

345. A 1948 ad for the Gourielli perfume "Five O'Clock". The bottle was made by Wheaton.

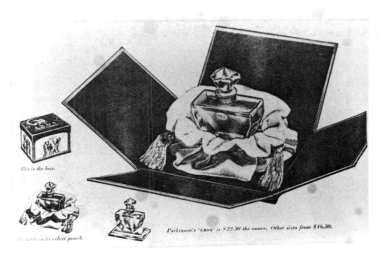

346. Illustration from a 1947 ad for the perfume "Eros" by George Robert Parkinson. The bottle and package was made in the United States.

347. A 1948 ad for "Eau de Fleurs" fragrance by Leonid de Lescinskis.

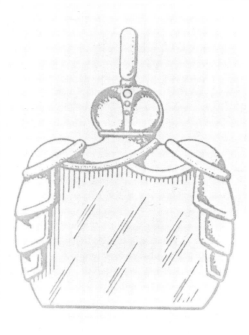

348. Patent drawing for a perfume bottle filed in 1949 and assigned to Gourielli.

349. A 1950 ad for the perfume "Célèbre" by De Heriot of Hollywood.

350. Patent drawing filed in 1950 for a bottle used by Helene Pessl, Inc. of New York.

351. A 1955 ad for the perfume "Notte Romana" by Borsari & F. of Italy.

352. A 1951 ad for the perfume "Loki, God of Mischief" by Loki of New York.

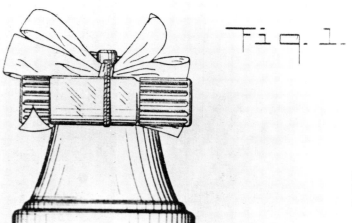

353. Patent drawing of a combined perfume bottle and bell-shaped holder filed in 1950 and assigned to Coty.

354. Patent drawing for a bottle filed in 1951 by Marie De Montesquiou Fezensac of Paris, France.

355. A 1952 ad for the perfume "Kis Royale" by Fauby of Paris.

356. A 1953 ad for the perfume "Private Affair" by Lenel of Dallas.

357. A 1954 ad for the Angelique perfume "Red Satin".

358. A 1954 ad for the perfume "Ricochet" by Ciro.

359. A 1955 ad for perfumes by Miahati of New York.

360. A 1951 ad for the perfume "Jealousy" by Blanchard.

361. A 1955 ad for the perfume "Folie de Minuit" by Lanier.

362. A selection of Caswell Massey perfumes
and toilet waters from the 1940's. Photo
courtesy of Caswell Massey.

Perfume and Manufacturers Directory

The following directory is the result of long, extensive research using trademarks, patents, magazines, wholesale and retail catalogs, and company information. I hope the following information will be helpful to the readers in dating their commercial bottles.

Directory Key

tm/ = U.S. trademark. The first date is the year in which the trademark was filed; the second date is the year which the company claimed use of the name from.

Ad = U.S. advertisement. Date of the oldest U.S. advertisement I found for a perfume.

Fr. Ad. = French advertisement. Date of the oldest French advertisement I found for a perfume.

Cat. = Catalog. Date of the oldest wholesale or retail American catalog I found the perfume was listed in.

Art. = Article. Date of magazine article, beauty column, or book in which a perfume was mentioned.

New = Year that a perfume was launched.

AARON BEAUTY SUPPLY, Brooklyn, NY: "Nora Adams", tm 1937/1935; "Zeŕe", tm 1938/1937.

AARSLEFF & CO., Copenhagen, Denmark: "Esprit du Roi", tm 1949/1948.

ABRAHAM & STRAUS INC., Brooklyn, NY: "Mirabelle", tm 1938/1936.

CHRISTINE S. ACKER, Santa Barbara, CA: "Naranjada", tm 1928/1928.

ADAM'S PERFUMES INC., NY, NY: "Fleurs Flotante", tm 1952/1950.

ADRIAN, NY, NY: "Saint", Ad 1944; "Sinner", Ad 1944.

AFFILIATED PRODUCTS, Jersey City, NJ: "Gallivanting", tm 1943/1943; "Tom-Tom", tm 1945/1945; "Vaness", tm 1941/1940.

AGNEL, Paris, France: "Dolly", Ad 1913; "Mon Doux Pays", Ad 1910.

AGRA, Detroit, MI: "Ci-Mi", tm 1923/1923.

AID LABORATORIES, Camden, NJ: "Cinde Lee", tm 1946/1934.

ETIENNE AIGNER: "#1 Cuir de Chasse", Ad 1963.

ROBAIRE ALAIN, Los Angeles, CA: "Canibelle", tm 1963/1962; "Cote D'Or", tm 1963/1962; "Durango", tm 1963/1962; "Jaguar", tm 1963/1962; "Rafifi", tm 1963/1962.

DR. M. ALBERSHEIM, Frankfort, Germany: "Khasana", tm 1924/1906; "Li", tm 1927/1925; "Salugen", tm 1925/1924.

JEAN D' ALBRET, Paris, France: "Casaque", Ad 1957; "Ecusson", Ad 1953.

ALEXA INC. (MARTIN DE BOTELHO), NY, NY: "Enigma", tm 1946/1944.

JANE ALEXANDER, Valley Stream, NY: "Pluggin' Jane", tm 1945/1944.

ALLAN COSMETIC CO. (KATHRYN A. ALLAN), NY, NY: "Seven Faces", tm 1925/1924.

ROGER S. ALLAN, NY, NY: "Celia", tm 1929/1929; "Whoopee", tm 1930/1929.

ALLEN PERFUMER, Detroit, MI: "Lady Allen", tm 1936/1932; "Lenore Dee", tm 1937/1936; "Prep", tm 1927/1927; "Vita-Fleurs", tm 1921/1920; "Ze Paree", tm 1926/1924.

LUCRETIA ALLEN, NY, NY: "Bluebonnet", art 1936; "Bouquet", ad 1934; "Gardenia", ad 1934; "Honeysuckle", ad 1934; "Wild Rose", ad 1934; "Violet", ad 1934.

ALLIANCE ART PRODUCTS CO., Alliance, OH: "Sea Treasure", tm 1927/1925.

ALLIED PRODUCTS INC., NY, NY: "L'Affaire", tm 1939/1939.

ALLIED TOILETRIES, NY, NY: Philadelphia, PA: "Carole Anne", tm 1944/1942; "Caucasian Lilac", tm 1944/1943; "Russian Lilac", tm 1944/1943; "Shandor", tm 1944/1943; "Spicy Flowers", tm 1945/1943.

ALMAY PHARMACEUTICAL, NY, NY: "Parasol", tm 1935/1935; "Truly Yours", ad 1953.

B. ALTMAN & CO., NY, NY: "Premier Amour", tm 1925/1925; "Sans Egal", tm 1926/1925; "Tout Seul", tm 1925/1925.

ALYS, NY, NY: "A Paris", cat 1922; "Chinois", cat 1922; "Chypre Ambre", cat 1922; "Elysees", cat 1922; "Parfum Filigree", tm 1921/1920; "Frivolite", cat 1922; "Jardinet", cat 1922; "L'Etoile", cat 1922; "Modeste", cat 1922; "Sheik", tm 1922/1921; "Un Jour de Printemps", cat 1922.

AMERICAN BEAUTY PERFUMERS, NY, NY: "Comac", tm 1927/1926.

AMERICAN DRUGGISTS SYNDICATE, Long Island, NY: "D'Arline", tm 1924/1923; "Delectol", tm 1927/1927; "Tijade", tm 1924/1923.

AMERICAN PRODUCTS CO., Cincinnati, OH: "Dream Girl", tm 1923/1917; "Faith Avery", tm 1932/1930; "La Bara", tm 1923/1917.

AMERICAN TOILET GOODS, Boston, MA: "Bokemia", cat 1922; "Cape Jasmine", cat 1922; "Fresh Violet", cat 1922; "Jardin De Lilas", ad 1918; "Jardin de Marie", ad 1918; "Jickee", cat 1922; "Kismidir", cat 1922; "L'Azora", cat 1922; "Lilas de Syria", cat 1922; "Lucille", cat 1922; "Pavlow", cat 1922; "Rozina", cat 1922.

AMORSKIN INC., Paris, France; NY, NY: "Fleurs Prisonnières", tm 1932/1931; "La Peele Aude", tm 1932/1931; "Le Rouge et Le Bleu", tm 1932/1931.

AMZELL, NY, NY: "Windswept", tm 1946/1945.

ARTHUR O. ANDERSON, Cedar Rapids, IA: "Blue Bonnet", tm 1938/1938.

ETHEL G. ANDERSON, Chicago, IL: "Jeunesse doreé", tm 1932/1930.

KARL O. ANDERSON, Omaha, NE: "Celebrity", tm 1939/1930.

M. V. ANDERSON & CO., Lewiston, ME: "Maban", tm 1923/1921.

ANDRE-LEE, NY, NY: "Bachelor's Bait", tm 1949/1944.

ANGELIQUE, Wilton, CT: "Black Satin", tm 1958/1946; "Gold Satin", tm 1958/1950; "Red Satin", tm 1958/1954; "White Satin", tm 1958/1949.

ANJOU, NY, NY: "Apropos", tm 1950/1940; "Devastating", tm 1944/1943; "Side Glance", ad 1952.

ANRE (HARRY D. KOENIG), NY, NY: "Caramba", tm 1947/1945; "Gay Divorcee", tm 1942/1941; "Trique", tm 1941/1941.

BENJAMIN ANSEHL, St. Louis, MO: "Amethyst", tm 1934/1927; "Futura", tm 1937/1936; "Lavender and Old Lace", tm 1934/1934; "Orchids in the Moonlight", tm 1934/1934.

THE ANTIQUE SHOPPE (RUBICON), NY, NY: "Tinsel", tm 1945/1944.

ANTOINE DE PARIS, Paris, France; NY, NY: "Blithe Spirit", tm 1942/1941; "Nuance", tm 1941/1940; "Rue Cambon", ad 1937; "Sunbask", tm 1947/1946.

ROSE APPELBAUM, Brooklyn, NY: "Lucille Savoy", tm 1928/1916.

ELIZABETH ARDEN, NY, NY: "Arden Jasmin", cat 1922; "Arden Rose", cat 1922; "Black Lace", tm 1939/1938; "Blackout", tm 1942/1941; "Blue Grass", tm 1934/1934; "Box Office", tm 1950/1949; "Brise d'Orient", cat 1922; "Carnival", tm 1945/1916; "Cupid's Breath", tm 1928/1916; "Corsage", tm 1935/1935; "Cyclamen", ad 1938; "Eau de France", tm 1949/1948; "Eau de Nile", tm 1947/1926; "For Her", ad 1937; "Gone With The Wind", tm 1938/1937; "Italian Lilac", cat 1922; "It's You", tm 1940/1938; "June Geranium", tm 1949/1917; "Ladies and Gentlemen", tm 1942/1941; "Lady in Black", tm 1941/1941; "La Jardin d'Elizabeth", tm 1928/1928; "la joie d' elizabeth", tm 1928/1928; "l'amour d'elizabeth", tm 1929/1929; "Le Bouquet d'Elizabeth", tm 1928/1928; "le êve d' élizabeth", tm 1928/1928; "1 élan d' elizabeth", tm 1931/1930; "L' Etoile d' Elizabeth", tm 1928/1928; "Ma Rue", tm 1932/1932; "Mémoire Chérie", ad 1956; "Millie Fleurs", ad 1942; "Miss Jezebel", tm 1938/1938; "Mon Amour", tm 1949/1948; "Mountie", tm 1941/1940; "My Love", tm 1949/1948; "Nothing Sacred", tm 1938/1937; "On Dit", tm 1945/1944; "Prince's Feather", tm 1938/1938; "Profile", tm 1947/1945; "Surprise", tm 1951/1940; "Thousand Flowers", tm 1941/1940; "Tuberose d' Elizabeth", tm 1933/1932; "Velva", tm 1925/1910; "Winged Victory", tm 1945/1944; "Younger Set", tm 1954/1953.

ARE-JAY, NY, NY: "Three little minks", tm 1939/1938.

ALSONO Y. ARENAS, Habana, Cuba: "Campos de Amor", tm 1932/1928.

MARC ARIF, Paris, France: "Contact", tm 1958/1953.

ARKWRIGHT MERCHANDISING CORP., NY, NY: "Franchette", tm 1933/1929.

ARLT, Brooklyn, NY: "Artistique", tm 1925/1924; "Orchard Wedding", tm 1927/1926; "Veragen", tm 1927/1914.

ARLY, Paris, France: "La Bohême", tm 1916/1915; "Lilas", ad 1915; "Ninique", ad 1934; "Rose Arly", cat 1922. (See also: DELETTREZ; V. VIVAUDOU.)

ARMAND CO., Des Moines, IA: "Beau 'K", tm 1928/1927; "Peridore", tm 1924/1923; "Taquine", tm 1926/1926; "Too Lovely For Words", tm 1948/1946.

IRMA ARMANET, San Francisco, CA: "Fleurs Des Alpes", tm 1941/1940.

ARMOUR, Chicago, IL: "La Richesse", tm 1949/1907.

ARMOUR & CO., Chicago, IL: "Floriana", cat 1922; "Karnak", cat 1922; "Luxor", cat 1922; "Mayfair", cat 1922.

F. R. ARNOLD & CO., NY, NY: "Allumettes", tm 1927/1926; "Lilacblooms", tm 1890/1890; "Lily-Bells", tm 1887/1887; "May Bells", tm 1885/1885; "Pavot", tm 1927/1924.

ARROW LABORATORIES, NY, NY: "Mad Hatter", tm 1945/1945.

ARTRA COSMETICS, NY, NY: "H R H", tm 1940/1937.

ARYS, Paris, France: "Ambre Vermeil", Fr. ad 1920; "Croyez Moi", Fr. ad 1931; "Cyclamen", Fr. ad 1919; "Diamant Impérial", ad 1927; "En Fermant Les Yeux", Fr. ad 1920; "Faisons un Reve", ad 1922; "Faites Lui Mes Aveux", cat 1922; "Fox Trot", Fr. ad 1920; "L'Amour Dans Le Coeur", Fr. ad 1919; "L'Anneau Merveilleux", Fr. ad 1919; "Muguet", cat 1922; "Musky", ad 1922; "Oeillet", Fr. ad 1919; "Parlez-Lui de Moi", Fr. ad 1919; "Premier Oui", Fr. ad 1919; "Rose", Fr. ad 1919; "Rose sans fin", Fr. ad 1920; "Secret d'Arys", ad 1922; "Un Jardin La Nuit", ad 1922; "Un Jour Viendra", Fr. ad 1919; "Violette", Fr. ad 1919; "Vouloir C'Est Pouvoir", cat 1922.

ASSOCIATED DISTRIBUTORS INC., Chicago, IL: "Chen Yu", tm 1939/1938; "Chinalac", tm 1941/1938; "Guillotine", tm 1938/1937; "Honolulu Moon", tm 1938/1936; "Linger", tm 1940/1938; "Lush", tm 1938/1937; "Sweet Escape", tm 1944/1934; "Taboo", tm 1936/1932; "Tattoo", tm 1944/1932; "Voodoo", tm 1938/1937.

ASSOCIATED MERCHANDISING CORP., NY, NY: "Jodelle", tm 1927/1927; "Louise André", tm 1937/1927.

ASSOCIATED PERFUMERS INC., West Haven, CT: La Castello", tm 1934/1926.

ASSOCIATED PRODUCTS, Chicago, IL: "Chez Nous", tm 1946/1945; "Cloudswept", tm 1946/1945; "Dynasty", tm 1946/1946; "Firebird", tm 1945/1945; "Glitter", tm 1947/1945; "Isolde", tm 1946/1946; "Lancelot", tm 1946/1945; "Lelani", tm 1947/1946; "Ming Yu", tm 1947/1945; "Red-Witch", tm 1947/1946; "Shantu", tm 1946/1945; "Tip and Toe", tm 1947/1946; "Yenshu", tm 1946/1945.

ASTORIA PRODUCTS (WILLIAM J. MIMS), Birmingham, AL: "Lucky Seven", tm 1946/1930.

J. & E. ATKINSON, London, England: "24 Flowers", tm 1951/1949; "Ballet Russe", tm 1952/1949; "Carillon", tm 1941/1936; "Columbine", tm 1924/1920; "Egesia", tm 1910/1910; "Eonia", tm 1902/1902; "Insouciance", tm 1924/1919; "Royal Briar", tm 1949/1941.

AUBER PERFUMS, Paris, France: "Fra Diavolo", tm 1953/1949; "Lac Des Fees", tm 1952/1949.

FERNAND AUBRY, Paris, France: "Visagiste", tm 1959/1951.

AUBRY SISTERS, NY, NY: "Reve d'Amour", tm 1917/1915.

AUCOIN, New Orleans, LA: "Chanson D'Amour", tm 1946/1942; "Nuit de Fleurs", tm 1946/1938.

AUDREY LOUISE, NY, NY: "Farouche", tm 1941/1941; "Nayade", tm 1941/1941.

WILLIAM J. AUSTEN, Oswego, NY: "Forest Flower", tm 1878/1878.

AUSTIN & MELVILLE, NY, NY: "Bouquet America", tm 1879/1879.

AUTRAN & ARDISSON, Paris, France: "Veni-Vici", tm 1913/1911.

AUVERGNE, Springfield, MA: "After Five", tm 1946/1937.

AUZIERE, Nashville, TN: "Secret d'Amour", tm 1949/1947.

AVON, NY, NY: "Andalusia", tm 1957/1957; "Applause", tm 1947/1946; "Attention", tm 1942/1942; "Blue Angel", tm 1950/1950; "Brass Buttons", tm 1942/1942; "Bright Night", tm 1955/1954; "Crystal Glory", tm 1963/1961; "Daisies Won't Tell", tm 1957/1956; "Deep in Clover", tm 1947/1947; "Devotedly Yours", tm 1949/1946; "Disarming", tm 1946/1945; "Elegance", tm 1957/1956; "Falling in Love", tm 1957/1957; "Flower Cluster", tm 1950/1948; "Flowers in the Wind", tm 1951/1950; "Forgive Me", tm 1947/1946; "Furlough", tm 1942/1942; "Hope Chest", tm 1947/1947; "June in January", tm 1952/1949; "Just For Fun", tm 1947/1945; "Kavon", tm 1963/1959; "Lovelight", tm 1946/1945; "Nearness", tm 1956/1955; "Occur!", tm 1963/1962; "Persian Wood", tm 1951/1951; "Quaintance", tm 1954/1948; "Rapture", tm 1963/1961; "Return Engagement", tm 1947/1946; "To A Wild Rose", tm 1959/1950; "Unforgettable", tm 1963/1960; "Violets-Are-Blue", tm 1949/1948; "White Moiré", tm 1946/1945; "Wishing", tm 1946/1945.

CECILE D'AVRIL, Rochester, NY: "Bombshell", ad 1941; "Concerto", ad 1941; "Daze", ad 1941; "Event", ad 1941; "Finale", ad 1941; "Heyday", ad 1941;

"Overture", ad 1941.

AVRAY (ROBERT LEFORT), Paris, France: "Ambre", ad 1946; "Briza Media", ad 1946; "Chypre", ad 1946; "Marjolaine D'Avray", ad 1946; "Muguet", ad 1946; "Symphonie Amoureuse", ad 1946.

HARRIET HUBBARD AYER, NY, NY: "Apres Lout", tm 1922/1922; "Brin D'Amour", tm 1922/1922; "Christmas Card", tm 1951/1948; "Darling", tm 1922/1922; "Doux Baiser", tm 1922/1922; "Golden Chance", tm 1950/1948; "Golden Hour", ad 1945; "Golden Note", tm 1949/1948; "Golden Splash", tm 1949/1948; Harriet Hubbard Ayer", ad 1937; "Honeysuckle", cat 1943; "Ivresse D'Amour", tm 1922/1922; "L'Ondée", tm 1922/1922; "Mes Fleurs", tm 1922/1922; "Muquet", ad 1932; "Papillon", tm 1922/1922; "Pink Clover", tm 1940/1938; "Pretty Package", tm 1950/1948; "Prince Charming", cat 1922; "Sweet William", ad 1951; "Tuliptime", tm 1940/1940; "Winter Carnival", tm 1949/1947; "Yu", tm 1937/1937.

AYER CO., Lowell, MA: "Ardeur', tm 1931/1931.

ANNA AYERS, Chicago, IL: "Ayers Doris Bouquet", cat 1922.

AZZARO, Paris, France: "Azzaro", new 1970; "Azzaro 9", new 1984.

BABANI, Paris, France: "Abdulla", tm 1927/1926; "Afghani", tm 1925/1920; "Ambre De Delhi", Fr. ad 1920; "Chinois", cat 1922; "Chypre Egyptien", ad 1928; "Daïmo", tm 1924/1921; "Fleurs D'Annam", tm 1925/1921; "Gardenia", ad 1937; "Giardini", ad 1937; "Gougouki", tm 1923/1922; "Hindou", cat 1922; "Japonais", cat 1922; "Jasmin de Corée", Fr. ad 1920; "Just A Dash", new 1928; "Ligeia", tm 1946/1920; "Ming", Fr. ad 1920; "Nandita", tm 1925/1925; "Oeillet du Japon", tm 1925/1920; "Pao—Pé", tm 1944/1937; "Parfum de Manille", cat 1922; "Parfum Persian", cat 1922; "Pin Fleuri", ad 1937; "Rose Gullistan", Fr. ad 1920; "Saïgon", tm 1925/1920; "Secret Princesse Nefertiti", tm 1938/1937; "Shogun", Fr. ad 1920; "Sousouki", ad 1928; "Yasmak", tm 1924/1920.

BABBITT, Philadelphia, PA: "Fleur de Nuit", tm 1924/1924; "Nuit Joyeuse", tm 1925/1925.

A. P. BABCOCK, NY, NY: "Acme", cat 1922; "Ann Hathaway", tm 1934/1934; "Black Bottom", tm 1927/1926; "Cho Cho San", cat 1922; "Cigarette", tm 1925/1925; "Corylopsis of Japan", cat 1922; "Cut Roses", cat 1922; "Eventide", ad 1934; "Flower of Savoy", cat 1922; "La Bud Parisienne", tm 1927/1926; "La Romance", tm 1937/1920; "Lady Nicotine", tm 1926/1926; "Love Petals", cat 1922; "Ma Cheri", ad 1936; "Morn", ad 1934; "Noon", ad 1934; "Numerology", tm 1931/1931; "Prettiest", cat 1922; "Queen Cologne", tm 1927/1899; "Romany", tm 1929/1920; "Superfumes", tm 1925/1925; "This", tm 1930/1930; "Tip Tap", tm 1923/1923; "Violet Elise", cat 1922; "We Moderns", tm 1928/1928.

BABS CREATIONS, NY, NY: "Blossomscent", tm 1943/1941; "Forever Yours", tm 1940/1940; "Gay Whirl", tm 1941/1940; "Hurdy Gurdy", tm 1941/1941; "Mint Julep", tm 1942/1941; "Wood Nymph",

tm 1943/1942; "Yesteryear", tm 1939/1939.

CHARLES R. BAILEY, NY, NY: "Trilby", tm 1895/1894.

ERWIN H. BAKER, San Jose, CA: "Evening Chimes", tm 1920/1904.

BALDWIN PERFUMERY, Chicago, IL: "Blue Beauty", tm 1917/1912; "Cheron", tm 1930/1929; "Nous Jasmin", tm 1926/1926; "Otesa", tm 1924/1920; "Passion", tm 1930/1929; "Peach Blow", tm 1924/1886; "Queen Bess", tm 1886/1884; "Silver Lake", tm 1917/1898; "Wild Plum Blossom", tm 1919/1892.

BALENCIAGA, Paris, France: "28", tm 1953/1948; "Cialenga", new 1973; "La Fruite des Heures", art 1947; "Le Dix", tm 1952/1947; "Prélude", ad 1982; "Michelle", new 1979, "Quadrille", tm 1956/1952.

BALLARDE INC., Paris, France; NY, NY: "Alexa", tm 1944/1944; "Arcadi", ad 1933; "L'Automne En Arcadi", ad 1935; "Le Charme D'Arcadi", ad 1935; "Le Magnolia d'Arcadi", ad 1936; "Le Muguet d'Arcadi", ad 1936; "L'Ete En Arcadi", ad 1935; "Le Tuberose d'Arcadi", ad 1936.

PIERRE BALMAIN, Paris, France: "Elysees 64-83", tm 1956/1945; "Jolie Madame", tm 1955/1952; "Ivoire", ad 1981; "Miss Balmain", ad 1967; "Vent Vert", tm 1955/1947.

L. BAMBERGER & CO., Newark, NJ: "Chantrey", tm 1928/1922.

BRIGITTE BARDOT (ANNE MARIE BARDOT), Paris, France: "Parfums de Brigitte Bardot", tm 1960/1959.

BARDIN, Paris, France: "Chypre", Fr. ad 1920; "Cyclamen", Fr. ad 1920; "La Perle", Fr. ad 1920; "Lilas", Fr. ad 1920; "Luxe de Paris", Fr. ad 1920; "Violette", Fr. ad 1920.

MARIE BARKER CO., St. Louis, MO: "Foolish Moments", tm 1951/1950; "Marie Barker", tm 1949/1932.

FRANK W. BARNUM, Danbury, CT: "Peerless", tm 1878/1877.

F. E. BARR & CO., Chicago, IL: "Gibson Girl", cat 1922.

BARROCHE INC., Paris, France; NY, NY: "Diavolo", tm 1947/1946; "Prologue", tm 1947/1946.

DONALD BARRY PRODUCTIONS, Los Angeles, CA: "Calamity Jane", tm 1952/1951.

BATHES, England: "Devon Violets", ad 1938.

TONI BAXTER (GERTRUDE LEMAN), Honolulu, Hawaii: "Remini", tm 1950/1946.

ALICE BAYLY, Los Angeles, CA: "Hollywood Nights", tm 1930/1929.

BEAN, Philadelphia, PA: "Our Pet", tm 1892/1888; "Peep O'Day", tm 1885/1885; "Queen", tm 1879/1877.

BEATRU LABORATORIES INC., Milwaukee, WI: "Moonlight Girl", tm 1929/1926.

BEAUTY COUNSELORS, Grosse Pointe, MI: "Encore", tm 1957/1943; "Flight of Fancy", tm 1954/1953.

JOSEPH W. BEAVAN, Syracuse, NY: "Cupid's Dream", tm 1921/1921.

BECHOFF, Paris, France: "21", art 1925.

BECKER FILS (LOUIS BECKER), Paris, France: "Keepsake", tm 1926/1925.

BEECHAM'S LABORATORY, Oscawana, NY: "Ambrosia", cat 1922; "Fleur d'Ete", cat 1922; "Lady Teasel", tm 1926/1925; "La Rie", tm 1927/1919; "Royal English Rose", cat 1922.

GEOFFREY BEENE: "Geoffrey Beene", ad 1971.

BEIA CO. (GEORGE YORITA), Los Angeles, CA: "Flowers of Paridise", tm 1923/1922.

EDWARD T. BEISER, Riverside, CT: "Black Tulip", tm 1928/1924.

BELCANO, Jersey City, NJ: "All Agog", tm 1953/1950; "Animation", tm 1946/1945; "Chalance", tm 1940/1940; "Filigree", tm 1946/1945; "Lofty", tm 1945/1944; "Night Bloom", tm 1946/1945; "Temple Bells", tm 1945/1938; "Twano", tm 1945/1938.

BELCO CHEM CO. (WILLIAM B. COHEN), St. Paul, MN: "Radio Girl", tm 1925/1922.

BONNE BELL, Cleveland, OH: "Casual", tm 1946/1946; "Coeur de Gardenia", tm 1936/1927; "English Bluebells", tm 1941/1940; "The Final Touch", tm 1952/1948; "Gadabouts", tm 1939/1937.

BELL PERFUME CO. (SAMUEL M. FREID), Chicago, IL: "Gypsy Queen", tm 1926/1926.

MURIEL BELL, NY, NY: "Anniversary", tm 1952/1947; "Sarouk", tm 1952/1947.

BENARD ET HONNORAT, Grasse, France: "Sketch", tm 1963/1953; "Tabatchin", tm 1950/1929.

HENRI BENDEL, INC., NY, NY: Paris, France: "No 7", tm 1927/1927; "10 West", tm 1943/1943; "Checkmate", tm 1942/1940; "Dites-Moi Oui", tm 1933/1932; "Eau de Sachet", tm 1945/1941; "Etoile Filante", tm 1936/1935; "Folle Journée", tm 1928/1927; "Gout du Jour", tm 1928/1927; "Chute D'un Ange", tm 1928/1927; "Cinque Triple Cinque", tm 1928/1928; "Jasmin de Japan", tm 1930/1929; "Ma Rose", tm 1929/1927; "Ma Violette", tm 1929/1927; "Mon Jasmin", tm 1929/1927; "Sans-gêne", tm 1939/1939; "Si Rare", tm 1939/1937; "Suede", tm 1938/1938; "Un Peu d'elle", tm 1948/1915; "White Freezia", tm 1944/1940; "Zita", tm 1932/1932.

BENDINER & SCHLESINGER (MAURINE F. SCHLESINGER), NY, NY: "Dorothy West", tm 1927/1924.

S. DE BENVENISTE, Paris, France: "Eteignons Tout", tm 1947/1945; "Francois Villon", tm 1947/1945; "Gribouillage", tm 1947/1942; "Interim", tm 1947/1941.

BERGDORF GOODMAN, NY, NY: "No. 101", tm 1928/1927; "Fireworks", tm 1952/1950; "Flower Shower", tm 1959/1948; "Nandi", tm 1956/1955.

BERGEL, Hollywood, CA: "Seduction", ad 1945; "Seventh Heaven", ad 1945.

POLLY BERGEN: "Tortue", ad 1969.

BERGERE, NY, NY: "Follies Bergère", tm 1943/1943; "Liegfeld Follies", tm 1947/1946; "Musette", tm 1946/1945; "Tabarin", tm 1947/1945.

BERGHOLT, Minneapolis, MN: "Peace Garden", tm 1946/1937.

JACOB S. BERLINER, NY, NY: "American Woman", tm 1927/1927.

ROCHELLE BERNARDO, NY, NY: "Romance", tm 1921/1921.

DAVID MAS DE RODA Y BERNAL, Barcelona, Spain: "Diamante", tm 1942/1935.

EUGENE BERNINGHAUS CO., Cincinnati, OH: "Roxanna", tm 1925/1922.

BERTAE: "Narcissus", ad 1928.

A. BERTELLI & CO., Milan, Italy: "Venus", tm 1908/1908.

ALFRED BERTI, NY, NY: "Jasér", tm 1963/1960; "Sobriqué", tm 1963/1960.

THE BERTLE CO., NY, NY: "Bertlay", tm 1927/1926.

BEST & CO., NY, NY: "Qui M'Aime?", tm 1925/1925.

GEORGE H. BETTS, NY, NY: "Glebeas Adoration", tm 1916/1915; "Inspiration Violet", tm 1915/1913.

BETTS & MUMPETON, NY, NY: "Finesse", tm 1927/1924.

MARIAN BIALAC: "Deepwoods Heather", ad 1971; "Rainforest Fern", ad 1971; "Weeping Willow", ad 1971.

ANDREE BIALLOT, France: "Fanfaron", ad 1968; "Sue Sue", ad 1968.

BICHARA, Paris, France: "Ambre", cat 1922; "Bosphora", cat 1922; "Cabiria", Fr. ad 1921; "Delices de Pera", cat 1922; "Gaudika", cat 1922; "Liliana", Fr. ad 1921; "Myrbaha", Fr. ad 1921; "Niruana", art 1913; "Saisit la Fortune", tm 1924/1917; "Sakountala", cat 1914; "Syriana", Fr. ad 1921; "Yavahna", Fr. ad 1921.

THOMAS M. BIDDLE, Fort Wayne, IN: "Satisfaction Bouquet", tm 1877/1877.

BIENAIME, Paris, France; Neiully, France: "Caravane", tm 1949/1936; "Dentelle", tm 1952/1948; "Enfin Jeuls", tm 1950/1949; "Eveil", tm 1936/1935; "Fleurs de Provence", tm 1948/1937; "Fleurs D'Ete", tm 1936/1935; "Jours Heureux", tm 1951/1948; "La Vie en Fleurs", tm 1936/1935; "Les Carnations", tm 1949/1943; "Sur les Aimes", tm 1949/1935; "Vermeil", tm 1936/1935.

BIJA, U.S., "Treasure Chest", ad 1939.

BIJAN, Beverly Hills, CA: "Bijan", ad 1980.

BIPPUS & BREIDENBACH, Dayton, OH: "Empress Josephine", tm 1892/1892.

BIRO, MEYNE, & BIRO, NY, NY: "No. 71", tm 1947/1946; "No. 72", tm 1947/1946; "No. 73", tm 1947/1946; "No. 74", tm 1947/1946; "No. 75", tm 1947/1946; "Anaitis", tm 1947/1946; "Birome", tm 1947/1946; "Chant De Paris", tm 1947/1946; "Chant D'Espoir", tm 1947/1946; "Chant D'etoile", tm 1947/1946; "Chant Du Ciel", tm 1947/1946; "Chou-Chou", tm 1947/1946; "Flowers Speak", tm 1947/1946; "Fragrance Foutaine", tm 1947/1946; "Parforce", tm 1947/1946; "Pathetique", tm 1947/1946; "Sympathy", tm 1947/1946; "Voix De La Foret", tm 1947/1946; "Voix De France", tm 1947/1946; "Voix De Paris", tm 1947/1946; "Voix Du Ciel", tm 1947/1946; "Voix Du Coeur", tm 1947/1946.

BIROTO, INC., NY, NY: "Debs", tm 1927/1926; "Gigolo", tm 1927/1924.

BIZET: "Adagio", ad 1946; "Ballade", ad 1946; "Baton", ad 1946; "Prelude", ad 1946; "Rhapsody", ad 1946; "Symphony", ad 1946.

CLEMENT BLACK & CO., Melbourne and Sydney, Australia: "Charmosan", tm 1929/1922.

ROSS W. BLACK, Pittsburg, PA: "Sincerity", tm 1910/1910.

MR. BLACKWELL, Los Angeles, CA: "Mr. Blackwell", ad 1964.

WILLIAM J. BLACKISTON, Denton, MD: "After the Ball", tm 1894/1893.

IRENE BLAKE COSMETICS, NY, NY: "Diversion", tm 1945/1943; "Lingerie", tm 1944/1942; "Twixteen", tm 1945/1944.

C. P. BLAIZE: "Brise d'Orient", cat 1922.

BLANCHARD, NY, NY: "Climax", tm 1946/1945; "Conflict", tm 1946/1945; "Gardenia, new 1932; "Evening Star", tm 1951/1949; "Intrepid", tm 1944/1943; "Jealousy", tm 1944/1943; "Plaid", tm 1944/1936.

MAURICE BLANCHET, Suresnes, France; Paris, France: "Coryse", tm 1929/1925; "Creation", tm 1962/1954; "Epilogue", tm 1950/1940; "Florilege", tm 1961/1950; "Malaisie", tm 1950/1935; "Opera De Paris", tm 1961/1960; "Peche Permis", tm 1958/1957; "Plus Que Jamais", tm 1961/1946; "Salomé", tm 1951/1938.

BLASCO, Brooklyn, NY: (See Gaston J. Block).

BLISS LABORATORIES, NY, NY: "Felix", cat 1922.

HARRY L. BLISS, NY, NY: "Mme. Duvigné", tm 1934/1930.

GASTON J. BLOCK, NY, NY: "Blasco", tm 1916/1915; "Cleopatra", tm 1919/1918; "Temptation", 1932/1931; "Wedding Bells", tm 1929/1929.

JOHN BLOCKI & SON, Chicago, IL: "Empress", cat 1922; "Esprit d'Amour", tm 1916/1916; "Flower-in-the-Bottle", tm 1923/1907; "Lilies", cat 1922; "Ollantay", cat 1922; "Orange Petals", cat 1922; "Sanrovia", tm 1911/1911; "Thais", tm 1911/1911; "Unique", cat 1922.

BLONDEAU ET CIE, London, England; NY, NY: "Jequilla", tm 1893/1892; "Marequil", tm 1893/1892.

WILLIAM BLOOM & CO., INC., NY, NY: "South Sea Flowers", tm 1927/1926.

BLOSSOM, Brooklyn, NY: "Breath of Orchards", tm 1920/1912.

BLUE WALTZ INC., NY, NY; Jersey City, NJ: "A Toi Cherie", tm 1934/1927; "Countess Joubert", tm 1934/1934; "The Duke", ad 1939; "The Duchess", ad 1939; "Empress Eugenie", tm 1934/1931; "Mischief", ad 1939. (See also: JOUBERT; JOLIND)

BLUEKAMEL, Detroit, MI: "Parfum Commeil Faut", tm 1932/1930; "Carnation", cat 1933; "Lilac", cat 1933; "Lily of the Valley", cat 1933; "Sweet Pea", cat 1933.

JACK BLUEMANTLE, Paris, France: "Jabley", tm 1927/1926.

BLUM'S INC., Chicago, IL: "Le Préféré", tm 1924/1924.

BOAG, INC., River Forest, IL: "Zephyr Zweet", tm 1930/1929.

BO—KAY, NY, NY; Jacksonville, FL: "Orange Blossom", ad 1924; "Fleur de Gloire", tm 1954/1921; "Preview", tm 1937/1937.

J. C. BOLDOOT, Amsterdam, Netherlands: "Boldoot Imperiale", tm 1953/1925; "Boldoot Veritable", tm 1953/1892; "Holland Flowers", tm 1932/1931; "Princesse Royale", tm 1924/1923.

BOMBI, NY, NY: "Black Magic", ad 1945; "Entre Nous", ad 1948; "Strange Venture", tm 1947/1946.

BONHEUR, Syracuse, NY: "Budda", cat 1922; "La Mona", cat 1922.

BONNEY, INC., Chicago, IL: "Flame-O-Youth", tm 1928/1924.

BONWIT TELLER INC., NY, NY: "721", tm 1936/1935; "Chamois", tm 1945/1944; "Fleur de Jasmin", tm 1926/1925;

"Foulard", tm 1945/1944; "Hour Glass", tm 1946/1944; "Malicious", tm 1945/1944; "Remember", tm 1946/1944; "Staffordshire Rose", tm 1946/1944; "Venez Avec Moi", tm 1924/1924; "Victorian Keepsake", tm 1947/1944.

BOOKERS, La Penitence, British Guiana: "Limacol", tm 1959/1938.

GEO. BORGFELDT & CO., NY, NY: "Précieuse", tm 1926/1926.

BONSARI, Italy: "Notte Romana", ad 1955.

BORUN BROS., Los Angeles, CA: "Regent House", tm 1940/1939.

BOTOT, Paris, France: "Chu-Chin-Chow", Fr. ad 1921.

CHARLINE BOUCHERY, Paris, France: "Dionysos", tm 1961/1960; "Taormina", tm 1961/1960.

BOUE SOEURS, NY, NY: "Quand Les Fleurs Rèvent", tm 1923/1922.

BOURBON FRENCH PERFUME MANUFACTURING CO., New Orleans, LA: "Kuskus", tm 1928/1915.

BOURGET, France: "Gardenia", ad 1931; "Jasemine", ad 1931; "Rose", ad 1931; "Sweet Pea", ad 1931.

BOURJOIS, Paris, France: "Ashes of Roses", tm 1912/1909; "Ashes of Sandal", tm 1914/1913; "Ashes of Violet", tm 1913/1913; "Beau "Belle", tm 1950/1949; "Clin d'oeil", art 1984; "Courage", tm 1940/1939; "Currant-Rose", tm 1924/1923; "Dialogue", tm 1963/1962; "eau légère", new 1973; "Empire", cat 1922; "Endearing", tm 1946/1946; "Etoile D'Amour", tm 1913/1903; "Evasion", new 1970; "Evening in Paris", tm 1929/1928; "Fantasio", tm 1951/1950; "Femina", ad 1928; "Flamme", tm 1935/1935; "Folies Bergere", tm 1952/1943; "Frozen Assets", tm 1954/1953; "Ga—Ga", tm 1953/1953; "Glamour", new 1953; "Heus Persane", tm 1927/1925; "Infralet", tm 1932/1931; "Je T'Aime", tm 1929/1928; "Karess", tm 1931/1921; "Kobako", tm 1937/1936; "L'Avenue", tm 1931/1929; "La Rose Pompon", tm 1914/1907; "La Violette", cat 1912; "Leczinska", cat 1922; "Liprubi", tm 1912/1911; "Lisbeth", cat 1922; "Louis XV", tm 1914/1891; "Mais Oui", tm 1938/1938; "Mandarine", tm 1930/1911; "Manon Lescaut", tm 1908/1907; "Marguerite Carré", tm 1927/1910; "Mimi Pinson", tm 1908/1907; "Modern Style", cat 1922; "Moia", cat 1922; "Mon Perfum", tm 1928/1914; "Montmartre", tm 1954/1953; "Number Thirty", tm 1933/1933; "Perfusion", tm 1954/1953; "Pergola", cat 1922; "Premier Muguet", new 1955; "Ramage", new 1951; "Rendezvous", tm 1930/1929; "Roman Holiday", ad 1955; "Rose Pompon", cat 1922; "Spirit of Paris", tm 1930/1930; "Springtime in Paris", tm 1932/1931; "Talis", art 1912; "Two's Company", tm 1953/1953; "Ultralet", tm 1931/1931; "Ultra Violet", tm 1932/1931.

BOUTON (GEORGE W. BUTTON CO.), NY, NY: "Ambre d'Or", ad 1933; "Audacious", tm 1945/1945; "Caution", tm 1943/1943; "Gardenia", ad 1933; "Hit", tm 1945/1944; "Honeysuckle", ad 1933; "Inescapable", tm 1946/1945; "Jasmin", ad 1933; "Muguet", ad 1933; "Pearl D'Or", ad 1928; "Rave", tm 1945/1944; "Reckless", tm 1943/1943; "Sweet Pea", ad 1928.

WM. BOWDEN & CO., Houston, TX: "Houston Girl", tm 1928/1918.

BOYD MANUFACTURING CO., Birmingham, AL: "Brown Beauty", tm 1928/1921; "La Nola", tm 1943/1915.

JOHN G. BOYLE, Saginaw, MI: "Beaute d'Or", tm 1937/1933.

ATHLEY BRADFORD, Los Angeles, CA: "California Poppy", tm 1945/1944.

D. R. BRADLEY & SON, NY, NY: "Amra", tm 1909/1909; "Auras", cat 1922; "Beauty Rose", tm 1905/1905; "Chiquita", cat 1922; "Classique", tm 1909/1909; "Coeur de Gitane", cat 1922; "Coronation Violet", tm 1906/1905; "Fanrita", tm 1908/1908; "Genee", tm 1908/1908; "Irisia", cat 1922; "Morning Dew", tm 1905/1905; "Nila Rose", cat 1922; "Oriel", cat 1922; "Princess Tulip", cat 1922; "Rolia", cat 1922; "Rose Maid", cat 1922; "Stem", tm 1905/1905; "Tre Flora", tm 1906/1905; "Vesta", tm 1905/1905; "Wildwood", tm 1905/1905; "Woodland", tm 1905/1905.

BRAJAN, Colombes, France: "Loukita", ad 1927; "Matin Clair", tm 1926/1926; "Secret de Minuit", ad 1927.

BRADSHAW, Boston, MA: "Woodbine", ad 1940.

BRAVO MANUFACTURING CO., Chicago, IL: "Dama de Noche", tm 1946/1944.

JOHN H. BRECK, Springfield, MA: "Golden Chalice", tm 1960/1959; "Misque", tm 1961/1959.

A. BRESLAUER CO., NY, NY: "Charleston Gardens", tm 1942/1941; "Contouré", tm 1940/1934; "Copacabana", tm 1951/1950.

JOSEPH H. BRIMEYER, Minneapolis, MN: "Russian Madness", tm 1929/1929.

NORMA BRINDLEY, Miami, FL: "Lu—Noma", tm 1934/1932.

BRISSON, Paris, France: "Toboggan", tm 1950/1948.

BROCARD OF MOSCOW: "Milaja", ad 1913.

BROCARD, Paris, France: "Taïmyr", Fr. ad 1922.

BRONISLAWA, Salem, MA: "Count-down", tm 1963/1962; "Oil of Grass of Jamaica", tm 1953/1952.

H. BRONNLEY & CO., London, England: "Havaneta", tm 1910/1908; "Viotto", tm 1909/1908.

BROSIS, Chicago, IL: "Theme", tm 1956/1943.

JEAN—CHARLES BROSSEAU, Paris, France: "Ombre Rose", new 1982.

DAVID S. BROWN & CO., NY, NY: "Bonanza", tm 1878/1878; "Brownie", tm 1895/1895; "Forest Fringe", tm 1896/1895.

WILLIAM H. BROWN & BRO., Baltimore, MD: "Dixie Blossoms", tm 1914/1913; "Dream Violet", cat 1922; "Dreamerie", tm 1923/1923; "Eileen", cat 1922; "Garden of Allah", tm 1914/1912; "Heliotrope Blossom", cat 1922; "Jess", cat 1922; "Marguerite", cat 1922; "Orchard Blossom", cat 1922; "Pearls of Hyacinths", cat 1922; "Siren Lilac", cat 1922; "Snow Violet", cat 1922; "Violet Simplicity", tm 1914/1900.

BROWNY OF HONOLULU, Honolulu, Hawaii: "Hawaiian Plumeria", tm 1959/1958; "Mai Tai", tm 1963/1961.

BRYENNE (JACQUES BRACH), Paris, France: "Brenny", tm 1949/1929; "Chu-Chin-Chow", tm 1921/1918; "Heure Exquise", tm 1924/1911; "Mabrouka", Fr. ad 1927; "Sentimental", Fr. ad 1927; "Ambre Persian", Fr. ad 1927.

BUCK AND RAYNER, Chicago, IL: "Jacrose", tm 1927/1890; "Mars", tm 1876/1876.

HARRY K. BUCK, Philadelphia, PA: "Colonial", tm 1898/1898.

BUERGER BROTHERS, Denver, CO: "Sorority Prom", tm 1936/1936.

WALDO E. BUGBEE, NY, NY: "Esquire", tm 1934/1932.

BULLOCK'S INC., Los Angeles, CA: "L'Eté du Jardin", tm 1938/1936; "Palm Springs", tm 1937/1937.

EDWARD BURNHAM, Chicago, IL: "Gen-Tsa", tm 1920/1911; "Moon Kiss", tm 1920/1911.

W. J. BUSH & CO. INC., NY, NY: "Mitcham", tm 1934/1888.

BUSH AROMATICS, NY, NY: "Indecision", tm 1942/1941; "Invasion", tm 1943/1943.

JEAN W. BUTLER, Chicago, IL: "Buena Locust", cat 1922; "Buena Violette", cat 1922.

GEORGE W. BUTTON CO., NY, NY: "A wee bit bold", tm 1945/1944; "A wee bit saucy", tm 1945/1944; "Black Jasmine", tm 1924/1924; "Boucar", tm 1926/1925; "Dareis", tm 1926/1925; "Duvinne", tm 1926/1925; "Fresh Flowers", tm 1935/1934; "Her Majesty", tm 1935/1934; "Laverne", tm 1926/1926; "Mah-Jongg", tm 1924/1923; "Noireise", tm 1926/1925; "Prière", tm 1926/1926; "Rajé", tm 1926/1925; "Rouget", tm 1926/1926; "Sardoux", tm 1926/1926; "Sealed Secrets", tm 1936/1934; "Sport Wear", tm 1937/1937; "Thrill", tm 1932/1931; "Vanly", tm 1926/1926. (See also: BOUTON)

BYCK BROS., Louisville, KY: "Magnolia White", tm 1946/1945.

CACHAREL, Paris, France: "Anais-Anais", new 1978.

CADOLLE FRERES, Paris, France: "Amour en Cage", tm 1927/1926; "Après le tennis", tm 1927/1926; "Bien-Etre", tm 1931/1930; "Le Bois Sauvage", tm 1927/1927; "Le No. 9", tm 1927/1927; "Magicia", tm 1933/1929; "Rêve d'infante", tm 1927/1927.

CAFE SOCIETE PARFUM CO., Milwaukee, WI: "Cuddle", tm 1946/1945; "Dreams Come True", tm 1946/1945.

CAIRE (MRS. R. SCOTT LINSLEY), Fairfield, CT: "Moods", tm 1932/1931.

CALIFORNIA PERFUME CO., NY, NY: "Bolero", tm 1935/1934; "Cotillion", tm 1935/1934; "Courtship", tm 1937/1937; "Gertrude Recordon's", tm 1928/1927; "Marionette", tm 1938/1938; "Topaze", tm 1935/1935; "Sonnet", tm 1938/1938.

A. B. CALISHER & CO., NY, NY: "Sweet Marie", tm 1895/1894.

CALMAC, NY, NY: "Zodiac", tm 1954/1953.

CALLOT SOEURS, Paris, France; NY, NY: "Bao", tm 1949/1947; "Dieu du Jour", tm 1950/1947; "Chichicallot", ad 1925; "Il Pleut des Baisers", ad 1925; "La Fille du Roi de Chine", ad 1925; "Le Louis d'Or", ad 1925; "Mariage D'Amour", tm 1949/1947.

CAMPANA. (See OLD SOUTH)

JOSE CAMPDERA, Mexico: "Regis", tm 1930/1928.

CANNON COSMETICS CO., Atlanta, GA: "Cannolene", tm 1934/1923; "Touchdown", tm 1935/1930.

CAPATONE PRODUCTS, NY, NY: "Femme D'Amour", tm 1944/1942.

FERNAND CAPELLE, Lamouroux, France: "Les Drags", tm 1937/1935; "Mon Faible", tm 1947/1936.

CAPUCCI, Paris, France: "Filly", new 1983; "Graffiti", ad 1963; "Parce Que", new 1963; "Yendi", new 1974.

CARAVAGLIOS, Paris, France: "Mon Parfum", art 1913.

PIERRE CARDIN, Paris, France: "Cardin", new 1976; "Choc", new 1981; "Paradoxe", new 1983; "Suite 16", tm 1959/1959.

CARDINAL, NY, NY: "Book of Perfume", ad 1939; "House of Groydon", tm 1940/1939; "Moon Magic", tm 1938/1938; "Tantalux", ad 1938; "Tru-Scent", tm 1962/1961.

CARILLON PARFUMERIE (CARL J. PETERSON), San Francisco, CA: "La Faveur", tm 1926/1925.

CARLE, INC., Des Moines, IA: "Cytherea", tm 1930/1930; "Interlude", tm 1931/1930.

CARLEY, Haddonfield, NJ: "Sweet Victory", tm 1963/1963.

CARLOVA, NY, NY: "Narcissus", ad 1923; "Peggy", tm 1925/1924.

CARLYLE: "Far East", ad 1937.

CARMIGNANI, Parma, Italy: "Adam", tm 1957/1943.

HATTIE CARNEGIE, NY, NY: "7", ad 1944; "11", ad 1944; "49", tm 1950/1944; "50", tm 1950/1949; "Agogo", ad 1969; "Any Time", tm 1948/1946; "Any Where", tm 1948/1946; "Carnegie Blue", ad 1944; "Carte Bleue", tm 1952/1949; "Carte Verte", tm 1952/1949; "Hattie Carnegie", tm 1928/1938; "Hypnotic", tm 1940/1939; "Miss Hattie", tm 1961/1958; "Whirlpool", tm 1946/1944.

CARON, Paris, France: "Acasiosa", tm 1929/1923; "Adastra", tm 1939/1939; "Affolant", new 1908; "Alpona", tm 1939/1939; "Avion", tm 1931/1930; "Bain de Champagne", tm 1924/1923; "Bel Amour", tm 1923/1906; "Bellodgia", tm 1928/1927; "Bichon Fard", tm 1928/1922; "Chantecler", new 1906; "Chez Moi", tm 1928/1927; "Coup de Fouet", new 1954; "Elegancia", new 1911; "Farnesiana", new 1947; "Fleurs de Rocaille", tm 1934/1933; "French Cancan", tm 1937/1936; "Infini", new 1970; "Isadora", new 1910; "Jacinthe Précieuse", new 1911; "L'Infini", tm 1923/1912; "La fête des roses", tm 1951/1949; "Le Narcisse Noir", tm 1923/1912; "Le Tabac Blond", tm 1923/1919; "Les Cent Fards", tm 1936/1935; "Les Rocailles de Caron", tm 1933/1933; "London-Paris", new 1917; "Madame Peau Fine", tm 1936/1935; "Mimosa", new 1917; "Modernis", new 1906; "Muguet Du Bonheur", new 1952; "N'Aimez Que Moi", tm 1916/1923; "Narcisse Blanc", new 1923; "Narcisse Noir", new 1911; "Nocturnes", new 1981; "N'Aimez Que Moi", new 1916; "Nuit D'Avion", tm 1933/1933; "Nuit de Noel", tm 1923/1922; "Or Et Noir", tm 1950/1949; "Pocahontas", tm 1924/1923; "Pois De Senteur De Chez Moi", new 1927; "Poivre", tm 1955/1954; "Pour Un Homme", new 1934; "Pour Une Femme", new 1942; "Radiant", tm 1923/1913; "Ravissement", new 1906; "Rose Précieuse", new 1910;

"Rose", new 1949; "Royal Bain de Champagne", new 1941; "Royal Caron", new 1904; "Royal Emilia", new 1904; "Tabac Blond", new 1919; "Tabac Noir", tm 1950/1948; "Voeu de Noël", tm 1940/1939; "With Pleasure", new 1949.

CAROSEL PARFUM CO. (MARVIN GORDON), NY, NY: "Haunting", tm 1946/1944; "Hubba Hubba", tm 1946/1944.

NELLIE CARR, Paris, France; NY, NY: "Carnell", tm 1935/1934.

CARREL, LTD., Chicago, IL: "Tahini", tm 1946/1937.

MAURICE BERTRAND CARRERE, Paris, France: "Signature Carrere", tm 1950/1946.

CARROLL. (See VIVINY).

CARTIER, Paris, France: "Panthere", new 1987; "Parfum Must", new 1981.

CARTIER (DERMAY INC.), NY, NY: "Chypre", ad 1926; "Jasmin", ad 1926; "Lilac", ad 1926; "Narcisse", ad 1926; "Rose", ad 1926; "Violet", ad 1926.

CARVEN, Paris, France: "Ma Griffe", tm 1946/1945; "Madame de Carven", new 1979; "Robe d'un Soir", new 1947.

CASELLA, Brooklyn, NY: "Pourquoi", tm 1946/1945.

CASINO DE PARIS, Paris, France: "Paris qui Brille", art 1931.

E. W. CASSEBEER, INC., Flushing, NY: "DOT", tm 1926/1926.

CASSELL PRODUCTS, NY, NY: "Esperanto", tm 1945/1945; "Rampage", tm 1952/1950; "Ricochet", tm 1957/1953.

JEAN-CHARLES DE CASTELBAJAC, Paris, France: "Première", new 1980.

CASTILIAN PRODUCTS CORP., Los Angeles, CA: "Chukker", tm 1939/1938; "Hollywood Girl", tm 1933/1933; "Huntress", tm 1945/1945; "Princess of Hollywood", tm 1935/1935; "Steeple Chase", tm 1939/1938. (See also: COURTLEY)

CASTILLA PRODUCTS, NY, NY: "Graziella", tm 1944/1943; "Iolanthe", tm 1944/1943.

E. CASTLEMAN & CO., Los Angeles, CA: "Russian Bouquet", tm 1945/1943.

CASWELL-MASSEY, NY, NY: "Number 6", tm 1952/1756; "Tricorn", tm 1958/1957.

CATO, Chicago, IL: "Junior Guild", tm 1944/1943; "Latin Quarter", tm 1945/1944.

ENRIQUE FERNANDEZ CAVADA, Habana, Cuba: "Heneol Iris", tm 1947/1945.

LINA CAVELIERO, Seattle, WA: "La Jolie", tm 1941/1932.

CEDA DIST., NY, NY; Rochester, NY: "Strange Music", tm 1945/1944; "Valse de Fleurs", tm 1945/1940.

CELAVIE PERFUMES, NY, NY: "C'est La Vie", tm 1960/1953.

NINO CERRUTI, Paris, France: "Fair Play", new 1984; "Nino Cerruti", new 1979.

CHABOT, Los Angeles, CA: "Lamy", tm 1932/1932.

CHALETTE, NY, NY: "Response", tm 1944/1944.

PH. CHALEYER INC., NY, NY: "Country Gardens", tm 1941/1940.

CHAMPREL, NY, NY: "Apple Blossom", ad 1941; "Bouquet", ad 1941; "Gardenia", ad 1941; "Pine", ad 1941.

CHANEL, Paris, France: "No. 2", tm 1926/1921; "No. 5", tm 1926/1921; "No. 11", tm 1926/1921; "No. 14", tm 1925/1922;

"No. 20", tm 1926/1921; "No. 21", tm 1926/1921; "No. 22", tm 1925/1922; "No. 27", tm 1926/1921; "No. 55", tm 1925/1922; "Bois des iles", tm 1950/1929; "Coco", new 1985; "Cuir de Russie", tm 1950/1936; "Cynique", tm 1946/1946; "Glamour", tm 1933/1933; "Ivoire de Chanel", tm 1932/1932; "Le 1940 Beige de Chanel", tm 1931/1931; "Le 1940 Blue de Chanel", tm 1931/1931; "Le 1940 Rouge de Chanel", tm 1931/1931; "Mademoiselle Chanel", tm 1949/1948; "Sycomore", tm 1930/1930; "Three Moods", tm 1935/1934; "Une Idée", tm 1931/1929.

ROY CHANTEUR, NY, NY: "Gypsy", tm 1935/1935.

CEIL CHAPMAN: "Ceil Blue", ad 1955.

CHAPMAN & RODGERS, Philadelphia, PA: "English Hawthorn", tm 1897/1895; "Princess Bonnie", tm 1894/1894.

CHARBERT, NY, NY: "21 W 52", tm 1937/1937; "730", tm 1946/1945; "1939", tm 1937/1937; "Amorous", tm 1946/1946; "As You Were", tm 1943/1943; "Breathless", tm 1939/1933; "Breathless Mist", tm 1954/1952; "Bridle Path", 1938/1937; "Carnation", ad 1936; "Censored", tm 1946/1945; "Consent", tm 1952/1951; "Deep Purple", tm 1947/1945; "De toi je chante", tm 1933/1933; "Drumbeat", tm 1936/1935; "Expressly Yours", tm 1941/1941; "Fabulous", tm 1941/1941; "The French Touch", ad 1947; "Grand Prix", ad 1938; "High Spirits", tm 1945/1945; "Hold Everything", tm 1946/1940; "Indian Summer", tm 1946/1945; "Junior Miss", tm 1941/1941; "Let's Make Up", tm 1949/1948; "Mountain Greenery", tm 1940/1939; "Notre Eleanor", tm 1933/1933; "Of Thee I Sing", tm 1937/1933; "Outrageous", tm 1946/1945; "Prix de Paris", tm 1936/1935; "They're Off", tm 1942/1942; "Three Star Cast", tm 1954/1953; "Tonight", tm 1943/1943; "Yours Sincerely", tm 1937/1936; "Warning", tm 1950/1948.

CHARLES OF THE RITZ, NY, NY: "A", new 1927; "B", new 1927; "C", new 1927; "An English Garden", tm 1946/1945; "Baby Pink", tm 1948/1947; "Country Wedding", tm 1953/1951; "Damask", tm 1946/1945; "Directoire", tm 1946/1945; "Floréal", tm 1962/1950; "Flower Show", tm 1942/1942; "French Provincial", tm 1951/1949; "Ishah", ad 1954; "Jester", tm 1945/1944; "Little Women", tm 1946/1945; "Love Potion", tm 1942/1941; "Ritual", tm 1946/1946; "Sea Shell", tm 1945/1944; "Simone Mounier", tm 1958/1957; "Soignée", tm 1944/1944; "Spring Rain", tm 1941/1941; "Spur", tm 1938/1937; "Summertime", tm 1939/1939; "Tingle", tm 1941/1938; "Water Sprite", tm 1944/1944; "Wintertime", tm 1941/1940.

CHARLES THE FIFTH: "Croyance", ad 1953.

CHARMIS, Paris, France: "Filou", tm 1955/1953.

CHEATHAM CHEMICAL CO., Atlanta, GA: "Polly Peachtree", tm 1927/1924.

DR. FELIX CHEDIAK, Habana, Cuba: "Jacquier", tm 1945/1943.

CHEMDRUG CORP., NY, NY: "Bonanza", tm 1946/1945; "D'Ormel", tm 1948/1947.

CHEMICAL CENTER CORP., NY, NY: "Shangrila", tm 1943/1943.

CHEMICAL SPECIALITIES CO., NY, NY: "Aphra", tm 1947/1940.

CHENIER, Paris, France; NY, NY: "Andaluza", ad 1931; "Lysystra", ad 1931.

CHERAMY, NY, NY: "April Showers", tm 1922/1921; "Blue Skies", tm 1928/1927; "Biarritz", tm 1927/1926; "Cadore", tm 1921/1921; "Cappi", cat 1922; "Carnation", ad 1939; "Chansonette", tm 1924/1924; "Ciel Bleu", tm 1925/1924; "Compliment", tm 1926/1926; "Cordon Blue", tm 1935/1935; "Cor D'Or", tm 1921/1921; "Dulcia", tm 1928/1928; "Espace", tm 1960/1959; "Fausta", tm 1924/1923; "Festival", tm 1925/1924; "Fifth Avenue", tm 1922/1922; "Frolic", tm 1922/1921; "Girly Girl", tm 1921/1921; "Joli Soir", tm 1924/1924; "Keep Cool", tm 1950/1950; "Ketty", tm 1926/1926; "Lido", tm 1924/1924; "Lido-Venice", tm 1925/1925; "Lov-Lor", tm 1921/1921; "May Flowers", ad 1933; "Myo-San", tm 1921/1921; "Nuée D'Or", tm 1924/1923; "Pal", tm 1922/1921; "Parfait Amour", tm 1929/1929; "Premiers Beaux Jours", tm 1929/1929; "Un Beau Dimanche", tm 1930/1929.

CHERIGAN (PERFUMES HABANA), Habana, Cuba: "Chance", tm 1947/1937; "Fleur de Cherigan", tm 1947/1935; "Fleurs de Tabac", ad 1945.

MARY CHESS, NY, NY: "Carnation", new 1939; "Chessmen", tm 1935/1933; "Chivalry", tm 1959/1958; "Desert Verbena", tm 1962/1932; "Elizabethan", new 1941; "Floral Odeurs", new 1935; "Song", ad 1946; "Souvenir D'un Soir", new 1956; "Strategy", tm 1942/1942; "Tapestry", tm 1940/1934; "Tuileries", tm 1962/1960; "Yram", tm 1940/1934.

DELILAH H. CHESTER, NY, NY: "Mlle. Delilah", tm 1926/1924.

CHEVALLIER, Maine, France: "Castel Bleu", tm 1960/1959; "Donjon Fleuri", tm 1960/1959.

CHEVALIER GARDE INC., NY, NY: "Arghavani", tm 1940/1940; "Fleur de Perse", art 1937; "H. R. H.", ad 1937; "Roi de Rome", tm 1940/1937.

CHEZ RELLEW, Bethelem, PA: "Chez-Re", tm 1924/1924; "Courle", tm 1924/1924.

CHICAGO MAIL ORDER CO., Chicago, IL: "Lady Conceta", tm 1925/1925.

CHIMENE, Paris, France: "Bleu Azuré", Fr. ad 1920; "Charme de Vivre", Fr. ad 1920; "Opale Du Matin", Fr. ad 1920; "Pourpre Du Soir", Fr. ad 1920.

NICKY CHINI, Milan, Italy: "Mon Ami", art 1957; "Mon Seigneur", tm 1951/1949.

CHINON, Courbevoie, France; Montrouge, France: "Cadiz", tm 1953/1951; "Cobalt", tm 1948/1944; "Happy Landing", tm 1947/1946.

CHYPRON, Seine, France: "Champic", tm 1936/1936; "Cyprême", tm 1960/1936; "Myriad", tm 1936/1936; "Sanicutan", tm 1961/1959.

MAURICIO CIA, Habana, Cuba: "Fibah", tm 1944/1941; "Frontiere", tm 1944/1941; "Jrenesi", tm 1944/1943.

HAUGRON CIENTIFICAL, Barcelona, Spain: "Flord", tm 1951/1936.

CIGOGNE, NY, NY: "Vintage", tm 1954/1953.

RALPH CILUZZI, NY, NY: "Mondo", tm 1919/1918.

CINDERELLA INTERNATIONAL, NY, NY: "On-The-Town", tm 1959/1958; "Rybaiyat", tm 1959/1958.

CIRO, NY, NY; Paris, France: "Acclaim", tm 1951/1950; "Ambre de Jadis", tm 1923/1923; "Batiste", tm 1957/1956; "Bouffante", tm 1957/1956; "Bouquet Antique", tm 1924/1923; "Camelia de Maroc", ad 1936; "Chevalier de la Nuit", tm 1924/1923; "Danger", new 1938; "Doux Jasmin", tm 1923/1923; "Esscent", tm 1954/1953; "Gardenia Sauvage", tm 1929/1928; "Le Chypre du Nil", tm 1924/1923; "L'Heure Romantique", tm 1929/1929; "Little Danger", tm 1958/1957; "Maskee", tm 1924/1923; "Mirelevres", tm 1924/1921; "New Horizons", tm 1941/1941; "Oh La La", ad 1959; "One On The House", tm 1952/1952; "Panaroma", tm 1961/1960; "Ptah", tm 1924/1923; "Reflexions", ad 1933; "Ricochet", tm 1955/1954; "Surrender", ad 1932; "Tete a Tete", tm 1961/1959; "Trois Notes de Ciro", tm 1938/1937.

CLAIRAC. (See LE CLAIRAC).

CLAIRE, Paris, France; Philadelphia, PA; NY, NY: "Le Beau Narcisse", tm 1924/1923; "Memorie", tm 1929/1927; "Numero II", ad 1929.

CLAMY, Paris, France: "Aire d'Ailes", Fr. ad 1928; "Femmes Ailées", ad 1927; "Qui M'Aime?", art 1913.

OTIS CLAPP & SON, Boston, MA: "Runic", tm 1953/1952; "Rasalka", tm 1924/1909; "Sanchia", tm 1924/1909.

F. S. CLEAVER & SONS, London, England: "Juvenia", tm 1891/1890.

CLEEVELANDT CORP., NY, NY: "D'Amour", ad 1940; "Maria Christina", tm 1945/1944.

CLOVER PRODUCTS, Los Angeles, CA: "Kwush-Ru", tm 1921/1920.

CLUNY, INC., NY, NY: "Delanne", tm 1930/1930; "Le Faun", tm 1930/1930.

FRANCES CLYNE (COUTURE), NY, NY: Paris, France: "C", new 1927; "F", new 1927; "FC", new 1927.

WALTER S. COBLE, Brooklyn, NY: "Rowéna", tm 1930/1927.

JACQUELINE COCHRAN, NY, NY: "Cultivay", tm 1952/1950; "Jacologne", tm 1948/1939; "Katalina", tm 1941/1941; "Shining Hour", tm 1941/1941; "Little Star", tm 1948/1940; "Merry-Go-Round", tm 1941/1941; "Perk-Up", tm 1948/1941; "Pursuit", ad 1949; "Shining Hour", tm 1948/1941; "Take-Off", tm 1948/1940.

CODELL, NY, NY: "Autumn Leaves", tm 1957/1956.

HARRY COHEN, NY, NY: "Mira de Paris", tm 1934/1927.

OTTO J. COHEN, NY, NY: "Vanard", tm 1926/1925.

WALTER COHEN, Baltimore, MD: "Florence Cole", tm 1933/1927.

CHARLES E. COLEMAN, Elgin, IL: "Flamingo", tm 1924/1923.

COLGATE, Jersey City, NJ: "Alba Violet", cat 1922; "Allegro", tm 1922/1921; "Amarna", tm 1923/1923; "Andor", tm 1954/1954; "Attá", tm 1922/1921; "Bast", tm 1923/1923; "Caprice", tm 1893/1883; "Carnival Violets", tm 1906/1906; "Cashmere Bouquet", tm 1893/1869; "Cha Ming", tm 1917/1917; "Clair de Lune", tm 1921/1921; "Coleo", tm 1890/1890;

"Dactylis", tm 1901/1901; "Dawn", tm 1921/1920; "Doña Flor", tm 1927/1926; "Eclat", tm 1911/1911; "Eleda", tm 1909/1908; "Facade", tm 1950/1949; "Fantasy", tm 1904/1904; "Fi Fi", tm 1923/1922; "Fleurette", tm 1891/1890; "Florrent", tm 1921/1912; "Hope", tm 1921/1921; "Italian Violets", cat 1922; "Kahira", tm 1923/1923; "Khepera", tm 1923/1923; "Knickerbocker", tm 1906/1905; "La France Rose", cat 1922; "La Liberte", cat 1922; "Les Fleurs Favorites", tm 1917/1917; "Lilac Imperial", tm 1921/1910; "Man Trap", tm 1960/1959; "Monad", tm 1901/1901; "Myself", tm 1920/1920; "Orchis", cat 1922; "Pansy Blossom", cat 1922; "Parami", tm 1939/1936; "Piquant", tm 1921/1921; "Princess Harran", tm 1921/1921; "Radiant", tm 1914/1914; "Robinia", tm 1906/1906; "Sandalay", tm 1921/1921; "Seventeen", tm 1928/1928; "Speciosa", tm 1886/1886; "Splendor", tm 1912/1912; "The Unknown Flower", tm 1921/1921; "Viodora", tm 1903/1903; "Violette de Mai", cat 1922; "Vioris", tm 1897/1897; "Vision de Fleurs", tm 1915/1915; "Watch Case", tm 1924/1923; "Wedding March", tm 1879/1879; "Week-End", tm 1904/1904.

D. R. COLLINS LTD., London, England: "Aqua Manda", tm 1944/1939; "Goya", tm 1942/1937; "Goyar", tm 1939/1937; "Decision", tm 1947/1946; "Great Expectations", tm 1947/1946.

COLONIAL DAMES CO., Los Angeles, CA: "Bachelor Button", tm 1946/1941; "Cloud 7", tm 1961/1958; "French Quarter", tm 1956/1954; "Tra La", tm 1957/1950.

COMMANDITE CHOME, Lille, France: "Maubert", tm 1924/1820.

COMMERCIAL LABORATORIES INC., Newark, NY: "Nemo", tm 1936/1932.

COMPACT PERFUME INC., NY, NY: "Bijou D'Enchant", tm 1930/1930.

COMPRE, Cleveland, OH: "Qu'est-ce que c'est", tm 1950/1949.

CONDE, NY, NY: "Tiger Lily", tm 1924/1923.

CONSOLIDATED COSMETICS, Chicago, IL: "A Drop Here-And There", tm 1946/1946; "Argentine", tm 1945/1940; "Bandit", tm 1948/1937; "Barcelona", tm 1946/1940; "Batu", tm 1946/1945; "Bermuda", tm 1947/1940; "Body And Soul", tm 1947/1946; "Bolivia", tm 1952/1940; "Cheetah", tm 1950/1949; "Ciné", tm 1946/1934; "Compliment", tm 1950/1949; "Dagger", tm 1947/1946; "Designer", tm 1948/1947; "Distracting", tm 1947/1947; "Extradri", tm 1946/1944; "Flora", tm 1945/1945; "Golden Violin", tm 1950/1932; "Havana", tm 1946/1940; "Heady", tm 1947/1942; "Honolulu", tm 1950/1936; "Isle of Capri", tm 1946/1945; "Jewelstick", tm 1950/1949; "Linger Longer", tm 1949/1944; "Maddening", tm 1947/1946; "Ming Toy", tm 1946/1945; "Nassau", tm 1946/1937; "No. T", tm 1947/1946; "Now", tm 1947/1947; "Oops", tm 1945/1945; "Perfume of Darkest Night", tm 1951/1949; "Peru", tm 1946/1940; "Purge", tm 1951/1949; "Rio", tm 1950/1940; "Show-Off", tm 1954/1953; "Sinister", tm 1950/1949; "Surprise", tm 1947/1946; "T", tm 1951/1931; "Tab", tm 1945/1932; "Tambo", tm 1952/1932;

"Tambor", tm 1950/1932; "Tabu", tm 1946/1932; "Thine Alone", tm 1950/1948; "Traveler", tm 1948/1947; "Trouble", tm 1946/1945.

ARNOLD CONSTABLE: "Le Premier Baiser", tm 1928/1926.

CONSTELLAIRE, Brooklyn, NY: "Capricorn", tm 1956/1955; "Libra", tm 1956/1955; "Leo", tm 1956/1955.

CONTESSA, NY, NY: "Gaye Contessa", tm 1956/1954; "Jaquar", tm 1956/1954; "Miramar", tm 1956/1954.

MARCEL CONTIER, Paris, France: "La Biosthétique", tm 1959/1946.

CONTOURE LABORATORIES INC., NY, NY: "Rendez-vous", tm 1934/1932.

SARA COOLEY, Los Angeles, CA: "Waterfall", tm 1947/1946.

CORDAY, Paris, France; NY, NY: "Attaque", tm 1947/1946; "Blanchette", tm 1925/1924; "Chevre Feuille", ad 1938; "Cordette", tm 1939/1939; "Eau de Cologne Brut", ad 1934; "Eau de Cologne Sec", ad 1934; "Eau de Lavande", ad 1934; "Eau de Lilas", as 1934; "Fame", tm 1947/1946; "Femme du Jour", ad 1927; "Frenzy", ad 1945; "Honeysuckle", ad 1938; "Jet", tm 1925/1924; "Kai Sang", tm 1925/1924; "Kis Royale", tm 1940/1939; "L'ardente Nuit", ad 1930; "La Plus Belle", art 1927; "La Promesse", tm 1934/1933; 'L'heure Romantique", ad 1930; "Orchidée Bleue", new 1925; "Possession", tm 1939/1939; "Quand?", ad 1930; "Romantique", tm 1951/1948; "Serre Fleure", tm 1925/1924; "Toodleoo", tm 1925/1924; "Toujours Moi", new 1923; "Toujours Toi", tm 1952/1951; "Trapèze", tm 1959/1956; "Tzigane", ad 1938; "Voyage A Paris", tm 1935/1933; "Zigane", tm 1950/1949.

CORDELL PRODUCTS, NY, NY: "Florence Benson", tm 1951/1950; "Love and Marriage", tm 1957/1956.

CORONADO MANUF. CO., St. Paul, MN: "Coronet", tm 1935/1933.

COROT, NY, NY: "Samba", tm 1944/1943.

CORYSE, Paris, France: "Vinca", Fr. ad 1928.

CORYSE SALOME, Paris, France: "Coryssima", new 1972; "Création", new 1951; "Epilogue", new 1946; "Intrépide", new 1977; "Opéra", new 1932.

COSMETICS, INC., Nashville, TN: "Danseuse", tm 1950/1943.

COSMETIC PRODUCTS CO., NY, NY: "Lily Dream", tm 1925/1923.

COSMETICS RESEARCH CORP., West Haven, CT: "Country Fair", tm 1941/1938.

COSMETIQUE LABORATORIES, Portland, OR: "Le Gui", ad 1937; "Mistletoe", tm 1935/1934.

COSMIC ARTS, NY, NY: "Aysgha", tm 1925/1925; "Dlacacia", tm 1925/1925; "Fleur D'Allah", tm 1925/1925; "Haroun", tm 1925/1925; "Myste're d'Orient", tm 1925/1925.

IRENE D. COTE, NY, NY: "Carrtee", tm 1931/1923.

COTTAN (COTTAN-PORTE), Paris, France: "Chypre", ad 1925; "Lilas Cottan", cat 1922; "Sybmée", art 1917; "Rouge De Basque", tm 1924/1922; "Rouge du Bengale", tm 1924/1857.

CYRUS L. COTTON, Earlville, NY: "Chrysanthemum Bouquet", tm 1893/1892; "Puritan", tm 1915/1890; "Queen of Lillies", tm 1893/1892.

COTY, Paris, France; NY, NY: "8 Mai", tm 1946/1945; "25 Août", tm 1946/1945; "A Suma", ad 1934; "Ambre Antique", tm 1921/1913; "Ambreine", tm 1921/1906; "Ballerina", tm 1939/1939; "Bali", tm 1935/1935; "Buckle", tm 1942/1941; "Cabochon", tm 1942/1941; "Cambo", tm 1943/1943; "Carousel", tm 1945/1945; "Chemin Dore", tm 1945/1944; "Chypre", art 1917; "Come-Seven", tm 1942/1941; "Complice", new 1973; "Continentale", tm 1935/1934; "Coquillage", tm 1947/1946; "Cyclamen", cat 1923; "Decoy", tm 1940/1939; "D'Orquille", tm 1945/1944; "Eau de Coty", tm 1921/1920; "Eldorado", tm 1945/1944; "Emeraude de Coty", new 1923; "Epreuve", tm 1944/1943; "Etrange", tm 1946/1945; "Excursion", tm 1942/1942; "Fairy Princess", tm 1957/1956; "Fleur du Lac", tm 1942/1942; "Fluorescent", tm 1946/1946; "Giselle", tm 1947/1946; "Grande Affair", tm 1954/1952; "Green Champagne", tm 1951/1950; "Heliotrope", cat 1923; "Idylle", cat 1922; "Imprèvu", ad 1965; "Inedit", tm 1938/1938; "Informal Fragrance", tm 1939/1939; "Iridescent", tm 1946/1945; "Iris", cat 1922; "Jacinthe", cat 1923; "Jasmin De Corse", before 1921; "L'Aimant", tm 1928/1927; "L'Effleurt", tm 1921/1909; "L'Oeillet France", cat 1923; "L'Or", tm 1921/1912; "L'Origan", tm 1921/1909; "La Fougeraie Au Crépuscule", tm 1932/1932; "La Jacee", tm 1925/1925; "La Rose Jacqueminot", tm 1921/1905; "La Violette Pourpre", tm 1921/1906; "Le Clou", tm 1946/1945; "Le Nouveau Cyclamen", cat 1922; "Le Nouveau Gardenia", ad 1936; "Le Soulier de Ballerine", tm 1947/1946; "Le Vertige", tm 1921/1906; "Les Muses", tm 1945/1945; "Lilas Blanc", cat 1922; "Lilas Poupre", cat 1922; "Little Miss Coty", tm 1960/1959; "Lumen", tm 1945/1924; "Macombo", 1947/1946; "Meteor", tm 1952/1949; "Mist de Paris", tm 1956/1954; "Moon Song", tm 1956/1954; "Moia", cat 1922; "Muguet des Bois", new 1923; "Obelisque", tm 1930/1930; "Oeillet France", cat 1922; "Panache", tm 1946/1945; "Pastel", tm 1947/1924; "Paris", tm 1926/1921; "Pearls of Paris", tm 1956/1954; "Pulsation", tm 1943/1943; "Red Ribbon", tm 1942/1942; "Rose Thé", tm 1936/1935; "Se Jour", tm 1945/1945; "Shakti", tm 1950/1950; "Sleigh Bells", tm 1942/1942; "Soleil D'Or", tm 1935/1935; "Sophisticate", tm 1943/1943; "Spectator", tm 1942/1942; "Spirituelle", tm 1945/1924; "Stow-Away", tm 1935/1935; "Styx", tm 1921/1912; "Sub-Deb", tm 1935/1935; "Superfine", cat 1922; "Tandem", tm 1927/1927; "Teindor", tm 1943/1943; "Tell Tale", tm 1942/1941; "Tovarich", tm 1945/1945; "Valiance", tm 1945/1945; "Vanid 'Or", tm 1945/1944; "Variations", tm 1939/1938.

COUDRAY, Paris, France; NY, NY: "Charme de France", ad 1930; "Je Vous L'Offre", Fr. ad 1919; "Le Trio", Fr. ad 1919; "Onyx Noir", ad 1930; "Rêve de Paris", ad 1930.

COUNT DORELIS LTD., NY, NY: "Royal Gem", tm 1954/1953.

COUNTESS MARITZA, NY, NY: "Rare Jewel", ad 1948; "Silent Night", ad 1947.

COURREGES, Paris, France: "Amérique", new 1974; "Courrèges in Blue", new 1983; "Empreinte", new 1971.

COURT PERFUMERY, NY, NY: "Gloriana", tm 1898/1897.

COURTISANES, NY, NY: "Salambô", 1923/1923; "Tonnerre", tm 1961/1959; "Yang-Yin", tm 1961/1959.

COURTLEY, Los Angeles, CA: "Afternoon", ad 1941; "Evening", ad 1941; "Grand Derby", tm 1944/1944; "Morning", ad 1941. (See also: CASTILIAN PRODUCTS).

JEAN COUTURIER, Paris, France: "Coriandre", new 1973; "Keora", new 1983.

COUTURIERS: "Tricot", art 1941.

IRENE F. CRAFT, Ridgewood, NJ: "Overture", tm 1952/1949; "Teen Date", tm 1952/1949.

MARK CROSS CO., NY, NY: "Cross Country", tm 1936/1935.

CROWN CHEMICAL, Indianapolis, IN: "Boncilla", cat 1922; "Ideal Bouquet", cat 1922.

CROWN PERFUMERY, London, England; NY, NY: "Crab-Apple Blossoms", tm 1918/1886; "Jeunesse Doree", tm 1908/1908.

ALBERTO CRUSELLAS, Habana, Cuba: "Ofelia", tm 1919/1915; "Safirea", tm 1919/1916.

CRYSTAL-LEE INC., NY, NY: "Rain", tm 1925/1925.

DAVID CRYSTAL, NY, NY: "Above All", tm 1942/1941; "Cheerio", tm 1942/1941.

HELENE CURTIS, Chicago, IL: "Birds in Guilded Cage", tm 1961/1960; "Cabana", tm 1960/1958; "Pink Lady", tm 1962/1961; "Tweedie", tm 1958/1957.

COUSSONS, SONS & CO., Manchester, England: "Imperial Leather", tm 1954/1939.

CYBER, Paris, France: "Cybera De Cyber", tm 1926/1925; "Moi-Même De Cyber", tm 1926/1925.

LILLY DACHE, NY, NY: "Because", tm 1946/1945; "Dachelle", tm 1963/1962; "Dashing", tm 1942/1941; "Drifting", tm 1942/1941; "Fan-Freluches", tm 1944/1944.

DAGGETT & RAMSDELL, Newark, NJ; NY, NY: "Arabesque", tm 1950/1949; "Dagelle", tm 1930/1929; "Debonair", tm 1950/1949; "Debutette", tm 1956/1956; "Debutante International", tm 1961/1960; "French Secret", tm 1959/1957; "French Sonata", tm 1958/1956; "Gay Manhattan", ad 1946; "Magic Moment", tm 1951/1949; "Miss Teen", tm 1960/1958; "Mountain Heather", ad 1946; "Personal Choice", tm 1954/1953; "Ruffles", tm 1959/1958; "Sonata", tm 1937/1937; "Sparkling Gold", tm 1961/1952; "White Ruffles", tm 1954/1952.

DAINTY DABS, NY, NY: "Royal Dabs", ad 1939.

DALMORA, Chicago, IL: "Be True", tm 1945/1944; "Carols", ad 1946; "Chee Wee", tm 1945/1944; "Dignity", ad 1946; "Haunting", ad 1946; "Inloo", tm 1945/1944; "Modesty", ad 1946; "Shambi", tm 1945/1944; "Shola", tm 1945/1943; "Take Me", tm 1945/1944; "Tarra", tm 1946/1943; "Tear Drop", ad 1946; "Twang", tm 1945/1944.

DANA, Paris, France; NY, NY: "100%", tm 1947/1947; "20 Carats", tm 1953/1933; "Aloha", tm 1939/1938; "Ambush", ad 1955; "Analergic", tm 1946/1945; "Bois de Boulogne", tm 1949/1948; "Bon Voyage", tm 1960/1951; "Canoe", tm 1946/1945; "Claude Fontaine", tm 1950/1949; "Cuir de Canada", tm 1950/1948; "Danalak", tm 1945/1945; "Danamask", tm 1951/1949; "Danita", tm 1958/1957; "Emir", tm 1937/1936; "Halago", tm 1944/1933; "Impulse", tm 1961/1960; "Intervalle", tm 1946/1946; "Kali", tm 1952/1944; "Lenia", tm 1941/1946; "Marquisette", tm 1952/1949; "Perfide", tm 1948/1947; "Pink Blue Pink", tm 1954/1945; "Platine", tm 1940/1939; "Platinum", tm 1953/1939; "Presage", tm 1947/1946; "Priority", tm 1947/1947; "Rocio", tm 1944/1933; "Sabotage", tm 1948/1946; "Sillage", tm 1946/1946; "Superstition", tm 1946/1945; "Tabu", new 1932; "Totem", tm 1939/1936; "Tundra", tm 1950/1948; "Utopie", tm 1946/1946; "Vendetta", tm 1946/1946; "Voodoo", tm 1953/1932; "Yoga", tm 1940/1940.

CAROLYN T. DARE, Atlantic City, NJ: "Sin", tm 1923/1923.

MARTI DARE (OLD 97 MANUFACTURING), Tampa, FL: "Antigua Royale", tm 1957/1956; "Florida Fragrance", tm 1956/1955; "truly fair", tm 1955/1953; "Tammy", tm 1958/1956.

DARIA: "Babiole", cat 1922; "Nina", cat 1922.

BELLEZA IRENE DARIE, Habana, Cuba: "Rejane", tm 1949/1944.

DARNEE INC., NY, NY: "La Spangla", tm 1929/1928.

D'ARNOT, Hollywood, CA: "Hollywood Blossoms", tm 1927/1927.

D'ARTIMON, NY, NY: "Clairvoyant", tm 1946/1943; "Deep Water", tm 1946/1943; "Fair Weather", tm 1945/1943; "Muting!", tm 1945/1943; "Northern Lights", tm 1946/1943; "Sinbad", tm 1946/1943; "Stormy Weather", tm 1945/1943.

KAY DAUMIT. (See KATHRYN).

DAUSSE, Paris, France: "Nelombo", tm 1933/1931.

CHARLES DAVIS, Paris, France: "Nildé", tm 1920/1915.

JOHN DAVIS, West Bay, MI: "Nun Betta", tm 1878/1878.

D'AVRAY, (See AVRAY).

DAY LIGHT LABORATORIES, St. Louis, MO: "Y-Dalight", tm 1925/1924.

D'CINY, St. Paul, MN: "Blossom Time", tm 1927/1926; "Liberty Bell", tm 1942/1941; "Masterpiece", tm 1933/1931.

DE CORTOT, Brooklyn, NY: "Madoue", tm 1954/1953; "Priceless", tm 1954/1953; "Prima Donna", tm 1954/1953.

MARYON DE FOE, NY, NY: "Fleur De Passion", tm 1925/1925.

DE HERIOT, Los Angeles, CA; NY, NY: "1001 Nights", tm 1945/1944; "Always In My Heart", tm 1945/1943; "Célèbre", tm 1952/1949; "Gardenia", ad 1939; "In Person", tm 1947/1945; "La Premiere", ad 1939; "Pink Line", ad 1943; "Violet", ad 1939; "White Lace", tm 1943/1935; "Woodlilac", ad 1939.

DE LUXE PRODUCTS, Chicago, IL: "Hollywood Queen", tm 1937/1936.

DE LUZY, Paris, France: "Le Chypre de De Luzy", ad 1919; "Poyrpre Antique", ad 1919.

DE MARBEL, Neuilly, France: "Ambassade de Paris", tm 1946/1931.

DE MUSSET INC.: "Poème", tm 1928/1927;

"pour l'amour", tm 1930/1928; "Ze Breath of Paris", tm 1930/1930.

DE RAYMOND, Paris, France; NY, NY: "Demain", ad 1930; "Deviltry", tm 1936/1936; "Elfe", tm 1927/1927; "Fleur de Pré", tm 1927/1927; "Guile", tm 1940/1940; "JB", ad 1936; "Man Alive", tm 1946/1945; "Mimzy", tm 1940/1925; "Mon Gardenia", tm 1929/1928; "Persian Lamb", tm 1944/1943; "Pinx", tm 1941/1931; "Rama", ad 1935; "Sa Fleur", ad 1936; "Sweet Peas", ad 1929; "Valli Lily-X", ad 1936. (See also: DE SEGHERS).

L. DE ROQUEFEUIL, Paris, France: "Nuit de Montmartre", tm 1925/1924.

DE SEGHERS, Paris, France; NY, NY: "Appel d'Amour", tm 1929/1928; "Gardenia", ad 1933; "Gardenia-X", ad 1935; "Honeysuckle", ad 1932; "Jasmin", ad 1933; "La Pensée Dorée", tm 1929/1928; "Larmes de Fleurs", tm 1929/1928; "Pinxx", ad 1932; "Sept Fleurs", tm 1929/1928; "Sweet Magnolia", ad 1932; "Teza", tm 1931/1930; "Valli Lily", ad 1933. (See also: DE RAYMOND).

DE VAUCHAY, NY, NY: "June Moon", tm 1930/1930.

DE VERNON, Paris, France: "My Dream", tm 1963/1961.

DEGAS, Paris, France; NY, NY: "Danseuse Etoile", ad 1947; "Estampe", ad 1947.

DEL VALLE, Buenos Aires, Argentina: "Julio Romero", tm 1952/1943.

DELAFINE, London, England: "Lytia", tm 1926/1923.

DELAVELLE, London, England: "Carnation", ad 1939; "Extra Scotch Spirit", ad 1939.

ELLYN DELEITH, NY, NY: "Pampa", ad 1946; "Spindrift", ad 1946.

DELETTREZ, Paris, France; Long Island City, NY: "Aluria", tm 1917/1915; "Aglaia", ad 1902; "Awake", tm 1941/1941; "Bonheur D'Aimer", tm 1928/1925; "Bridal Wreath", tm 1939/1939; "Country Clover", tm 1940/1939; "Esora", tm 1928/1925; "Florise", tm 1918/1915; "Fulfillment", tm 1940/1939; "Inalda", ad 1934; "Jeanne Baird", tm 1928/1927; "La Danse des Fleurs", tm 1928/1926; "Lais", tm 1928/1925; "Mainliner", tm 1940/1939; "Moonlight & Lace", tm 1941/1941; "Nuit Blanche", tm 1928/1926; "One Night", tm 1941/1941; "Palma", tm 1887/1886; "Racing Red", 1940/1939; "Renée", tm 1917/1915; "Reveillon", ad 1925; "Righi", tm 1928/1925; "Silver Butterfly", tm 1929/1927; "Storm", tm 1941/1941; "Together", tm 1941/1941"; "Tourmaline", tm 1928/1925; "Violettes Celestes", ad 1902; "Wildflower", ad 1940; "Zakieh", tm 1920/1916. (See also: ARLY; V. VIVAUDOU).

DELEX PRODUCTS, NY, NY: "Frame", tm 1946/1945; "Indeed", tm 1946/1945.

M. DELIA, Paris, France: "A la Cocarde de France", ad 1938.

DELTAH: "Ecstasy", cat 1934; "Midnight Hour", cat 1934; "Mon Bijou", cat 1934; "Une Sentour", cat 1934.

GABRIELLE CUISINIER DELVALLEE, Paris, France: "Tour Eiffel", tm 1954/1950.

JAMES LOUIS DEMOVILLE, NY, NY: "Fancea", tm 1928/1927.

DENNEY & DENNEY, Philadelphia, PA: "Crème Mercedes", tm 1927/1927;

"Myana", tm 1920/1918; "Silver Narcisse", tm 1926/1926.

FRANCES DENNY, Philadelphia, PA: "Do-Re-Mi", tm 1940/1940; "Gay Mood", tm 1957/1956; "Hope", tm 1953/1952; "Interlude", new 1962; "Mrs. Santa Claus Comes To Town", tm 1951/1949; "Night Life", tm 1939/1939; "Shining Star", tm 1940/1939; "Snow Blossom", tm 1952/1950; "Whirlwind", tm 1942/1942; "Yes, Yes", tm 1939/1939; "You and I", tm 1938/1938.

DENVER DRY GOODS CO., Denver, CO: "Coudrai-Roseau", tm 1926/1926; "Madame Cecile", tm 1932/1931.

DERMAY PERFUMERS INC., NY, NY: "Bath Flowers", tm 1928/1927; "Cartier", tm 1926/1926; "Charing", tm 1937/1936; "Fete de Coeur", cat 1928; "Honeysuckle", ad 1934; "Les Parfums Lucien", tm 1926/1926; "Nuit d'Extase", ad 1934; "Pagliacci", ad 1937; "Warwick Lavender", ad 1938.

DERMETIES, NY, NY: "Academy Award", tm 1947/1946; "Aged in Wood", tm 1945/1944; "Goddess of Crete", tm 1947/1947; "1199", tm 1947/1945; "Perclogne", tm 1947/1947; "Reincarnation", tm 1946/1945.

DEROC, Paris, France; Asnieres, France: "Gai Montmartre", tm 1926/1925.

PARFUMS DESIREE CO., NY, NY: "Broadcast", tm 1926/1926.

JEAN DESPREZ, Paris, France: "40 Love", tm 1951/1947; "Bal à Versailles", ad 1962; "Etourdissant", ad 1939; "Grande Dame", new 1939; "Jardanel", new 1972; "Sheherazade", art 1939; "Votre Main", new 1939.

RENE DESSEIGNES, Asnieres, France: "Ting-Shang", tm 1925/1924.

JEAN DESSES, Paris, France: "Celui", new 1938; "Diffusion", ad 1949.

DESTI, Paris, France; NY, NY: "Beatrice d'Este", ad 1914; "Devinez", ad 1914; "Lilas", ad 1914; "L'Invitation à La Danse", ad 1914; "Moi-Même", ad 1914; "Saphir", ad 1914; "Whither Thou Goest", ad 1914.

FAREL DESTIN INC., NY, NY: "Strange Music", tm 1945/1945; "Wine In The Air", tm 1946/1946.

D'ESTREE, Paris, France: "No. 7", ad 1954.

GWENDOLYN DESVEAUX, Alpena, MI: "Yours", tm 1952/1950.

JEAN D'HENNERY, Paris, France; NY, NY: "Chantaco", tm 1947/1946; "Dogaresse", tm 1947/1946; "Guitte-Amour", tm 1947/1946; "Kim", ad 1946; "Langueur", tm 1947/1946; "Magnificat", tm 1947/1946; "Mouky", tm 1947/1946; "Réconciliation", tm 1948/1946; "Reine de Saba", tm 1948/1946; "Retour", tm 1947/1946; "Reverence", tm 1948/1946; "Tendre Espoir", tm 1947/1946; "Toutounne", tm 1947/1946; "Triomphe D'Amour", tm 1947/1946.

D'HERAUD, Paris, France: "Jasmin", ad 1925; "Marjoline", ad 1925; "La Phalène", ad 1923; "Semis Des Fleurs", ad 1923.

MAXIME D'HOTMAN DE VILLIERS, Paris, France: "Les Parfums du Lys d'Or", tm 1924/1921; "Lys D'Or", tm 1924/1921.

DIEDRE PRODUCTS, Forest Hills, NY: "Cliche", tm 1960/1958.

DILL CO., INC., Norristown, PA: "Dilnorpa", tm 1926/1922.

MARTIN & JARED DILLEY, Los Angeles, CA: "Mist 'O The Moon", tm 1931/1931.

DIMITRY: "Credo", new 1933.

DINARD, NY, NY: "Jou Jou", tm 1946/1945; "Plaisir D'Amour", tm 1963/1943.

DINY INC., NY, NY: "En Amour", tm 1927/1927.

CHRISTIAN DIOR, Paris, France: "Diorama", tm 1950/1947; "Diorella", new 1972; "Dioressence", new 1979; "Diorissimo", tm 1960/1956; "Eau Sauvage", new 1967; "Fleurs Fraîches", tm 1962/1955; "Miss Dior", tm 1953/1948; "Poison", new 1986.

DIVORCONS-PARIS, INC., NY, NY: "Evening in Bermuda", tm 1935/1935.

JACQUES DOBAIS, NY, NY: "Momentum, tm 1952/1951; "Say So", tm 1952/1951.

FRANCISCUS DOBBELMANN, Amsterdam, Netherlands: "Casanova", tm 1931/1929.

DOBBS & CO., NY, NY: "Bagatelle", tm 1924/1924.

DOLEITH INC., Chicago, IL: "Clair de Lune", tm 1942/1940; "Gay Patton", tm 1946/1945.

GEORGE M. DOMENICE, NY, NY: "Ruby", tm 1927/1925.

DONAT, Chicago, IL: "Evening Capers", tm 1953/1952.

DONNA LO, St. Louis, MO: "Lingering Melody", ad 1944.

JULIA DONNELLY, St. Davids, PA: "Arlette de Fallaise", tm 1925/1924.

LOUIS D'OR, Paris, France: "Amour D'Or", ad 1963; "Ceil D'Or", ad 1963; "D'Or D'Or", ad 1963; "Mademoiselle D'Or", ad 1963; "Reve D'Or", ad 1963.

DORALDINA INC., West Hollywood, CA; NY, NY: "Chartreuse", tm 1932/1931; "Gypsy Lure", tm 1930/1929; "La Conga", tm 1940/1939.

DORELIS, NY, NY: "Belle of New York", tm 1945/1944; "Canzonetta", tm 1945/1944.

DORIAN, NY, NY: "Exquise", ad 1968.

DORILLY, Paris, France: "Fin d'Automne", art 1923; "L'Elu", tm 1950/1946; "Vanikoro", art 1922.

DORLAND INTERNATIONAL, NY, NY: "Tognac", tm 1939/1938.

WILL B. DORMAN, Georgetown, MA: "Champagne Cologne", tm 1875/1875.

DORON, Portland, OR: "Forever After", tm 1927/1926; "My Folly", tm 1927/1926; "Orange Valencia", tm 1927/1926.

DOROTHEA (CHAUNCEY FREEDMAN), Mt. Vernon, NY: "Letty Lynton", tm 1934/1930.

D'ORMIDOR & CO., NY, NY: "Peantine", tm 1893/1892.

D'ORMO, New Haven, CT: "Dainty Maid", ad 1921; "Garden Blossoms", cat 1922; "Kiss-Me", ad 1921; "La Victoire", ad 1921; "Naturelle Flowers", cat 1922; "Peg O' My Heart", tm 1914/1913; "Triumph", cat 1922; "Two Lips", cat 1922.

D'ORSAY, Paris, France: "Alarme", tm 1947/1946; "Ambre d'Orsay", Fr. ad 1914; "Arome 3", ad 1958; "Belle de Jour", tm 1938/1938; "Bouquet D'Orsay", ad 1914; "Casino", tm 1932/1932; "Charme d'Orsay", ad 1920; "Chevalier D'Orsay", tm 1928/1912; "Comtesse D'Orsay", tm 1932/1931; "Cyclamen", ad 1913; "Divine", ad 1947; "Duo D'Orsay", tm 1929/1928; "Eau De Cologne Du Chevalier", tm 1949/1912; "Fantastique", ad 1953;

"Fleurette Bleue", ad 1920; "Ganika", tm 1928/1923; "Grâce", Fr. ad 1920; "Grinette", Fr. ad 1914; "Intoxication", tm 1942/1942; "Jasmin", ad 1923; "L'Aveu", Fr. ad 1914; "La Flambee", art 1913; "Le Dandy", tm 1927/1926; "Le Jardin", tm 1932/1931; "Le Porte-Bonheur", art 1913; "Les Fleurs", ad 1914; "Les Roses D'Orsay", ad 1914; "Leur Coeurs", ad 1913; "Meggy", art 1911; "Milord", tm 1948/1932; "Muguet", ad 1923; "Mystere D'Orsay", tm 1928/1915; "Nelly D'Orsay", ad 1914; "Panier de Roses", ad 1914; "Pirouette", tm 1948/1946; "Poesie", ad 1914; "Toujours Fidele", tm 1928/1912; "Trophee", Fr. ad 1935.

DOEUILLET DOUCHET, Paris, France: "Mareva", tm 1929/1929.

DOUCE-O'DEUER, Baltimore, MD: "Three Graces", tm 1927/1927.

D'OUCHY, Paris, France; NY, NY: "Ambre", ad 1929; "Bouquet d'Ouchy", ad 1929; "Chypre", ad 1929; "Extrait d'Ouchy", ad 1929; "L'Amazone", ad 1929; "Olympiades", ad 1929; "Princess de Legende", ad 1929; "Simoun", ad 1929.

DOUSSAN FRENCH PERFUMERY CO., New Orleans, LA: "The Sweet South", tm 1888/1887.

B. W. DOWS & CO., Lowell, MA: "East End", tm 1876/1876.

DR. DYS: "Auberpine", cat 1922; "Ambre", cat 1922; "Oeillet", cat 1922; "Royal", cat 1922; "Shamrina", cat 1922.

GEORG DRALLE, Hamburg, Germany: "Illusion", tm 1933/1909.

F. F. DREXEL & CO., Baltimore, MD: "Vienna Cologne", tm 1874/1874.

D'RUVYL, Cleveland, OH: "Choisi", tm 1926/1924.

DU TOUR: "Satyre", ad 1955; "Volage", ad 1955.

DUBE PARFUM CO., Chicago, IL: "Blue Book", tm 1947/1946; "Lonely", tm 1947/1946; "Michigan Avenue", tm 1947/1946.

DUBARRY PERFUMERY CO., Hove, England: "Dalcrose", tm 1926/1916.

DUBUIS & ROWSELL, Croydon, England: "Duroma", tm 1932/1923.

DUCAREL PERFUMERY CO., NY, NY: "La Vare", tm 1927/1924.

DUCHESS D'ANDRE: "Eventide", ad 1946.

DUKE & BENEDICT, NY, NY: "Enchanted Evening", tm 1950/1949; "Monsoon", tm 1951/1947.

MARY DUNHILL, NY, NY: "Amulet", new 1938; "Bewitching", tm 1941/1941; "Escape", tm 1945/1943; "Frou Frou de Gardenia", ad 1934; "White Hyacinth", ad 1941.

DUPRE: "Affinite", cat 1922; "Floradol", cat 1922.

RAYMOND R. DU PRE, Waterloo, IA: "Adrienne", tm 1927/1927; "Clotaire", tm 1927/1927.

DURALE CO. INC., St. Louis, MO: "Paris Charm", tm 1932/1931.

DURE, NY, NY: "Air de Jeunesse", tm 1932/1925; "Comme Ci, Comme Ca", tm 1930/1927; "Lalay", tm 1931/1930; "Toujours Rouge de Tuscany", tm 1931/1929; "Whip", tm 1930/1930.

DURITE CORP., Detroit, MI: "Record", tm 1947/1945.

ARMAND DUVAL: "Valencia D'Amour",

tm 1929/1925.

DUVINNE: "Bouquet Duvinne", ad 1926; "Narcissum", ad 1926; "Jasmine", ad 1926.

MARIE EARLE INC., Paris, France; NY, NY: "Arc de Triomphe", tm 1930/1930; "Legion D'Honneur", tm 1930/1930; "Redbud", tm 1940/1940; "Roseraie", tm 1937/1937; "Secret des Fleurs", ad 1923; "Soufflé", tm 1940/1940; "Tropicolor", tm 1942/1942.

C. M. EARL MANUFACTURING CHEMIST, Detroit, MI: "Purple Narcise", tm 1924/1923.

EASTMAN & BROTHER, NY, NY; Philadelphia, PA: "Aloha", tm 1885/1885; "Snow Lily", ad 1890.

EATON PRODUCTS (MELVIN H. JACOBS), Chicago, IL: "Lady Charm", tm 1941/1941.

ECKERD'S OF ERIE, INC., Erie, PA: "Loupay", tm 1933/1932.

EDDY BROTHERS, NY, NY: "Royal Dagmar", tm 1875/1874.

EDEN CO. (EDWARD LANE), NY, NY: "Garden of Eden", tm 1945/1943.

EDOUARD, Cleveland, OH: "S", tm 1951/1948; "WS", tm 1951/1948.

CHARLES EDOUARD, Paris, France: "Mon Numéro", tm 1947/1945; "Signet", tm 1947/1945.

EDOUARDO INC., NY, NY: "Bag-dabs", tm 1926/1925; "Egyptian", new 1927; "Lakme", tm 1926/1925; "Lilas De Paques", ad 1928; "Lotus", new 1927; "Nuit Divine", tm 1927/1926.

EISENBERG, Chicago, IL: "847", new 1938; "Enticing", tm 1950/1944; "Startling", tm 1949/1941; "Stirring", tm 1950/1942.

EL MOROCCO, NY, NY: "Gala", tm 1959/1956.

ELESBE, Paris, France: "Mossieu Gugusse", ad 1924; "Mossieu Clown", ad 1924.

ELIANE, Paris, France: "le Mélange d'Eliane", Fr. ad 1927.

ELIZABETH OF SWEDEN, Paterson, NJ: "Fjord", tm 1961/1959; "Three Crowns", tm 1961/1959.

ELMO, Philadelphia, PA: "Dalliance", tm 1946/1945; "El Patio", tm 1937/1937; "Going My Way", tm 1946/1945; "Lord Baltimore", tm 1947/1946; "Miosotys", tm 1930/1929; "Pretty Please", tm 1956/1953; "Rose", ad 1923; "Sesqui Fleurs", tm 1926/1926.

EMDEE LABORATORIES CO., Los Angeles, CA: "Sazon", tm 1931/1930.

EMEF, Rome, Italy: "Arabeske", ad 1939; "Argento", ad 1939; "Roma Antica", ad 1939; "Scherzo", ad 1939.

EMFO, NY, NY: "Aquascent", tm 1939/1938; "Genupine", tm 1939/1938.

EMKINS, Brooklyn, NY: "De Gu-Sai", tm 1931/1921.

GI. VI. EMME, Milan, Italy: "Ampolle", ad 1922; "Contessa", ad 1922; "Dimmi Di Si", ad 1922; "G.V.M.", tm 1951/1947; "Giardino Antico", ad 1925; "Insidia", tm 1948/1945; "La Rosa", ad 1922; "Malia", ad 1922; "Nina Sorfidi", ad 1922; "Ricordo d'Autunno", tm 1951/1948; "Ricordo d'Estate", tm 1951/1948; "Ricordo d'Inverno", tm 1951/1948; "Ricordo di Primavera", tm 1951/1948; "Subdola", ad 1922; "Venezia Mia", ad 1925.

ERTE INC., NY, NY: "Dadá", tm 1927/1926.

H. H. ERWIN CO., Philadelphia, PA: "Easte

Bells", tm 1927/1927; "Erwinia", tm 1927/1927; "Velestra", tm 1927/1927.

ERWYN PRODUCTS INC., NY, NY: "Crinoline", tm 1939/1938.

ESME OF PARIS, Paris, France; NY, NY: "A May Morning", ad 1941; "Green Eyes", ad 1946; "Indian Summer", ad 1946; "On Fifth Avenue", ad 1943; "Sophisticated Lady", ad 1946.

ESTALL, NY, NY: "Love & Kisses", ad 1948.

ESTON MANUFACTURING CO., Birmingham, AL: "Lolaline", tm 1926/1924.

CECILE ETIEVE, Paris, France: "Midsummer Night", tm 1935/1935; "Saint-Jean-D'été", tm 1934/1934.

ETTA PERFUMES, NY, NY: "Un Souvenir de Budapest", tm 1939/1937.

EURO AMERICAN CORP., Newark, NJ: "Lucky Drop", tm 1930/1929.

H. SUGDEN EVANS, Montreal, Canada: "De Leon", tm 1881/1881.

EVENOD PERFUMER INC., NY, NY: "Another Day", tm 1931/1930.

EVYAN, NY, NY: "Beach and Travel", tm 1955/1955; "Bright Stars", ad 1945; "Gay Diversion", tm 1945/1945; "Gay Glitter", ad 1945; "Golden Hearts", tm 1957/1956; "Golden Shadows", tm 1953/1950; "Great Lady", tm 1958/1957; "Menace", tm 1943/1943; "Moonlight Menace", tm 1947/1946; "Most Precious", tm 1949/1947; "M. P.", tm 1961/1957; "My Pet", tm 1960/1958; "Satin Glide", tm 1959/1959; "Splash", tm 1951/1946; "Stolen Heaven", ad 1945; "Surf Club", tm 1951/1950; "Tiny Waist", tm 1950/1949; "Torrent", tm 1946/1945; "Treasure Trove", tm 1960/1950; "White Shadows", tm 1946/1945; "White Shoulders", tm 1943/1943; "White Shoulders Splash", tm 1951/1946; "W. S.", tm 1961/1957.

EXCITEMENT, Chicago, IL: "Enticing", tm 1944/1944; "Startling", tm 1942/1941; "Stirring", tm 1942/1942.

FABERGE, NY, NY: "Act IV", tm 1952/1949; "Aphrodisia", tm 1937/1932; "Babe", new 1977; "Cavale", new 1975; "Esprit De Parfum", tm 1962/1960; "F#", ad 1959; "Fabergette", tm 1949/1947; "Feminin", new 1982; "Flambeau", tm 1956/1955; "Straw Hat", tm 1963/1938; "Tigress", tm 1963/1938; "Woodhue", art 1949; "Xanadu", ad 1969.

FABIELO (RAFAEL GUITART), Havana, Cuba: "Flor de Caña, tm 1958/1957.

MAURICE FABRICANT, NY, NY: "Magic Charme", tm 1953/1951; "Magic Mystery", tm 1953/1951; "Matador", tm 1953/1952; "Trickery", tm 1953/1952.

MAX FACTOR, Hollywood, CA: "Autograph", tm 1953/1950; "Chaster", tm 1960/1959; "Cocoanut Grove", tm 1939/1938; "Diamont", tm 1960/1959; "Electrique", ad 1954; "Golden Lavender", tm 1956/1954; "Golden Woods", tm 1952/1951; "Hi-Fi", tm 1956/1954; "Rubis", tm 1960/1959; "Signature", tm 1953/1950; "Trocadero", tm 1939/1938.

FAD BEAUTY PRODUCTS, NY, NY: "Chiquita", tm 1947/1946.

FAITOUTE MUNN: "Carnation", art 1923; "Lilac", art 1923; "Orange-blossom" art 1923; "Oriental bouquet", art 1923; "Violet", art 1923.

PERCIVAL E. FALKINGHAM, NY, NY: "Ambre B", tm 1930/1929; "Evenod", tm

1930/1929; "Percefal", tm 1933/1933; "Jules V. Riviere", tm 1930/1929.

FALLIS INC., Cincinnati, OH: "Peter Pan", tm 1926/1920.

FAMILEX PRODUCTS CO. (ROMEO PARENT), Montreal, Canada: "Jacquello", tm 1938/1928.

FAMOUS PRODUCTS (VALMOR PRODUCTS), Chicago, IL: "Double Lucky", tm 1956/1936; "Good Times", tm 1939/1938; "High John The Conqueror", tm 1939/1930; "Hold Your Man", tm 1939/1937; "Kiss Me Again", tm 1939/1937; "Lucky", tm 1956/1955; "Lucky Cat", tm 1939/1937; "True Love", tm 1939/1937; "Van Van", tm 1937/1930.

FAROS, NY, NY: "Bretton Woods", ad 1940; "Lido", ad 1940; "White Lilac", ad 1940.

FASHIONEL, Baltimore, MD: "Alcofleur", tm 1945/1938.

JACQUES FATH, Bois, France; Paris, France: "Canasta", tm 1953/1950; "Chasuble", tm 1949/1945; "Expression", ad 1977; "Fath de Fath", tm 1957/1953; "Fath's Love", ad 1968; "Green Water", tm 1926/1953; "Iris Gris", tm 1952/1946.

FAUBY, Paris, France: "Kis Royale", new 1939.

FAXON & GALLAGHER, Kansas City, MO: "Brookwoods", cat 1922; "Dream Kiss", tm 1917/1911.

FAY: "Absolute Essence of Gardenia", art 1936.

BETTY FAYE CO., New Haven, CT: "Jean La Solle", tm 1929/1925; "Jipsee Fleurs", tm 1928/1925. (See also: VIVINY).

FEBOE, NY, NY: "Fancy Free", tm 1945/1944.

FELICE CO. (EVELYN WESTALL), NY, NY: "Now Or Never", tm 1948/1946.

LOUIS FERAUD, Paris, France: "Fantasque", new 1981; "Feraud 2", ad 1972; "Jour", new 1984.

FERBO CO., Madison, NJ: "L'Dianelle", tm 1945/1944.

BIENVENIDO FERNANDEZ, Habana, Cuba: "Nuit Romantique", tm 1930/1928.

PAUL F. FERRIERE, NY, NY: "Brise d'Or", tm 1916/1915.

FIDELWOOD. (See HOUSE OF FRAGRANCE).

JOSEPH A. FIELDS, NY, NY: "Allez Hop", tm 1924/1924.

HENRIETTE HOTERMANS FIEULLIEN, Brussels, Belgium: "Robymona", tm 1946/1945.

FINLAY, DICKS, & CO., New Orleans, LA: "La Valliere", tm 1910/1910.

FIORET, Paris, France; NY, NY: "Ambre Byzantin", ad 1922; "Chose Promise", ad 1921; "Chypre", ad 1923; "Fatalitas", cat 1922; "Hommage A La Femme", cat 1922; "Jouir", ad 1921; "La Fleur Sacre", cat 1922; "La Muse", ad 1923; "L'Au-Dela", cat 1922; "Le Dernier Roman", ad 1923; "L'Elan", ad 1921; "Le Roy de Paris", ad 1923; "Les Parfums des Jardins", tm 1924/1920; "L'Impromptu", ad 1921; "Monar", cat 1922; "Orchid", ad 1940; "Prévert", ad 1922; "Priere", cat 1922; "Prince Rival", ad 1921; "Sweet Pea", ad 1921.

FISHER & CO., NY, NY: "The Orphans' Boquet", tm 1874/1874.

F. W. FITCH, Des Moines, IA: "Lois", tm 1921/1903.

FLAMOUR, Sao Paulo, Brazil: "Flor de

Café", tm 1951/1949.

ALFRED A. FLASTER, NY, NY: "Cordially Yours", tm 1943/1942; "Gay Goddess", tm 1947/1946; "My Reputation", tm 1946/1946; "Russian Sable", tm 1944/1942; "Wanton Miss", tm 1944/1943.

FLEMING BROS., Pittsburg, PA: "Mikado", tm 1886/1886.

FLORALATOMS CO., Chicago, IL: "Exhaltation", tm 1947/1946; "Heavenly Night", tm 1947/1946.

FLORASYNTH, NY, NY: "Chancing", tm 1954/1933; "Comfort Me", tm 1956/1954; "Entrapped", tm 1954/1951; "Modesty", tm 1956/1954; "Shelter Me", tm 1956/1954.

FLORIS (1730), London, England: "English Bluebells", U.S.; "Lily of the Valley", U.S.; "Red Rose", new 1730.

FLOSSY DENTAL MFG., Evanston, IL: "Lucky-Love-Lure", tm 1924/1923; "Sheik Lure", tm 1925/1923.

FONTAINE PERFUME CORP., NY, NY: "Enchanted Evening", tm 1950/1949; "Golden-Necklace", tm 1951/1948; "Kismet", tm 1955/1954; "Oriental Wood", tm 1950/1948; "This & Heaven Too", tm 1950/1948.

FONTANIS, Paris, France; Neuilly, France; NY, NY: "Ananya", tm 1925/1924; "Blue Isle", tm 1947/1946; "Daisette", tm 1924/1922; "Damoya", tm 1925/1924; "Fleurs de Bagdad", ad 1923; "Madhva", tm 1925/1923; "Prelude", tm 1939/1928; "Quel Delice", ad 1924; "Rahna", tm 1925/1924; "Sourire de France", art 1926; "Sous La Charmille", tm 1924/1919; "Tamya", tm 1925/1924; "Tawao", tm 1925/1924; "Vivette", tm 1922/1920.

FOOTE & JENKS, Jackson, MI: "Betsy Ross", tm 1916/1904; "Swas-ti-ka", tm 1907/1907.

PARFUMERIE FOREST (LEON COHN), Paris, France: "Beaucaire", tm 1926/1925; "Lucky Scents", new 1924; "Ming Toy", tm 1923/1923; "Monceau", tm 1926/1926.

FORST LABORATORIES, Cincinnati, OH: "La Gloire", tm 1925/1922.

J. FORSTREM (J. BAUDOIN), Paris, France: "Après Minuit", tm 1934/1930; "Bouquet Pourpre", tm 1934/1927; "Florel", tm 1934/1927; "Fruit Vert", tm 1934/1928.

FORTY SECOND STREET SALES CO., Chicago, IL: "Theater Box", tm 1937/1935.

FORVIL, Paris, France: "A Vos Ordres", tm 1950/1938; "Ayménée", tm 1950/1941; "Equivoque", tm 1952/1951; "La Perle Noire", tm 1924/1922; "Le Parfum", art 1927; "Les 5 Fleurs", ad 1926; "Les Yeux Doux", tm 1950/1941; "Poeme", tm 1955/1954; "Trois Valses", tm 1950/1937.

ROSARIA MARIA FOSCOLO, Paris, France: "Nuit de Decembre" tm 1947/1946.

CHARLES H. FOSTER, NY, NY: "T. N. T.", tm 1945/1944; "Tease", tm 1942/1942; "To New Triumphs", tm 1944/1944.

FOUILLAT, Paris, France: "Tècherose", Fr. ad 1921.

JACQUES FOURCY, Paris, France: "Comme-ci Comme-Ça", tm 1963/1962.

ADRIENNA FOY, Paris, France: "Maudy", tm 1946/1928.

MARCEL B. FOY, NY, NY: "Bourget", tm 1930/1929; "Morlet", tm 1929/1929; "Myette", tm 1926/1926.

FRACY, Paris, France: "Charmeuse", ad 1924; "Fracy", tm 1923/1922; "Jasmin,

Passionata", ad 1924; "Rose-Joli", ad 1924; "Silhouette", ad 1924.

FRAGONARD, Paris, France: "Belle De Nuit", tm 1947/1933; "Evernia", tm 1946/1935; "Lancry", tm 1947/1942; "Moment Vole", ad 1947; "Pur Hasard", tm 1946/1935; "Source Bleue", tm 1946/1935; "Zizanie", tm 1946/1935.

FRANAD, Chicago, IL: "105", tm 1961/1958.

FRANCO AMERICAN HYGIENIC CO., Chicago, IL: "Dearest", tm 1945/1911; "Franco", cat 1922; "Hygrade", cat 1922; "Inspirante", cat 1922; "La Joie", cat 1922; "Opalescent", cat 1922; "Patrician", cat 1922; "Persian Garden", cat 1922; "Sandalon", cat 1922.

FRANK TEA & SPICE CO., Cincinnati, OH: "Mazda", tm 1926/1926.

FRANKEL & SMITH INC., Boston, MA: "Franquelle", tm 1926/1926.

GEORGE FRANKS CO., St. Paul, MN: "Song Of Love", tm 1928/1927.

FRASER & CO., NY, NY: "Fraser's Cologne", tm 1952/1901.

W. & D. FRASER, Inverness, Scotland: "Culloden Moor", tm 1959/1957.

JOHN FREDERICS, NY, NY: "Crystal Arrow", tm 1935/1935; "The Golden Arrow", tm 1935/1935; "Good Afternoon", tm 1944/1943; "Good Night", tm 1944/1943; "Silver Arrow", tm 1935/1935; "Upper Level", tm 1945/1943.

WILLIAM D. FREEMAN, Cincinnati, OH: "Hiawatha", tm 1888/1888.

FRENCH, Philadelphia, PA: "Purity", tm 1906/1906; "Rose-Violet", tm 1906/1906.

FRENCH ART SILK CREATIONS, NY, NY: "d'Arsac", tm 1942/1941; "Prince Vezy", tm 1948/1945.

FRENCH BEAUTY PRODUCTS CO., INC., NY, NY: "Princess Mary", tm 1926/1926.

FRENCH PERFUMED PRODUCTS, INC., NY, NY: "Junonia", tm 1935/1934; "Touchdown", ad 1935.

FRENCH PERFUME CO., Pittsburgh, PA: "Artemis", tm 1925/1924.

FRENCH PERFUMERY CO., Johnstown, PA: "Cupid Kiss", tm 1925/1923.

FRENCH, RICHARDS, & CO., Philadelphia, PA: "Sweet Chimes", tm 1890/1889; "White Musk", tm 1890/1890.

LUDWIG B. FREY, NY, NY: "Silver Slipper", tm 1934/1933.

EUGENE FREZZATI, Paris, France: "Mademoiselle de Paris", tm 1954/1952.

FRIENDLY TIP CO., Chicago, IL: "Frentico", tm 1937/1927.

THE FRIES & FRIES CO., Cincinnati, OH: "Jeanne d'Arc", tm 1926/1926; "La Fête", tm 1926/1926; "Les Beaux Arts", tm 1926/1926.

ALICE HOWARD FRYE, Salem, MA: "Beau Brummel", tm 1887/1886.

GEORGES FUCHS LTD., NY, NY: "Oberon", tm 1949/1948.

FULLER BRUSH CO., Hartford, CT: "Blue Hedge", tm 1960/1959; "From A Misty Garden", tm 1962/1961; "Golden Accent", tm 1960/1959; "Leading Lady", tm 1957/1956; "Midnight Mood", tm 1961/1960; "Night Fire", tm 1961/1960; "So Different", tm 1963/1962; "The First Rose", tm 1961/1960; "Tracery", tm 1963/1962.

FULLER & FULLER, Los Angeles, CA: "Ardath", tm 1927/1924.

FUNEL, France: "Ciel de Cannes", tm 1963/1958; "Never On Sunday", tm 1962/1961; "Revanche", tm 1963/1962; "Tea For Two", tm 1963/1962.

FURMAN-WEILAND ASS. INC., NY, NY: "Jarice", tm 1936/1935.

GABILLA, Paris, France: "Ambre de Gabilla", cat 1922; "Ambre Merveilleux", cat 1922; "Bijou D'Amour", tm 1928/1928; "Bouquet de Gabilla", cat 1922; "Bruyere", Fr. ad 1926; "Chin-Li", Fr. ad 1925; "Chrysantheme", cat 1922; "Chypre", ad 1924; "Columbine", cat 1922; "Cordiality", cat 1922; "Dream For Two", ad 1940; "Fleur Du Jour", ad 1920; "Fleuri", cat 1922; "Foin Coupe", cat 1922; "Folle Passion", tm 1956/1910; "Foolish Virgin", ad 1940; "Fougere", cat 1922; "Glycine", Fr. ad 1926; "Heliotrope", Fr. ad 1926; "Hossegor", tm 1931/1929; "Jasmin", Fr. ad 1926; "L'Ambre", cat 1922; "La Bouquet", cat 1922; "La Vierge Folle", tm 1931/1910; "Les Jeux et les Ris", Fr. ad 1922; "Le Reve", cat 1922; "Le Succes", cat 1922; "Lilas", Fr. ad 1926; "L'intrigant", Fr. ad 1923; "Longchamp", tm 1931/1921; "Marguerites", cat 1922; "Mimosa", Fr. ad 1926; "Minne", tm 1931/1912; "Moda", tm 1931/1920; "Mon Chéri", tm 1931/1910; "Mon Talisman", tm 1928/1928; "Mousardises", tm 1931/1912; "Musardises", tm 1927/1912; "Muquet", Fr. ad 1926; "Musc du Tonkin", cat 1922; "Narcisse", Fr. ad 1926; "Opoponax", cat 1922; "Oui ou Non", tm 1939/1933; "Peau d'Espagne", Fr. ad 1922; "Petite Folie", Fr. ad 1922; "Pois De Senteur", Fr. ad 1926; "Pour Changer", ad 1920; "Quadrille", tm 1938/1938; "Rêve A Deux", tm 1937/1936; "Rose", Fr. ad 1926; "Sinful Soul", tm 1934/1933; "Tout la France", cat 1922; "Tout le Printemps", cat 1922; "Toutes Les Fleurs", Fr. ad 1926; "Vineuil", tm 1939/1933; "Violette", Fr. ad 1926; "Xantho", tm 1927/1911; "X Y Z", tm 1939/1932.

ANDREA GAIL, NY, NY: "Deep Orchid", tm 1958/1955; "Hi!", tm 1958/1956; "Orchid Mist", tm 1958/1955; "Spray of Orchids", tm 1958/1955.

GAL, Madrid, Spain: "Agua de Colonia Añeja", tm 1949/1917; "Alma", ad 1924; "Dens", tm 1949/1913; "Flores de Talavera", tm 1919/1917; "Heno de Pravia", tm 1949/1912; "Jardines de España", tm 1925/1923; "Marisol", tm 1949/1948; "Pravía Hay", ad 1924; "Talavera Flowers", ad 1924.

GALLI SALES CO., Brooklyn, NY: "Jean Gail", tm 1936/1936; "Polka dot", tm 1936/1936.

GAMBOA INC., NY, NY: "Should I?", tm 1942/1941.

AGUSTIN REYES GARCIA, Habana, Cuba: "Nuit Du Samedy", tm 1933/1930.

ROBERT W. GARDNER, NY, NY: "Lily D'Or", tm 1889/1889.

JULIUS GARFINKLE & CO., Washington, DC: "Heavenscent", tm 1924/1923.

GARRY & CO. INC., NY, NY: "Lavoscent", tm 1934/1933; "Stlyset", tm 1927/1927.

WILLIAM C. GARWOOD, Evanston, IL: "Kathryn", tm 1886/1886.

GASTON DE PARIS, NY, NY: "No Regrets", tm 1944/1944; "Toutes Saisons", tm 1941/1941.

JOHN D. GAUMER, Chicago, IL: "Te Amo", tm 1944/1939; "Temu", tm 1945/1940; "Tuba", tm 1945/1940.

GEORGES GAY, Colombes, France: "Gladys Pickford", tm 1930/1928.

FREDERIC GEILLE, Seine, France: "Bel Gazou", tm 1946/1942; "Pamphlet", tm 1946/1943.

GELLE FRERES, Paris, France: "Caprice de Fleurs", art 1923; "Etoile Noire", tm 1929/1927; "Nacréor", art 1912; "Noblesse Oblige", art 1910; "Nythis", tm 1926/1925; "Pour être Aimée", art 1911; "Seduction", tm 1924/1909; "Régina", tm 1925/1913.

GENERAL COSMETICS CORP., NY, NY: "Congratulations", tm 1930/1930; "Délassé", tm 1935/1935; "Je Plais", tm 1929/1929; "Louvet", tm 1929/1929; "Surrey House", tm 1935/1935; "Vouret", tm 1929/1929.

GENERAL PURCHASING CO., Paris, France: "Gossip", tm 1938/1937.

GENESEE COSMETICS CO., NY, NY: "Betty Brae", tm 1933/1933; "Yolande", tm 1947/1946.

HUGH GENSKE, Philadelphia, PA: "Aorist", tm 1946/1945; "Envoy", tm 1946/1945.

GEORGES INC., NY, NY: "Polonaise", tm 1946/1945.

GERARD BROTHERS, Nottingham, England: "Sobano", tm 1938/1919.

ANNE GERARDE: "Mistral", new 1927.

GERRE INC., NY, NY: "Jirré", tm 1927/1927.

GERVAIS, NY, NY: "June Rose", tm 1928/1922.

MAX GESELLSCHAFT, Dresden, Germany: "Biox", tm 1923/1909.

DOROTHY GIBSON, Brooklyn, NY; NY NY: "Baudelaire", tm 1948/1948; "Dunrovin", tm 1948/1947; "Gibson Girls", tm 1948/1947; "Impatient", tm 1948/1947; "I Remember Mama", tm 1950/1948; "Jusweetu", tm 1948/1947.

LEON W. GIELLERUP, Bronxville, NY: "Two Doves", tm 1929/1929.

EGBERT W. GILLETT, Chicago, IL: "Florentine", tm 1882/1882.

ANDRE GILLIER, Troyes, France: "Jildor", tm 1930/1929.

SAVONNERIE GILOT, Paris, France: "Brise d'Orient", tm 1921/1913.

GILVO CHEMICAL, Melbourne, Australia: "No. 7777", tm 1947/1942.

GIMBEL BROTHERS, NY, NY: "Gimay", tm 1924/1918; "Inviting", tm 1944/1943; "Pierre Jacoulet", tm 1930/1929.

MORIS GIMELSTEIN, Habana, Cuba: "Capricho de Mujer", tm 1941/1936.

J. GIRAUD FILS: "Bouquet Royale", cat 1922; "Dans Les Nues", cat 1922; "Fleur de Jasmin", cat 1922; "Fleur de Rose", cat 1922; "Japtis", cat 1922; "L'Oeillet", cat 1922; "Lysmina", cat 1922; "Mariana", cat 1922; "Mysteriose", cat 1922; "Odorantis", cat 1922; "Parfum Reve", cat 1922.

JULES GIRAUX, Rouen, France: "Gix", tm 1932/1920.

GIVENCHY, Paris, France; NY, NY: "Givenchy III", new 1970; "Le De Givenchy", ad 1965; "L'interdit", tm 1958/1957; "Monsieur de Givenchy", tm 1963/1959; "Rose Des Vents", tm 1959/1943; "Ysatis", new 1984.

GIVIEMME. (See GI. VI. EMME).

GUSTAVE GLATZER, NY, NY: "Lela

L'Avenay'', tm 1929/1927.

GLEBEAS IMPORTATION, NY, NY: "Adoration", ad 1916; "Finesse", tm 1925/1924; "Inspiration", ad 1915; "Maid of the Mist", tm 1924/1922; "Rosetone", tm 1924/1922; "Tic Toc", tm 1934/1934.

S. GLENBY'S SONS, NY, NY: "Jeanette", tm 1924/1924; "Joan", tm 1924/1924; "Tien", tm 1924/1924; "Tiltil", tm 1924/1924.

ALEXANDER GOBERT, Neuilly, France: "Miss Univers", tm 1955/1954.

GODET, Paris, France: "Divinité", Fr. ad 1924; "Jerusalem", art 1913; "Nuit D'Amour", tm 1925/1925; "Parfum d'Ambre", art 1911; "Parmi les Fleurs", Fr. ad 1924; "Petite Fleur Bleue", tm 1926/1921; "Sous-Bois", Fr. ad 1924; "Trésor De Jasmin", tm 1926/1911; "Tut-An-Kham", ad 1923; "Week-End", ad 1953.

GODISSART, Hollywood, CA: "Cette Nuit ou Jamais", tm 1932/1927; "Rhythme", tm 1937/1934.

TATIANA GODUNOV, Elmhurst, IL: "Snow Maiden", tm 1952/1947.

GOLDEN ARROW, NY, NY: "Cábalá", tm 1946/1944; "Diane", tm 1946/1944; "Duette", tm 1946/1944; "Hocus-Pocus", tm 1946/1944; "Jack of Clubs", tm 1946/1945; "Jack of Diamonds", tm 1946/1945; "Jack of Hearts", tm 1946/1945; "Jack of Spades", tm 1946/1945; "King of Clubs", tm 1946/1945; "King of Diamonds", tm 1946/1945; "King of Hearts", tm 1946/1945; "King of Spades", tm 1946/1945.

GOLDENBERG'S, Washington, DC: "Smart Set", tm 1927/1922.

GOLNAY, Paris, France: "Yapana", ad 1922.

GOLDSTEIN & LALL, NY, NY: "Sheherazade", tm 1940/1937.

HENRI S. GOMPES, NY, NY: "Mephisto", tm 1937/1936; "Opéra", tm 1931/1930.

GOODIER CO., Dallas, TX: "Personal Charm", tm 1932/1932.

GOODMAN CHEMICAL CO., Brooklyn, NY: "Silver Nymphe", tm 1934/1932.

L. E. GOODRICH, Los Angeles, CA: "La Dame Aux Camellias", tm 1931/1930.

GOODRICH DRUG CO., Omaha, NE: "Velvetina", tm 1915/1909.

GOSNELL & GOSNELL, London, England: "Cherry Blossom", tm 1885/1885.

DAVID E. GOTHE, NY, NY: "Voici", tm 1953/1952; "Voila", tm 1953/1952.

GOUBAUD OF PARIS, NY, NY: "Cha-Cha", tm 1957/1955; "Habibi", tm 1953/1952.

BARBARA GOULD, LTD., NY, NY: "10", tm 1933/1933; "No. 25", tm 1938/1933; "30", tm 1933/1933; "40", tm 1933/1933; "Bridge Set", ad 1934; "Collector's Choice", tm 1954/1953; "Exaltée", tm 1962/1961; "Garden Club", tm 1952/1951; "Garden Fragrance", cat 1950; "Lovers-Knot", tm 1948/1942; "Moon Struck", new 1947; "Nocturne", new 1952; "Skylark", tm 1940/1940; "Whimsical", tm 1954/1951.

GOURIELLI, NY, NY: "Bow Tie", tm 1942/1942; "Five O'Clock", tm 1947/1947; "Four Loves Have I", tm 1957/1954; "Fourth Dimension", new 1953; "Heart to Heart", tm 1947/1947; "Moonlight Mist", tm 1955/1944; "Something Blue", new 1943; "Tipsy", tm 1947/1947. (See also HELENA RUBINSTEIN)

MICHEL GOURLAND, Paris, France: "Lait de Cologne", tm 1936/1934.

ANDRE GOUTAL & CO., NY, NY: "Dudauvrai", tm 1927/1927.

GOYA, NY, NY: "Corvette", tm 1952/1951; "Let's Celebrate", tm 1951/1950; "Love Affair", tm 1961/1958; "Yachting", tm 1950/1944.

GRALENE, Chicago, IL: "Evening Star", ad 1935; "Mondel", ad 1935; "Nona", ad 1935.

GRANT CO., Sabina, OH: "Ta Wa Na", tm 1951/1950.

HENRY GRANT, Latrobe, PA: "Meta", tm 1939/1937.

GRASSE, France: "Christmas Bells", ad 1927.

A. GRAVIER (ALPHONSE GRAVIER), Paris, France; Neuilly, France; Seine, France: "Ambre Mysterieuse", cat 1922; "Aux Violettes", cat 1922; "Coeur de Poete", cat 1922; "Dans Les Bles", cat 1922; "Dely", cat 1922; "Hantige", art 1912; "Hotivia", cat 1922; "Jane Marnac", cat 1922; "Jardin de Mai", cat 1922; "Je Viens de Paris", tm 1928/1928; "Joie de Nice", cat 1922; "Kantia", cat 1922; "La Cascade", art 1926; "La Joie de Aimer", cat 1922; "L'envoûtement", art 1911; "Malice", cat 1922; "Me Voici", tm 1921/1914; "Orgueil de Reine", cat 1922; "Pluie D'Or", tm 1921/1906; "Secret de France", cat 1922; "Toute la Prairie", cat 1922; "Voltigy", cat 1922.

DOROTHY GRAY, Bloomfield, NJ: "Aureate", art 1957; "Beautiful Lady", cat 1922; "Bouquet Yvette", cat 1922; "Dee Gee", ad 1971; "Doritina", cat 1922; "Elation", tm 1937/1936; "Figurine", ad 1954; "Flutter", tm 1939/1938; "Lady in the Dark", ad 1941; "Nosegay", tm 1941/1938; "Savoir Faire", ad 1947; "Wedgewood", ad 1953.

GREAT AMERICAN LABORATORIES (GREAT AMERICAN TEA CO.), Brooklyn, NY: "Golden Key", tm 1925/1924.

LE GRELLIER, INC., NY, NY: "Volumes of Scentiment", tm 1929/1927.

GRENOVILLE, Paris, France; Asnieres, France: "Ambre Hindou", tm 1921/1910; "Avant L'été", tm 1932/1931; "Bluet", tm 1922/1910; "Byzance", tm 1926/1925; "Casanova", tm 1933/1929; "Chaine d'Or", cat 1922; "Charny", tm 1924/1912; "Cypria", ad 1926; "Dancing", tm 1934/1934; "Dans un Jardin", tm 1939/1933; "Eau de Cologne Chaine D'Or", tm 1921/1920; "Eau De Cologne Russe", tm 1921/1910; "Envoi De France", tm 1947/1945; "Jasmin Blanc", tm 1921/1910; "Le Rouge du Diable", tm 1933/1932; "Les Quatre Saisons", tm 1937/1936; "Muguet D'Orly", tm 1921/1910; "Nuit de Mai", tm 1921/1910; "Oeillet Fané", tm 1921/1910; "Rêverie", tm 1921/1910; "Rose Myrto", cat 1922; "Rosier du Roy", art 1913; "Un Piege", tm 1939/1936; "Victrix", art 1913; "Violette Grenoville", tm 1921/1910; "Violettes Russes", tm 1921/1910; "X X Vincent", art 1917.

GRES, Paris, France: "A", ad 1947; "Alix", new 1982; "Cabochard", tm 1962/1958; "Chouda", tm 1960/1959.

GRIET & CIA, Buenos Aires, Argentina: "Nantes 18", tm 1947/1940.

JACQUES GRIFFE, Paris, France: "Griffonnage", art 1949; "Mistigri", tm 1953/1950.

A. GRIMAUD, Nice, France: "Norante", tm 1935/1934.

GROSHUR TONIC CO. INC., NY, NY: "The New Yorker", tm 1931/1931.

JOHN LIPSCOMB GROSSMITH, London, England: "Bethrothal", tm 1895/1893; "Golden Still-Brand", tm 1919/1914; "Hasu-No-Hana", tm 1890/1887; "Phul-Nana", tm 1893/1890; "Shem-El-Nessim", tm 1907/1907; "Tsang-Ihang", tm 1923/1922.

NICOLE GROULT (COUTURE), Paris, France: "Le Bleau", ad 1928; "Le Rose", ad 1928.

GROVILLE SALES INC., NY, NY: "Truyu", tm 1934/1934.

GUCCI, Italy: "Parfum 1", ad 1972; "No. 3", new 1985.

GUELDY, Paris, France: "Antar", cat 1922; "Doux Songe", ad 1921; "Gotic", cat 1922; "La Closeric", cat 1922; "La Feuilleraie", Fr. ad 1920; "Le Bois Sacré", ad 1921; "Le Glycines", cat 1922; "Le Lyes Rouge", Fr. ad 1920; "L'Empyree", ad 1922; "Le Prestige", ad 1922; "Les Glycines", Fr. ad 1920; "Les Inmosees", cat 1922; "Le Triomphe", Fr. ad 1920; "Loki", Fr. ad 1920; "Mirage", Fr. ad 1929; "Sergy", tm 1923/1910; "Stellamare", cat 1922; "Vasthi", ad 1922.

GUENFAUX, Asnieres, France: "Aziadé", tm 1930/1920.

GUERLAIN, Paris, France: "A Travers Champ", new 1924; "Ai Loe", new 1905; "Après L'Ondee", tm 1923/1906; "Aroma Helio", cat 1922; "Atuana", tm 1952/1951; "Belle France", new 1892; "Bon Vieux Temps", new 1902; "Bouquet de Faunes", tm 1923/1923; "Cachet Jaune", ad 1937; "Candide Effleuve", ad 1924; "Chamade", new 1969; "Champs-Elysées", art 1904; "Chant D'Aromes", new 1962; "Chypre 53", new 1909; "Coque D'Or", tm 1938/1938; "Cuir De Russie", new 1875; "Cyprisine", new 1894; "Dawamesk", new 1942; "Dix Petales de Roses", new 1899; "Djedi", tm 1927/1927; "Eau Hegemonienne", new 1890; "Elixir de Guerlain", tm 1923/1923; "Excellence", new 1890; "Faëna", tm 1962/1961; "Fleur de Feu", tm 1949/1948; "Fleur D'Italie", new 1884; "Fleur Qui Meurt", new 1901; "Fol Arome", art 1912; "Fragrance", cat 1922; "Ger d'Espagne", cat 1922; "Guerlarose", ad 1930; "Guerlilas", ad 1930; "Guerlinade", tm 1923/1922; "Hegemonienne", art 1890; "Imperiale", tm 1923/1853; "J'Aimais Rosine", new 1900; "Jacinthe", cat 1922; "Jardin de Mon Curé", new 1895; "Jardins de Bagatelle", new 1983; "Jasmin d'Siam", cat 1922; "Jasmiralda", new 1917; "Jicky", new 1889; "Kadine", new 1911; "Kriss", tm 1945/1945; "La Violette de Madame", cat 1922; "Le Bon Vieux Temps", cat 1922; "Le Quai Aux Fleurs", tm 1950/1948; "L'Heure Bleue", tm 1944/1912; "Liu", tm 1929/1929; "Mi-Mai", new 1914; "Mitsouko", new 1919; "Mouchoir de Monsieur", new 1904; "Muguet", new 1873; "Nahema", new 1979; "Ne Moub Liez Pas", tm 1923/1923; "Ode", tm 1956/1955; "Parure", new 1975; "Pois De Senteur", new 1917; "Poudre Aux Ballons", tm 1923/1920; "Pour Troubler", new 1911; "Quand Vient L'Ette", new 1910; "Rococo A La Parisienne", new 1887; "Rue de La

Paix", tm 1924/1908; "Secret de Bonne Femme", tm 1923/1906; "Shalimar", tm 1926/1926; "Sillage", tm 1947/1907; "Skine", new 1885; "Sous Le Vent", tm 1935/1934; "Superdulci", tm 1923/1912; "Tsa-Ko", new 1898; "Une Rose", new 1908; "Vague Souvenir", new 1912; "Vega", tm 1937/1936; "Vera Nova", cat 1922; "Veritable Eau De Cologne", tm 1945/1875; "Verveine", ad 1936; "Vetiver", cat 1922; "Violette A Deux Sous", new 1936; "Violette de Madame", new 1904; "Viola Pourquoi", new 1900; "Vol de Nuit", tm 1932/1932.

MARCEL GUERLAIN, Paris, France: "8 et 9", tm 1927/1927; "Caravelle", tm 1927/1924; "Contes Choisis", art 1927; "Kadour", tm 1927/1923; "Masque Rouge", tm 1927/1925; "Pate D'Or", tm 1927/1924; "Pavillon Royal", tm 1927/1924; "Rolls Royce", tm 1930/1929.

GUERMANTES (CLAUDE CARON), Paris, France: "Allegretto", tm 1947/1938; "Le Temps Retrouvé", tm 1947/1944.

PEREZ GUERRA LTD, Los Angeles, CA: "Ajmir", tm 1945/1944; "Lama", tm 1944/1944.

JEANNE GUILLEAUMAUD, Nice, France: "Sorcière", tm 1939/1937.

LOUIS PIERRE GUILLON, Ivry-Sur-Seine, France: "Les Parfums de Montfort", tm 1940/1938; "Premeditation", tm 1939/1938; "Pretender", tm 1939/1938.

GUIMET, Paris, France; NY, NY: "Chypre", ad 1929; "Jasmin", ad 1929; "Les Pois De Senteur", ad 1928; "Multi-Fleurs", ad 1929; "Sweet Pea", ad 1929; "Tout Paris", ad 1929.

S. & G. GUMP, Honolulu, Hawaii: "Fern Lei", tm 1936/1935; "Hawaiian Night", tm 1936/1935; "Pikaki Lei", tm 1936/1935; "Plumenia Lei", tm 1936/1935.

HENRY GUSTIN, Saint Maur, France: "Montin", tm 1955/1954.

GWEN-AWY CO. (PAUL T. LAWRENCE), Cleveland, OH: "Bel Ayr", tm 1944/1944.

H. W. MFG. CO. INC., Bessemer, AL: "Flossy", tm 1931/1929.

HAARMANN-DE LAIRE-SCHAEFER CO., Marwood, NJ: "Iraldeine", tm 1903/1902.

AMEEN F. HADDAD, NY, NY: "Midhat Pasha", tm 1909/1909; "Napoleon's Cologne", tm 1895/1895; "Sultan's Bouquet", tm 1895/1894; "Sultan's Favorite", tm 1909/1909; "Young Turkey", tm 1909/1909.

HAHN DEPARTMENT STORES INC., Wilmington, DE: "Avona", tm 1932/1921; "Latour", tm 1932/1921.

WILLIAM H. HALL, NY, NY: "Companion", tm 1886/1886; "Sozodont", tm 1886/1877.

HALLE BROS. CO., Cleveland, OH: "Gossip", tm 1937/1937.

HALSTEAD SPECIALTIES CO., Oakland, CA: "Burning Blossoms", tm 1925/1924.

A. HAMBURGER & SONS, Los Angeles, CA: "La Cigale", tm 1894/1893.

HANSON-JENKS, NY, NY: "Halcyon Rose", ad 1918; "Ilys", cat 1922; "Many Flowers", cat 1922; "Natoma", tm 1912/1912; "Phyllis", cat 1922; "Snow Drop", cat 1922; "Springtime Symphony", cat 1922; "Violet Toilet Water", ad 1920.

HARAD, NY, NY: "Bright Stars", tm 1952/1944; "Gay Glitter", tm 1952/1944;

"Saint & Sinner", tm 1951/1944; "Stolen Heaven", tm 1952/1944.

HARBOUR ISLANDERS LTD., Bahamas: "Royal Lyme", tm 1959/1958.

HAREM PERFUME CO., NY, NY: "Salome", tm 1923/1923.

B. HARRIS CO., Los Angeles, CA: "Toujenais", tm 1943/1942.

HERBERT H. HARRIS, NY, NY: "Méchante", tm 1933/1933.

LOUIS R. HARRISON & CO., NY, NY: "Zaza", tm 1900/1900.

HART-ALBIN CO., Billings, MT: "Why Pay More", tm 1932/1931.

ELIZABETH HARTLEY, NY, NY: "Garden of Eden", ad 1945.

HARTNELL. (See EVYAN).

NORMAN HARTNELL, London, England: "In Love", tm 1953/1950.

HARZFELD'S, INC., Kansas City, MO: "Petticoat Lane", tm 1932/1932.

ANN HAVILAND (HAVILAND LABORATORIES), NY, NY: "Blue Hyacinth", tm 1950/1948; "Céleste", new 1939; "Daphne", art 1935; "First Love", tm 1944/1944; "Fleurs de Noel", tm 1959/1958; "Jasmin of the Night", tm 1950/1948; "Lily of the Valley", ad new 1939; "Perhaps", new 1939; "Purple Lilac", ad 1946; "Wood Violet", ad 1944.

HAWIN CO., Brooklyn, NY: "Bouquet Paradis", tm 1927/1926.

WILLIAM LEWIS HAYES, Atlantic City, NJ: "Wieayes", tm 1930/1918.

JANE B. HAYWARD, Babylon, NY: "Secrets", tm 1925/1924.

HEALODERM LABORATORIES, Fayetteville, NC: "Lejuven", tm 1927/1924.

JOHN J. HEALY, Far Rockaway, NY: "Shamrock", tm 1890/1889.

HEATHER CO., NY, NY: "Light Glow", tm 1927/1926; "Midnight Frolic", tm 1927/1925; "Or-Amber", tm 1923/1923; "Plastiko", tm 1923/1910; "Sunmade", tm 1923/1923.

CHARLES HEDDEN, NY, NY: "Lilac Echo", tm 1913/1912; "Rose Melody", tm 1912/1911; "Siren Lily", tm 1913/1911.

HEDDEN & EBERHARDT, NY, NY: "Indra", tm 1912/1910.

HEDLEY, Cleveland, OH: "Hedley 51", tm 1960/1956; "Ivre D'Amour", tm 1960/1956; "Noble 55", tm 1960/1956; "Paradis Perdu", tm 1960/1956.

JACQUES HEIM, Paris, France: "Shandoah", art 1960.

HEINRICH CHEMICAL, Minneapolis, MN: "Dedo", tm 1921/1920; "Jarvais", tm 1922/1920.

HELLER-DELTAH, NY, NY: "Ecstacy", tm 1931/1928; "L'Heure de Minuit", tm 1931/1928.

HELLMAN LABORATORY, St. Louis, MO: "Golden Princess", tm 1939/1939; "Indra", tm 1939/1938.

JACQUES HELM, Paris, France: "Ariane", tm 1953/1953; "J'Aime", art 1951.

HENNESSY, Paris, France: "Easter On Fifth Avenue", art 1931; "First Night At The Empire", art 1931; "Moonlight And Roses", art 1932; "New Year's Eve In Havana", art 1933; "Nuit Profonde", art 1931; "Serenata", art 1932; "Strictly Dishonorable", art 1932.

SIDNEY HENRY, NY, NY: "Chimère", tm 1943/1943; "La Sylphide", tm 1942/1940;

"Zodiac", tm 1942/1942.

HENSALKA PRODUCTS CO., NY, NY: "Ninotchka", tm 1945/1943.

HERAUD. (See D'HERAUD).

HERB FARM SHOP LTD., Elizabeth, NJ: "No. 37 Audley", tm 1948/1947.

JOSEPH HERMAN, NY, NY: "Venus Flacon", tm 1922/1921.

BAROUH HERMANOS, Paris, France; Habana, Cuba: "Jardin du Mystèrre", tm 1929/1928; "Merry Christmas", tm 1928/1926; "Nuit de Paques", tm 1928/1925.

HERMES, Paris, France: "Amazone", new 1974; "Calèche", ad 1962; "Doblis", ad 1956; "Parfume d'Hermès", new 1984.

HERMIONE, Glendale, CA: "Blue Note", tm 1947/1946.

HESS, Rochester, NY: "Arbor Violet", cat 1922; "Blush Rose", cat 1922; "Douxce", cat 1922; "Heather Bells", cat 1922; "Ideal Supreme", cat 1922; "Imperial Bouquet", cat 1922; "Indianola", cat 1922; "Japanotis", cat 1922; "Marlea", cat 1922; "Rochester Bouquet", cat 1922; "Spanish Beauty", cat 1922; "Yezzo", cat 1922; "Ziara", cat 1922.

HESSIG-ELLIS DRUG CO., Memphis, TN: "Beautibloom", tm 1925/1924.

GEORGE C. HESTER, Glendale, CA: "Brown Bomber", tm 1947/1946.

JANET HESTER, Hollywood, CA: "Acquisesce", tm 1946/1946; "Coax Me", tm 1946/1946; "Mamba", tm 1946/1946; "Three Little Words", tm 1946/1946.

THOMAS HETHERINGTON, Philadelphia, PA: "America's Laurels", tm 1907/1907.

HICKSON INC., NY, NY: "Heure D'Extase", tm 1925/1924.

A. J. HILBERT & CO., De Pere, WI: "Black Cap", tm 1928/1927; "De Luxe", tm 1904/1893; "Kismet", tm 1912/1897; "The Merry Widow", tm 1908/1908; "Revelation", tm 1918/1918; "Stolen Sweets", tm 1895/1894.

HARRIET HILL, Chicago, IL: "Remember Me", tm 1944/1937.

WARREN HILL, Boston, MA: "Nile Lily", tm 1887/1885.

HINDU INCENSE MANUFACTURING CO., Chicago, IL: "Chaunay", tm 1938/1936.

S. H. HIRSCH (SIDNEY HENRY), NY, NY: "Ambush", tm 1941/1941; "As You Like It", tm 1942/1941; "Gong", tm 1942/1941; "Honi Soit Qui Mal Y Pense", tm 1941/1941; "Priorité", tm 1942/1941; "Renouveau", tm 1942/1941; "Scentinel", tm 1942/1941; "Symbole", tm 1942/1941.

THOMAS G. HITT, Seattle, WA: "Fleurs des Indes", tm 1918/1917.

HOBE CIE, NY, NY: "Heavenly Body", tm 1944/1944; "The Night Before", tm 1944/1944; "Tu es a moi", tm 1930/1929.

ROBERT HOFFER, Detroit, MI: "June Bride", tm 1929/1921.

THEODORE HOFFMAN, NY, NY: "Soubise", tm 1927/1927.

W. R. HOLLINGSHEAD, Binghamton, NY: "Bingo Fragrance", tm 1920/1920.

HOLLYWOOD, INC., Dallas, TX: "Holly Voque", tm 1932/1931.

HOLLYWOOD BEAUTY PRODUCTS, Los Angeles, CA: "Aloma", tm 1927/1926; "Duano", tm 1927/1926.

HOLLYWOOD MARVEL PRODUCTS CO., Los Angeles, CA: "La Cherté", tm 1934/1928; "Song of the Flowers", tm 1932/1932.

HOLMAN SOAP CO., Chicago, IL: "Toketa", tm 1931/1910.

ARMAND HOLTZ, Paris, France: "Citiane", tm 1924/1923.

HOPPE & HOPPE, Chicago, IL: "Reddy", tm 1926/1925.

HORWITZ AND DUBERMAN, NY, NY: "The two of us", tm 1944/1944.

HOUBIGANT, Paris, France; NY, NY: "Abandon", tm 1932/1932; "A Demi Mot", tm 1932/1932; "Air Nouveau", tm 1946/1945; "Allegorie", tm 1932/1931; "Anneau D'Or", tm 1946/1945; "Au Bois", tm 1923/1923; "Au Loin", tm 1928/1928; "Au Matin", tm 1923/1923; "Autre Chose", tm 1932/1932; "Avant Premiere", tm 1932/1931; "Avante Scene", tm 1932/1931; "Bois Dormant", tm 1925/1925; "Boutade", tm 1936/1935; "Cadence", tm 1931/1931; "Celle Que Mon Coeur Aime", tm 1925/1925; "Chantilly", tm 1948/1940; "Chassé-Croisé", tm 1935/1935; "Chiberta", tm 1930/1930; "Ciao", new 1980; "Clé des Champs", tm 1933/1934; "Coeur De Jeannette", tm 1920/1899; "Consecration", tm 1931/1931; "Contraste", tm 1932/1932; "Couleur Du Temps", tm 1929/1929; "Country Club", ad 1936; "Croquis", tm 1932/1932; "Curiosité", tm 1925/1925; "d'Argent", cat 1922; "D'Argeville", art 1913; "Deci-Delà", tm 1930/1929; "Dedale", tm 1932/1931; "Dedicace", tm 1936/1936; "Demi-Jour", tm 1932/1929; "Desinvolture", tm 1932/1932; "Diapason", tm 1933/1932; "Dilettante", tm 1927/1927; "Dissonance", tm 1932/1932; "Dominante", tm 1931/1931; "Douce Illusion", tm 1923/1923; "Douce Quietude", tm 1930/1929; "Eau D'Houbigant", tm 1920/1899; "Eau Florale", tm 1938/1937; "Ebats", tm 1932/1932; "Echappée", tm 1932/1931; "Eden Roe", tm 1957/1956; "Emaux", tm 1931/1931; "En Butinant", tm 1923/1923; "En Sourdine", tm 1931/1931; "Entr' Acte", tm 1932/1931; "En Visite", tm 1923/1923; "Episode", tm 1931/1931; "Essence Rare", tm 1929/1928; "Etude", tm 1931/1931; "Evette", ad 1915; "Farandole", tm 1936/1936; "Faune & Flore", tm 1946/1945; "Festival", ad 1931; "Flatterie", tm 1923/1923; "Floraison Houbigant", tm 1932/1932; "Fougère Royale", tm 1920/1885; "Fraîcheur", tm 1928/1928; "Giroflée", ad 1915; "Grand Air", tm 1925/1925; "Halyard", tm 1957/1956; "Heureuse Surprise", tm 1926/1926; "Honeysuckle", ad 1938; "Incartade", tm 1936/1936; "Inconnu", tm 1921/1910; "Intermède", tm 1930/1929; "Interpretation", tm 1931/1931; "Jeux D'Orgue", tm 1931/1931; "La Belle Saison", tm 1924/1924; "La Fleur Bien Aimee", tm 1927/1927; "La Fleur Noble", tm 1926/1925; "L'Aile Du Rêve", tm 1930/1929; "La Nuit Tombe", tm 1935/1935; "La Rose France", new 1911; "L'Art De Plaire", tm 1928/1928; "Le Champ Des Oiseaux", tm 1923/1923; "Le Parfum Ideal", tm 1926/1900; "Les Heures Choisies", tm 1932/1932; "Le Temps Des Lilas", tm 1922/1921; "Lilac Time", tm 1940/1925; "L'ile De Beauté",

tm 1930/1930; "L'Oeillet Du Roy", tm 1921/1906; "Lyrisme", tm 1934/1934; "Magnolia", ad 1938; "Mes Dèlices", tm 1920/1920; "Mon Boudoir", tm 1921/1919; "Moulin Galant", tm 1923/1923; "Oeillet de Roy", cat 1922; "Parenthese", tm 1931/1931; "Peau d'Espagne", ad 1913; "Penny Merrill", tm 1953/1945; "Perseverance", tm 1946/1945; "Plein Eté", tm 1931/1931; "Premier Mai", tm 1921/1908; "Presence", tm 1933/1933; "Presentation", tm 1939/1939; "Princesse de Legende", tm 1925/1925; "Prophetie", tm 1931/1931; "Quelques Fleurs", tm 1920/1912; "Quelques Fleurs Refreshence", tm 1959/1955; "Quelques Violettes", tm 1920/1914; "Raffinée", new 1982; "Raffinements", tm 1928/1928; "Resonance", tm 1931/1931; "Ritournelle", tm 1931/1931; "Rose Ideale", cat 1922; "Royal Bouvardia", cat 1922; "Royal Fern", tm 1927/1927; "Sous La Charmille", tm 1946/1945; "Souverainete", tm 1926/1926; "Sports D'Eté", tm 1931/1931; "Sports D'Hiver", tm 1931/1931; "Subterfuge", tm 1931/1931; "Subtilité", tm 1923/1923; "Sur La Terre Endormie", tm 1926/1926; "Temps Nouveaux", tm 1926/1926; "Thunderbird", tm 1956/1955; "Tous-Deux", tm 1931/1931; "Town and Country", tm 1936/1936; "Transition", tm 1931/1931; "Transparence", ad 1940; "Trouvaille", tm 1936/1936; "Un Coin Du Ciel", tm 1927/1926; "Un Peu d'Ambre", tm 1921/1920; "Un Tour De Jardin", tm 1930/1929; "Versailles", tm 1937/1937; "Verte Foret", tm 1936/1936; "Vert Gazon", tm 1925/1925.

HOUSE OF FRAGRANCE, Bermuda: "Corsage", ad 1937; "Fidelwood", ad 1937; "Hibiscus", ad 1937; "Lily", ad 1937; "Wild Jasmine", ad 1937.

HOUSE OF GORDON, Chicago, IL: "Reminisce", ad 1945.

HOUSE OF HOLLYWOOD, Los Angeles, CA: "Furlough", tm 1942/1942.

HOUSE OF HUSTON, Coral Gables, FL: "Wicked Angel", tm 1951/1949.

HOUSE OF STUART, Newark, NY: "Caddenza", tm 1958/1944; "Massacre", tm 1960/1959; "Matinee", tm 1958/1957.

HOUSEHOLD UTILITIES CO., Chicago, IL: "Burselle", tm 1930/1928; "Les Fleurs Rendezvous", tm 1930/1929.

THE HOWELL CO., New Orleans, LA: "Hi-Qual", tm 1927/1926.

HOYT, NY, NY: "Apriculus", cat 1922; "Azira", cat 1922; "Elgecie", cat 1922; "Hoyt's Cologne", tm 1954/1868; "Hoyt's Dime Cologne", tm 1954/1882; "Locust Buds", cat 1922; "Marie", cat 1922; "Miolena", cat 1922; "Princess Violet", cat 1922; "Rose Supreme", cat 1922; "Some Flowers", cat 1922; "U-Ar-Das", cat 1922.

PEGGY HOYT, Paris, France; NY, NY: "Badinage", tm 1925/1925; "Flowers", tm 1920/1916; "Midsummer Night", tm 1925/1925; "Night Breeze", tm 1925/1925.

RICHARD HUDNUT, NY, NY: "Acrasia", tm 1920/1919; "Aimée", tm 1903/1902; "Angel Choir", tm 1947/1946; "Barcarolle", tm 1923/1923; "Blizzard", tm 1944/1944; "Bon Voyage", tm 1925/1925; "Cardinal", tm 1902/1902; "Champagne Taste", tm 1951/1950; "Charmed Circle", tm 1954/1954; "Chevron", tm 1932/1932;

"Chrysis", tm 1904/1904; "Cypresia", tm 1903/1902; "Deauville", tm 1924/1923; "Deauville Perfume Pats", tm 1927/1926; "Dream House", tm 1951/1949; "Drei Blumen", tm 1958/1957; "Du Barry", tm 1902/1900; "Elaine", tm 1912/1907; "Extreme", tm 1912/1895; "Extreme Violet", tm 1896/1895; "Fatale", tm 1961/1960; "Firebrand", tm 1946/1945; "Fleurs A Vous", tm 1924/1923; "Fragrance Frills", tm 1951/1950; "Frozen Champagne", tm 1948/1947; "Frozen Fragrance", tm 1951/1950; "Gemey", tm 1924/1923; "Gondola", tm 1925/1924; "Grand Gesture", tm 1948/1947; "Guys And Dolls", tm 1955/1954; "Harlequin", tm 1950/1949; "Heart Of The Heliotrope", tm 1912/1910; "Hudnutine", tm 1914/1893; "Indianotis", tm 1895/1895; "Kaleidoscope", tm 1950/1949; "La Pyramide", tm 1927/1927; "La Soirée", tm 1926/1926; "Le Debut", tm 1927/1927; "Le Rêve", tm 1904/1904; "Les Cascades", tm 1927/1927; "Magic Lantern", tm 1951/1949; "Maytime", tm 1924/1923; "Mitzi", tm 1924/1923; "Monalisa", tm 1903/1902; "Monkey Business", tm 1954/1954; "Mon Souvenir", tm 1925/1925; "Oh La La!", tm 1957/1957; "Perfume Jewels", tm 1954/1953; "Pet Fragrance", tm 1953/1952; "Phantom", tm 1895/1895; "Plaza", tm 1913/1913; "Pour Vous", tm 1924/1923; "Prediction", tm 1947/1946; "Primitive", tm 1946/1945; "Promenade", tm 1945/1944; "Richesse", tm 1928/1927; "Rose Of Omar", tm 1912/1911; "Rose Rosee", tm 1912/1910; "R. S. V. P.", tm 1936/1935; "Serenade", tm 1923/1923; "Seven Winds", tm 1957/1956; "Silhouette", tm 1923/1923; "Soul Of The Violet", tm 1912/1910; "Spring Song", tm 1923/1923; "Superba", tm 1912/1895; "Teak", tm 1937/1937; "Temple d'Amour", tm 1924/1923; "Three Flowers", tm 1923/1915; "Tout Mon Jardin", tm 1914/1914; "Tres Flores", tm 1929/1928; "Tres Gai", tm 1952/1948; "Twinkle Toes", tm 1954/1953; "Two Little Indians", tm 1955/1954; "Vanity", tm 1910/1910; "Veldt Blumen", tm 1903/1902; "Victorian Fragrances", tm 1954/1954; "Violet Sec", tm 1896/1896; "Violette Superba", tm 1896/1895; "Vogue", tm 1937/1902; "Watteau", tm 1920/1919; "Yadma", tm 1903/1902; "Yanky", tm 1898/1898; "Yanky Clover", tm 1948/1944; "Young Folks", tm 1956/1954.

HYMAN HUEBSCHMAN, Brooklyn, NY: "Chez-Ritz", tm 1929/1925; "Ritz Carlton", tm 1927/1926.

JEAN HUERRE, Seine, France: "Megeve", tm 1960/1950.

HUJARVIS, NY, NY: "Ambrette Napo", cat 1922; "Clos Joli", cat 1922; "Dionis", cat 1922; "Fleurance", cat 1922; "Javane", cat 1922; "Mon Secret", tm 1922/1921; "Rose Eternelle", cat 1922; "Son Envie", cat 1922; "Violane", cat 1922.

HUNTLEY, St. Thomas, Virgin Islands: "Raffia", tm 1963/1962.

LUCETTE HYDE, NY, NY: "Numéro 512", tm 1954/1953.

HYMAN & OPPENHEIM INC., NY, NY "Torcy", tm 1929/1928.

IBIS PERFUMER, NY, NY: "Golden Earrings", tm 1949/1948; "Parfum 69", tm

1945/1944.

ILLIDELA, Chicago, IL: "Moonlight Fragrance", ad 1930.

IMPERIAL CROWN, St. Louis, MO; Dallas, TX: "Amorilas", cat 1922; "Boketia", cat 1922; "Chantilly", cat 1922; "Hot House Rose", cat 1922; "La Tosca Bouquet", tm 1891/1890; "Lilacs of Sicily", cat 1922; "Marechal Neil Rose", cat 1922; "Parma Wood Violet", cat 1922; "Soul Kiss", cat 1922; "White Carnation", cat 1922.

IMPERIAL FORMULA, NY, NY: "Dawning", ad 1939; "Enchantment", ad 1939; "Moonlight", ad 1939; "Regal Splendor", ad 1938; "Twilight Meadows", ad 1939.

IMPRESSION PRODUCTS, Chicago, IL: "Grano", tm 1946/1940; "Kistic", tm 1945/1939.

INDIA INCENSE CO., Chicago, IL: "Fragrant Night", tm 1934/1932.

INDIANA MANUFACTURING CO., EVANS-VILLE, IN: "Black Gold", tm 1925/1925; 'Fayrins", tm 1925/1925.

INDIANAPOLIS DRUG CO., Indianapolis, IN: "Chrysanthemum Bouquet", tm 1894/1892.

IRICE, NY, NY: "Grape Cologne", ad 1939; "Piccadilly Perfume Bar", ad 1939; "Pineapple Cologne", ad 1940.

IRRESISTIBLE, NY, NY: "All Of Me", tm 1945/1945; "Bait", tm 1945/1945; "Flowerscope", tm 1939/1939; "Fragrant Showers', tm 1942/1941; "Fraternity", tm 1947/1946; "Gay Deceiver", tm 1940/1940; "Gingham", tm 1941/1941; "Hoot Mon", tm 1946/1945; "Lerner", tm 1947/1946; "Napoleon", tm 1947/1946; "Pace Maker", tm 1946/1945; "Persuasion", tm 1939/1939; "Place", tm 1946/1945; "Precious Moments", tm 1940/1940; "Princess Zina", tm 1939/1939; "Raphael", tm 1946/1945; "Rio Spice", tm 1940/1940; "Sacrifice", tm 1947/1946; "Special Reserve", tm 1946/1945; "Sugar And Spice", tm 1942/1941; "The Vogues Of 1890", tm 1940/1940; "Toughy", tm 1946/1945.

IRVING'S PERFUME SHOP, NY, NY: "L'Heure D'Amour", tm 1930/1929.

ISABEY, Paris, France: "Bleu de Chine", ad 1926; "D'Yvonne Printemps", Fr. ad 1929; "Grand Slam", ad 1935; "L'Ambre De Carthage", Fr. ad 1924; "La Perle d'Isabey", Fr. ad 1925; "La Route D'Emeraude", Fr. ad 1924; "Le Chypre Celtic", Fr. ad 1924; "Le Collier Isagey", tm 1927/1925; "Le Gardenia d'Isabey", Fr. ad 1928; "Le Jasmin d'Isabey", tm 1928/1924; "Le Lys Noir", Fr. ad 1924; "Mon Seul Ami", tm 1928/1928; "Rayon Vert", tm 1928/1927; "Sir Gallahad", Fr. ad 1924; "Sourire Fleuri", tm 1928/1926; "Tendres Nuits", tm 1945/1944.

MAURICE ISRAELVITZ, Philadelphia, PA: "Verne", tm 1934/1934.

IVEL PERFUMES, NY, NY: "Ivel", tm 1947/1946; "Mon Désir", art 1956.

J & J BEAUTY CULTURE, NY, NY: "Jano Jeanette", tm 1927/1927.

JACQUET, NY, NY: "Petit-Point", tm 1934/1931.

JACQUELINE, Paris, France: "Peut-Etre", Fr. ad 1927.

JADWIGA, Brooklyn, NY: "Cyganka", tm 1937/1928.

RICHARD JAECKEL. (See ARE-JAY).

JALAND PARFUM, NY, NY: "C'est Vous",

tm 1940/1936.

ALBERT F. JAMMES, NY, NY: "Exquisia", tm 1901/1891; "Léon Libert", tm 1897/1883.

JANAIN, NY, NY: "Aria", tm 1945/1944; "Esquilon", tm 1945/1944; "Etoile des Dunes", tm 1945/1944; "L'Aria", tm 1947/1945; "Milaya", tm 1945/1944; "Milonga", tm 1945/1944; "Pastorale", tm 1945/1944; "Searamouche", tm 1946/1945; "Vesperal", tm 1945/1944.

JANICE PERFUME CO., Sioux City, IA: "Sweet-Tulip", tm 1929/1928.

JANKEL, NY, NY: "Louvre", tm 1925/1924; "Secrets", tm 1925/1924.

JANVY INC., Brooklyn, NY: "Taffeta", tm 1934/1934.

JAPANESE PERFUME CO., NY, NY: "Wild Flower", tm 1923/1923.

JAQUET, NY, NY: "Fire Magic", ad 1942. (See FONTANIS).

JAQUET & MAXWELL, NY, NY: "Tanty", tm 1917/1904.

JARDIN, Paris, France; Boston, MA: "Jardin de Lilas Extract", ad 1920; "Jardin de Rose Extract", ad 1920.

JARNAC, Paris, France: "Shamly", ad 1951.

JASPY, Paris, France: "Buisson Fleuri", ad 1921; "Jasmin", ad 1924; "Kadoura", ad 1921; "Latulipe Noire", ad 1924; "Muscadin", ad 1921; "Myrodata", ad 1921; "Rose du Chemin", ad 1921.

JAYNARD, NY, NY: "Conservatoré", tm 1928/1928.

JAY-THORPE, NY, NY: "Jaytho", ad 1927; "Hearts & Flowers", new 1940.

JEAN GAIL, NY, NY: "Co-ed", ad 1939; "Forbidden Night", ad 1939.

JENEA, Rosemead, CA: "Deep South", tm 1962/1961; "Foggy Night", tm 1963/1961; "Westwind", tm 1963/1961.

JENNINGS MFG. CO., Grand Rapids, MI: "American Princess", cat 1922; "Chanticlere", cat 1922; "Clover Land", cat 1922; "Dorothy Vernon", tm 1920/1895; "Golden Genesta", cat 1922; "Lady Alice", tm 1919/1905; "Ma Joie", tm 1924/1923; "Maxie Rose", cat 1922; "Posy Garden", cat 1922; "Rose Saladin", tm 1919/1911; "Vernon", cat 1922; "Woodlawn Queen", cat 1922.

GEORG JENSEN, NY, NY: "Acacia", ad 1945; "Bal Blanc", tm 1956/1954; "Fire Orchid", tm 1946/1945; "Fleur Danoise", ad 1945; "Sachet Spray", tm 1945/1944.

ANDREW JERGENS, Cincinnati, OH: "Aloha", tm 1911/1883; "Atom Bomb", tm 1950/1948; "Ben Hur", tm 1919/1904; "Bijou de L'Air", tm 1928/1928; "Cupids Delight", tm 1947/1946; "Doris", tm 1915/1903; "Dream Stuff", tm 1959/1946; "Fleurs Dansantes", tm 1928/1928; "Jac-Lin", tm 1921/1921; "Lilac Frost", tm 1963/1962; "Marimba", tm 1945/1945; "Memoires de Paris", tm 1931/1931; "Morning Glory", tm 1948/1941; "Nifty", tm 1916/1916; "Ombres", tm 1929/1928; "Sorcery", tm 1960/1959; "White Veil", tm 1952/1951; "Zenobia", tm 1910/1909.

JEUNESSE, Paris, France: "Natacha", tm 1947/1945; "Nizami", tm 1947/1945; "Parfums Marny", tm 1947/1945; "Zortel", tm 1958/1953.

JEURELLE-SEVENTEEN, NY, NY: "Blue Field Flower", ad 1944; "Blue Grotto", tm 1941/1941; "Central Park", ad 1944;

"Constellation", tm 1942/1942; "Cool-ogne", tm 1938/1938; "English Boxwood", tm 1944/1944; "Gay Lothario", tm 1945/1945; "La Tuareg", tm 1944/1944; "Le Camelia de Jaurelle", ad 1933; "Le Cyclamen de Jeurelle", ad 1933; "Le Freesia de Jaurelle", ad 1933; "Le Gardenia De Jeurelle", ad 1936; "Le Mimosa de Jeurelle", ad 1933; "Libretto de Jeurelle", tm 1937/1936; "Limited Edition", 1937/1936; "Lisette", tm 1942/1941; "Old Vienna", tm 1938/1936; "Queen Alexandria", tm 1936/1936; "Rouvon", tm 1944/1938; "Saraband", tm 1945/1945; "Secret de Jaurelle", tm 1933/1933; "Seventeen", tm 1933/1928; "Six-Thirty", ad 1944; "Toreador", tm 1942/1941.

JOCEAU INC., Brooklyn, NY: "Narcisse Doré", tm 1925/1923.

ROBERT P. JOHNS, NY, NY: "Boutique", tm 1953/1952; "Peek-A-Boo", tm 1954/1952.

ABE JOHNSON, Waterbury, CT: "D'Vora", tm 1929/1928.

JOLIND, INC., NY, NY: "Duchess of Paris", tm 1934/1934. (see also: JOUBERT, BLUE WALTZ).

JOMARD: "Disguise", ad 1951; "Engaged", ad 1951.

JONAI INC., NY, NY: "Etes-Vous Décente?", tm 1944/1937.

T. JONES, Paris, France: "Jou-Jou", Fr. ad 1920; "Maida", Fr. ad 1920; "Veni-Vici", art 1917.

PAUL JONES, Beverly Hills, CA: "Flower Lei", tm 1936/1935; "Unconquered", tm 1948/1947.

JORDAN, MARSH, & CO., Boston, MA: "La Reine", tm 1892/1891; "Latour", tm 1892/1889.

JEAN JORDEAU INC., South Orange, NJ: "Camouflage", tm 1937/1937; "Zip", tm 1935/1912.

JORDELL MANUFACTURING CO., Philadelphia, PA: "Fleur de Jordell", tm 1926/1922.

JOUBERT, NY, NY; Jersey City, NJ: "Blue Garden", tm 1929/1927; "Blue Waltz", tm 1929/1927; "d'Anjou", tm 1929/1927; "Divine Kiss", tm 1934/1929; "Expectation", tm 1938/1937; "Imagination", tm 1938/1937; "Infatuation", tm 1938/1937; "Irresistible", tm 1934/1932; "Letty Lynton", tm 1934/1932; "Lip Lure", tm 1934/1932; "Mischief", tm 1937/1936; "Naughty", tm 1937/1937; "Oriental Lure", tm 1937/1937; "Singapore Nights", tm 1937/1937; "Sweet Moments", tm 1939/1939. (See also: JOLIND, BLUE WALTZ).

CHARLES JORDAN, Paris, France: "Un Jour", new 1982; "Vôtre", new 1978.

JOVOY, Paris, France: "Allez....Hop!", ad 1924; "Hallo Coco", ad 1924; "Severem", tm 1924/1923.

JULIANA UNDERWEAR CO., NY, NY: "Dream World", tm 1947/1944.

JUMELLES CORP., NY, NY: "Curtain Call", tm 1957/1957; "White Piqué", tm 1958/1957.

J. JUTRAS, Montreal, Canada: "Boule de Neige", tm 1924/1921; "Faites Moi Rever", tm 1924/1921.

KAIRY, NY, NY: "Air de Paris", tm 1930/1930; "Ladye Divine", tm 1928/1928.

KAMINIA PERFUMERY CO., Bombay,

India: "Dil-Bahar", tm 1923/1908.

JOHANNES KARBE, Berlin, Germany: "Jofrika", tm 1937/1932.

KAROFF, NY, NY: "Barette", ad 1939; "Cannonizer", ad 1941; "Canteen", tm 1943/1942; "Castanettes", ad 1937; "Celestial Dream", ad 1940; "Essence of Knowledge", ad 1940; "Love-All", ad 1941; "Old Acquaintance", tm 1944/1944; "Parfumes", ad 1939; "Perfume Blossoms", ad 1939; "Perfume Caravan", ad 1939; "Perfume of the Hour", ad 1940; "Private Number", ad 1942; "Queen's Court", ad 1940; "Sheltered Treasures", ad 1945; "Tap Cologne", ad 1939; "Topper", ad 1938; "Tri-Fumidor", ad 1940. (See also: STUART PRODUCTS CO.).

KATHRYN, Chicago, IL: "Amba-Aura", tm 1947/1946; "Arrogant", tm 1947/1945; "Beguiling Fuchsia", tm 1947/1945; "Dealer's Choice", tm 1948/1945; "Double Dare", tm 1947/1942; "Forever Amber", tm 1947/1945; "Furious", tm 1947/1945; "On Leave", tm 1947/1942; "Pouting", tm 1947/1945; "Rollicking", tm 1947/1945; "Whiteshirt", tm 1946/1945; "Wild Azalea", tm 1948/1945.

KAUFMAN-STRAUS, Louisville, KY: "Estelle", tm 1921/1905.

KATZ & BESTHOFF, New Orleans, LA: "Astra", tm 1914/1913; "Cleo", tm 1914/1913; "Electra", cat 1922; "Gladia", cat 1922; "Gloria", tm 1914/1913; "Golf Queen", cat 1922; "Jeu de la Reine", cat 1922; "Rose Minon", cat 1922; "Sphinx", tm 1914/1913; "Violet Imperiale", cat 1922.

HARRY KAYE, NY, NY: "Ambre Noir", tm 1924/1923; "Diables Bleus", tm 1924/1923; "Madouka", tm 1924/1924; "Nikylla", tm 1924/1924.

AUGUSTINE J. KENNEDY, Brooklyn, NY: "Mamzelle", tm 1927/1926; "Sparkle", tm 1927/1926.

BENJAMIN KENT, Paterson, NJ: "Silk City", tm 1889/1888.

ELIZABETH KENT, NY, NY: "Truly Yours", tm 1942/1942.

KERKOFF, NY, NY: "Djerkiss", tm 1908/1908; "Djer-Lady", tm 1928/1927.

KEYSTONE LABORATORIES, Memphis, TN: "Darboux", tm 1928/1928.

EMMETT M. KING, NY, NY: "Ballanciaga", tm 1945/1945; "Forever Amber", tm 1945/1945.

THOMSON KINGSFORD, Oswego, NY: "Regina Boquet", tm 1887/1886; "Oriental", tm 1887/1886.

KINGHILL LABORATORIES, NY, NY: "Career", tm 1941/1941; "Design", tm 1945/1944; "Gazette", tm 1941/1941; "Posh", tm 1946/1945.

F. KINGMAN & CO., Sacramento, CA: "Narcissus de Oriente", tm 1926/1926.

KIRBY'S PRODUCTS, Union, SC: "Happy Hearts", tm 1941/1941.

KISLAV (GANTS BUSCARLET), Paris, France: "6½", tm 1955/1954; "Kislav", ad 1955.

BEN KLEIN, Chicago, IL: "Me", tm 1924/1923.

GEBRUDER KLEINER, Berlin, Germany: "Cosa", tm 1957/1954; "Metroberlin", tm 1957/1955; "Renommée", tm 1963/1961.

SIMON KLEINKRAMER, NY, NY: "Elise", tm 1941/1940; "Turelle", tm 1941/1940.

H. & G. KLOTZ, Paris, France: "A La Corbeille Fleurie", tm 1925/1886; "Lilas de France", tm 1925/1890.

KNIZE & COMP., Paris, France: "The Knize Ten", tm 1936/1931.

WM. T. KNOTT CO., INC., NY, NY: "Beau-Knot", tm 1939/1931.

HARRY D. KOENIG, NY, NY: "1776", tm 1936/1936; "Martha Washington", tm 1927/1922.

FRANK KOENIGSBERGER, NY, NY: "Approach", tm 1940/1940.

WALTER F. KOKEN, St. Louis, MO: "Kosan", tm 1938/1919.

KOLYNOS CO., New Haven, CT: "Nalqiri", tm 1926/1925.

KONDAZIAN, Paris, France: "Fibi", tm 1927/1926.

LEROY H. KORB, Newark, NJ: "Barbara Lee", tm 1938/1932.

KREMOLA CO. INC., Chicago, IL: "Alice Blue Gown", tm 1936/1936.

KRESGE DEPARTMENT STORE INC., Newark, NJ: "Merlay", tm 1931/1930.

S. H. KRESS & CO., NY, NY: "Fonda", tm 1925/1925.

WILLIAM KROPFF, NY, NY: "No. 25", tm 1917/1917.

ROBERT L. KROUSE, Colorado Springs, CO: "d'Arell", tm 1927/1926.

J. P. KRUSE, Minneapolis, MN: "Castle", tm 1924/1920.

KUTNER AN HEITEL, NY, NY: "Roslyn", tm 1925/1920.

KYLE COSMETIC, Hollywood, CA: "Brise D'Amour", tm 1957/1956; "Tryst", tm 1945/1944.

LA CHARMA CO., Tampa, FL: "Aggravating Papa", tm 1940/1937; "Ding Dong Daddy", tm 1940/1937; "4 Leaf Clover", tm 1940/1938; "Pretty Mama", tm 1939/1938; "Two Time Mama", tm 1940/1937.

LA CIE REVE, NY, NY: "Midream", tm 1931/1928.

LA COLLA (JOSEPH LA COLLA), Brooklyn, NY: "Broadway Rose", tm 1923/1920.

LA DORE, Paris, France: "Lily of the Valley", cat 1923; "Narcissus", cat 1923; "Trailing Arbutus", cat 1923; "White Rose", cat 1923.

LA FLEUR LABORATORIES, Cleveland, OH: "Juvenis", tm 1925/1912.

LA FLOREAL PARFUM (HARY A. SIMON), Los Angeles, CA: "d'Arnel", tm 1946/1945; "Jasmine de Luxe", tm 1946/1940; "Night of Love", tm 1946/1935; "Pampered", tm 1945/1945; "Violet Time", tm 1946/1945.

LA FRANCE TOILET GOODS CO. INC., NY, NY: "Narcisse Ambre", tm 1926/1924; "Springtime", tm 1926/1926.

LA LETE, Paris, France; NY, NY: "Narcisse", ad 1925.

LA PERLE, Paris, France: "Perles Fines", tm 1922/1909.

LA SALLE PRODUCTS, INC., St. Paul, MN: "Cinderella", tm 1927/1926; "Collejet", tm 1926/1926; "Collejet Girl", tm 1927/1927; "Evolution", tm 1925/1925; "Femme de Nuit", tm 1927/1926; "Par", tm 1929/1929; "Truso", tm 1926/1926.

LA VALLIERE, New Orleans, LA: "Alluré", tm 1923/1914; "Ambrose", cat 1922; "Cape Jasmine", cat 1922; "Chan-Dra-Kan-Ta", cat 1922; "Desiree", tm 1923/1914; "Fantasie", cat 1922; "Fleur de Mai", cat 1922; "Golden Narcissus", tm 1928/1924;

"Grand Duke Jasmine", cat 1922; "Lilas de Louis XIV", cat 1922; "Mystique", cat 1922; "Ravise", tm 1929/1920.

LACASSIAN LABORATORIES, St. Louis, MO: "Coeur de L'Araby", tm 1926/1917.

RENEE LACOSTE, Detroit, MI: "Duchess of Windsor", tm 1937/1937; "Happy Landing", tm 1955/1951; "Lovingly Yours", tm 1948/1945; "Souvenir", tm 1955/1939.

LADD & COFFIN. (See LUNDBORG).

LADY GREY PERFUMERY, Boston, MA: "777", tm 1893/1893; "Algonquin", tm 1893/1893; "Toroco", tm 1891/1891.

LADY KNIZE, Paris, France: "Lady Knize", ad 1954.

LAGERFELD, Paris, France: "Chloé", new 1975; "K. L.", new 1982.

JOHN LAHOUD, Paris, France: "Fontenac", tm 1959/1958.

SERGE J. J. LAKHOVSKY, NY, NY: "Zig-Zag", tm 1944/1944.

CHARLES LALANNE, Paris, France: "Fraisy", tm 1924/1916.

LANCASTER, Monte Carlo: "Mademoiselle de Paris", ad 1958.

LANCHERE, Chicago, IL: "Blue Rose", tm 1947/1912; "By Candlelight", ad 1940; "Carillon", ad 1940; "Colonial Tradition", tm 1940/1940; "Gardenia", ad 1937; "Jasmine", ad 1937; "Lavender", ad 1937; "Lilac", ad 1937; "Naturelle", ad 1937; "Rose Geranium", ad 1937.

LANCOME, Paris, France: "Bel Automne", tm 1951/1947; "Bocages", tm 1946/1935; "Chiyat", ad 1969; "Climat", ad 1969; "Conquête", tm 1938/1935; "Cuir de Lancome", tm 1949/1947; "Eau de Senteur de Lancôme", tm 1952/1948; "Envol", ad 1958; "Fleches", tm 1946/1938; "Galateis", tm 1951/1942; "Kypre", tm 1948/1935; "Lait Des Hesperides", tm 1950/1942; "Lancôme d'Abord", tm 1958/1957; "La Vallee Bleue", tm 1946/1943; "Lavandes", ad 1954; "Magie", tm 1954/1949; "Magie Noire", new 1978; "Marrakech", tm 1947/1942; "Minlys", tm 1949/1945; "Nutrix", tm 1946/1935; "Qui Sait", tm 1946/1946; "Seul Trésor", tm 1955/1954; "Tendres Nuits", Fr. ad 1935; "Tressor", ad 1953; "Trophee Lancome", new 1982; "Tropiques", Fr. ad 1935.

LANCRY, Paris, France: "Bacchanale", ad 1946; "Guess", ad 1946; "Nous Deux", ad 1946; "Tango", ad 1946.

LANDER, NY, NY: "Black Orchid", tm 1940/1940; "Black Panther", tm 1963/1942; "Cave Man", tm 1943/1943; "Dorothy Deanne", tm 1940/1937; "Dorothy Reed", tm 1948/1937; "Emily Paige", tm 1950/1948; "Forbidden Secret", tm 1943/1943; "Golden Apple Blossom", tm 1948/1947; "Golden Corsage", tm 1949/1947; "Golden Gardenia", tm 1948/1947; "Movie Star", tm 1935/1935; "Pixie", tm 1954/1917; "Romantic Days", tm 1940/1939; "Samezi-Soir", tm 1952/1950; "Stolen Secret", tm 1943/1943; "The Untamed Perfume", tm 1944/1943; "Tiki", tm 1944/1943.

MAURICE J. LANGDON, Boston, MA: "Langdeau", tm 1923/1922.

LANGLOIS. (See UNITED DRUG CO.).

LANIER: "Folie de Minuit", ad 1955.

LANOLIN PLUS COSMETICS INC., Chicago, IL: "Plus Grande", tm 1951/1928.

LANSELLE PARFUMEUR, Paris, France:

"Banco", tm 1946/1938; "Cou Cou", tm 1946/1942; "Forcing", tm 1946/1941; "Martingale", tm 1946/1941; "Sans Atout", Fr. ad 1936.

LANVILLE, Paris, France: "Murmures", art 1939.

LANVIN, Paris, France: "Arpège", tm 1931/1927; "Clair de Jour", new 1983; "Crescendo", tm 1939/1939; "Eau de Lanvin", tm 1949/1946; "L'Ame Perdue", tm 1931/1928; "My Sin", tm 1934/1923; "Pétales Froissés", tm 1931/1928; "Prétexte", tm 1937/1937; "Prodige", tm 1949/1928; "Rumeur", tm 1934/1934; "Scandal", tm 1931/1931; "Spanish Geranium", tm 1951/1938; "Vétyver", new 1966.

TED LAPIDUS, Paris, France: "Envol", new 1981.

LARAY COSMETICS, Newark, NJ: "Elusive", tm 1945/1936.

L'ARGENE, NY, NY: "Le Couturier", tm 1958/1951; "Lis'n-Dear", tm 1957/1951; "Your Grace", tm 1958/1955.

LARIMORE LABORATORIES, INC., NY, NY: "Lari", tm 1926/1925.

LARKIN, Buffalo, NY: "Modjeska", tm 1944/1895.

GUY LAROCHE: "Drakkar Noir", new 1982; "Fidji", new 1966; "J'Ai Osé", new 1977.

LAS, Los Angeles, CA: "California Exotics", tm 1947/1942; "Play", tm 1947/1946.

LASCOFF LABORATORIES, NY, NY: "Golden Anniversary", tm 1950/1948.

ESTEE LAUDER, NY, NY: "Aliage", new 1972; "Aramis", new 1964; "Beautiful", new 1985; "Cinnabar", new 1978; "Private Collection", new 1972; "White Linen", new 1978; "Youth-Dew", tm 1955/1951.

LAUREN LIMITED, Toronto, Canada: "Sky Garden", tm 1947/1945.

LAUTIER FILS, Paris, France: "Bouquet Evangeline", tm 1886/1885; "Edelweiss", tm 1883/1872; "Maybells", cat 1922.

LAWRENCE CO., Laguna Beach, CA: "Strictly Tailored", tm 1948/1948.

LAWRENCE INC., Philadelphia, PA: "Une Fleur", tm 1927/1926.

F. & R. LAZARUS & CO., Columbus, OH: "Marianne", tm 1938/1938.

LAZELL, NY, NY; Newburgh, NY: "As-The-Petals", ad 1916; "Bellwood Flora", cat 1922; "Bocadia", cat 1922; "Cloth Of Gold", cat 1922; "Clover Buds", cat 1922; "Coeur de Fleur", cat 1922; "Coronaria", cat 1922; "English Ideal", cat 1922; "Hispania", tm 1895/1894; "Irisinia", tm 1888/1887; "Japanoda", cat 1922; "Lily of the Valley", ad 1916; "Massatta", tm 1913/1913; "Meadow Lily", tm 1893/1892; "Mignonette", ad 1916; "Narcissa", tm 1926/1923; "Perpetua", cat 1922; "Persian", tm 1883/1883; "Queen Isabella", tm 1893/1893; "Redwood", tm 1874/1874; "Rosalia", tm 1888/1887; "Rose Petals", ad 1916; "Samurai", cat 1922; "Valley Rose", cat 1922; "White Rose of Ceylon", cat 1922.

LE BLUME, NY, NY; Paris, France: "Chypre", ad 1924; "Jasmin", ad 1924; "Narcissus", ad 1924; "Rose", ad 1924; "Violette", ad 1924.

LE CERT, Milwaukee, WI: "Dating", tm 1947/1946; "Dreams Come True", ad 1946; "Secretly Yours", ad 1946.

LE CLAIRAC, Habana, Cuba: "Forbidden Love", tm 1936/1934; "Kismaju", tm 1936/1936; "Nuit Espagnole", tm 1936/1934.

CECILE LE DUC, Rochester, NY: "Aero Club", tm 1941/1940; "Cecile D'Avril", tm 1941/1940; "Xardia", tm 1941/1940.

LE GALION, Neuilly, France; Paris, France: "Bourrasque", tm 1946/1937; "Brumes", tm 1946/1937; "Cub", tm 1954/1953; "Eau Noble", new 1972; "Frac", tm 1955/1949; "Gardenia Le Galion", ad 1937; "Jasmin Le Galion", ad 1937; "Mégara", new 1978; "Shake-Hands", tm 1946/1937; "Snob", new 1952; "Sortilege", tm 1946/1937; "Whip", tm 1954/1953.

LE MAIRE PERFUMEUR INC., Chicago, IL: "Cereus", tm 1926/1924.

ELIZABETH LE MERDY, Vincennes, France: "Euphorie", tm 1947/1941.

JULIETTE ADOLPHINE LE RAY, Neuilly, France: "Nuit Des Rois", tm 1947/1943.

LE SONIER, Boston, MA: "Atlantis", tm 1947/1932.

LEADING PERFUMES & CHEMISTS INC., NY, NY: "Cartel", tm 1933/1920; "Pan-American", tm 1940/1939.

GERMAINE LECOMTE, Paris, France: "Soir de Fête", tm 1948/1946.

MARCEL LEDUC, Rochester, NY: "Boo", tm 1945/1944.

MARTHA LEE, Waco, TX: "Spicy Bouquet", tm 1946/1940.

PEARL LEESE, NY, NY: "Minx", tm 1945/1944; "Rigadoon", tm 1944/1944.

LEFCOURTE COSMETICS (ALBERT LEFCOURTE), NY, NY: "Cover Girl", tm 1943/1943; "Fleur d'Albee", tm 1945/1943.

LEFFLER MFG. CO., NY, NY: "Perfection", tm 1906/1905.

LEGENDRE, Los Angeles, CA: "Arreté", tm 1946/1946; "Clishay", tm 1946/1946; "Woo", tm 1947/1945.

ORIZA L. LEGRAND, Paris, France; NY, NY: "Breath Of Sping", tm 1927/1926; "Camélia du Nile", ad 1929; "Chypre Mousse", Fr. ad 1920; "Déja Le Printemps", tm 1924/1922; "Fin Comme l'Ambre", art 1913; "Jasmin d'Asie", art 1914; "Kadidja", cat 1922; "Le Bon Ton", tm 1924/1923; "Marions-Nous", ad 1928; "Muguet Fleuri", Fr. ad 1920; "Oeillet de la Reine", Fr. ad 1920; "Ouarda", Fr. ad 1920; "Rose du Roi", Fr. ad 1920; "Soleil de Minuit", tm 1932/1932; "Venise", tm 1926/1925; "Violette Fleur", Fr. ad 1920; "Violettes Du Czar", tm 1932/1862; "Zelmis", art 1913.

LEHN & FINK, NY, NY: "Bloomfield, NJ: "Be Mine", tm 1943/1943; "Columbus", tm 1890/1889; "Cordovan", tm 1946/1945; "Daredevil", tm 1942/1941; "D G", tm 1948/1933; "Elka", tm 1889/1889; "Estrellita", tm 1943/1942; "Figurine", tm 1954/1953; "Flower Mart", tm 1950/1949; "Hidden Charm", tm 1957/1956; "In The Pink", tm 1946/1943; "Lady In The Dark", tm 1941/1941; "Matchmaker", tm 1954/1945; "Music At Midnight", tm 1945/1945; "Pinafore", tm 1944/1941; "Play House", tm 1957/1956; "Red Letter", tm 1945/1942; "Ruby Fragrance", tm 1946/1945; "Savoir Faire", tm 1948/1947; "Turquoise", tm 1956/1955; "Wedgwood", tm 1953/1952; "Young Look", tm 1957/1948; "Young Time", tm 1945/1945. (See also: TUSSY; LESQUENDIEU).

LEIGH (SHULTON), NY, NY: "Ambar Nile", tm 1923/1923; "America", tm 1923/1923; "Bainaqua", tm 1925/1925; "Boquet Supreme", tm 1926/1910; "Desert Flower", ad 1947; "Dulcinee", tm 1926/1919; "Heartbeat", ad 1943; "Lady Leigh", tm 1929/1929; "Lochinvar", tm 1930/1930; "Man Fashion", tm 1930/1930; "Poetic Dream", tm 1930/1930; "Resplendent", tm 1930/1930; "Risque", tm 1926/1926; "Rose Marechal", cat 1922; "Sublime", tm 1930/1930; "Virginia Clover", cat 1922.

BENJAMIN LELAND & CO., St. Louis, MO: "Vivani", tm 1927/1925.

LECIEN LELONG, Paris, France; Chicago, IL: "A", ad 1928; "B", ad 1928; "C", ad 1928; "N", ad 1928; "J", ad 1928; "Abra Ca Dabra", tm 1944/1943; "Baguette", tm 1951/1929; "Balaiza", tm 1947/1946; "Balalaika", tm 1939/1939; "Big Moment", tm 1951/1950; "Cabochon", tm 1943/1942; "Cachet", ad 1949; "Camelot", tm 1950/1949; "Carefree", tm 1940/1939; "Carrousel", tm 1946/1935; "Castel", tm 1940/1940; "Cologne Of The Hour", tm 1953/1952; "Coolmist", tm 1941/1941; "Double Life", tm 1951/1950; "Duvetyn", tm 1937/1937; "Edition Limitée", new 1951; "Elle Elle", tm 1948/1937; "Falbalas", tm 1935/1935; "Fan Fare", tm 1935/1935; "Flacon de Sac", tm 1937/1936; "Flippant", tm 1939/1938; "French Lavender", ad 1935; "Grand Bouquet", tm 1949/1933; "Havoc", tm 1945/1944; "Hearsay", tm 1950/1949; "High Time", tm 1952/1950; "Honeysuckle", ad 1938; "Impromptu", tm 1937/1937; "Indiscret", tm 1941/1935; "Ingenue", tm 1936/1936; "Jabot", tm 1939/1939; "Joli-Bouquet", ad 1953; "Les Fleurs de Lucien Lelong", tm 1941/1934; "Les Plumes", tm 1939/1938; "Lilac", ad 1938; "Magnolia", ad 1938; "Mimosa", ad 1938; "Mon Image", tm 1933/1933; "Nicole", tm 1941/1938; "Opening Night", tm 1935/1934; "Orgueil", tm 1947/1946; "Papotage", tm 1945/1945; "Passionnement", tm 1940/1940; "Penthouse", tm 1934/1934; "Petits Fours", tm 1951/1949; "Philtre d'Amour", tm 1938/1937; "Round Trip", tm 1950/1949; "Sahara", tm 1948/1947; "Sextet", tm 1942/1942; "Sirôcco", tm 1948/1934; "Sweet Pea", ad 1938; "Taglio", tm 1945/1945; "Tailspin", tm 1940/1940; "Take Two", tm 1952/1951; "Tempest", tm 1948/1942; "Ting-A-Ling", tm 1950/1949; "Tout-Le-Long", tm 1927/1925; "Travel Pac", tm 1951/1936; "Turbulent", tm 1945/1944; "Whisper", tm 1945/1932.

LEMLER'S DRUG STORES (HARRY LEMLER), Baltimore, MD: "Fairy Bloom", tm 1927/1927.

G. LEMOINE, Paris, France: "Pour Moi Seule", Fr. ad 1928.

LENEL, Dallas, TX; NY, NY: "Bellezza", ad 1953; "Caressant", ad 1956; "Frosted Cologne", tm 1950/1944; "One Moment", tm 1950/1944; "Private Affair", tm 1953/1950; "Scent Sampler", tm 1951/1949; "Sublime", tm 1951/1950; "Trifling", tm 1944/1944.

LENGYEL, Dover, DE; NY, NY: "Gift Of An Empress", tm 1936/1936; "Impératrice Catherine", tm 1925/1924; "Imperiale Russe", tm 1936/1924; "Julika", tm

1928/1928; "Parfum Imperial", ad 1936.
LENIEF (COUTURE), Paris, France: "Devine?", art 1925.
LENORE PERFUME, Brooklyn, NY: "La Ronele", tm 1928/1927.
LENTHERIC, Chicago, IL; Paris, France; NY, NY: "A Bientot", tm 1931/1930; "Adam's Rib", tm 1954/1953; "Aeolian", tm 1926/1906; "Air De France", tm 1961/1960; "All Stars", tm 1955/1954; "Ambre Mousse", tm 1924/1912; "Anchors Aweigh", tm 1941/1941; "Anticipation", tm 1937/1937; "Ardans", cat 1922; 'Asphodèle", tm 1929/1928; "Atyche", tm 1924/1912; "Au Fil De L'eau", tm 1931/1924; 'Bal Masque", tm 1936/1936; "Band Box", tm 1941/1941; "Bataille de Fleurs", tm 1942/1942; "Beige", tm 1943/1941; "Belle Inconnu", cat 1922; "Beyond", tm 1946/1946; "Birds In A Gilded Cage", tm 1940/1940; "Birds Of A Feather", tm 1941/1941; "Black Sunlight", tm 1947/1945; "Blind Date", tm 1941/1940; "Cabaña", tm 1936/1935; "Caravan", tm 1938/1938; "Carnation", ad 1936; "Center Of Attraction", tm 1947/1946; "Cheops", cat 1922; "China Poblana", tm 1946/1946; "Clandestine", tm 1934/1934; "Cloak Of Night", tm 1938/1938; "Coeur De Paris", tm 1924/1912; "Coffret De Ma Poupée", tm 1924/1924; "Confetti", tm 1941/1939; "Critics' Choice", tm 1951/1948; "Daisy Chain", tm 1940/1940; "Dame en Noir", cat 1922; "Dark Brilliance", tm 1947/1946; "Deep End", tm 1946/1945; "Desir Princier", cat 1922; "Ditty Fox", tm 1941/1941; "Don Quijote", tm 1947/1946; "Durbar", tm 1938/1937; "Dykil", tm 1936/1935; "Escapade", tm 1934/1934; "Espionnage", tm 1937/1937; "Exposition", tm 1939/1939; "Feu Froid", tm 1946/1946; "Feu Sacré", tm 1945/1945; "Fleurs Helene", cat 1922; "Fleurs Polonge", cat 1922; "Folk Dance", tm 1942/1942; "Forêt Vierge", tm 1928/1928; "Formidable", tm 1946/1946; "Fougere Orchidee", cat 1922; "Gaieté", tm 1940/1939; "Galaxy", tm 1953/1953; "Gardenia De Tahiti", ad 1936; "Gay Bird", tm 1961/1960; "Gendarme", tm 1948/1948; "Heart Throb", tm 1941/1941; "Hell-Bent", tm 1941/1941; "High Tension", tm 1953/1953; "Home Spun", tm 1936/1935; "Iceberg", tm 1940/1940; "Icicle", tm 1951/1950; "Ingenue", cat 1922; "Jasmine Orkidee", cat 1922; "Jeanina", tm 1940/1939; "Jeune Fille", tm 1940/1940; "Kubla Khan", tm 1945/1944; "La Dame En Noir", tm 1924/1910; "La Feria", tm 1924/1912; "La Mien", cat 1922; "La Passant, cat 1922; "La Prenant", cat 1922; "Le Pirate", tm 1928/1928; "Le Triangle De Fleurs", tm 1939/1939; "Lilas Orkidee", cat 1922; "L'Intuition", tm 1935/1935; "Little Slam", tm 1942/1941; "Lotus D'or", tm 1924/1924; "Mavourneen", tm 1939/1939; "Mazurka Russe", tm 1937/1936; "Mimosa De Nice", tm 1924/1912; "Miracle", tm 1925/1924; "Mi Vida", cat 1922; "Mon Reve", cat 1922; "Muguet d'Altesse", cat 1922; "Musketeer", tm 1956/1955; "Nilus, cat 1922; "Numéro 12", ad 1933; "Numero Douze", tm 1931/1931; "Occasion", tm 1946/1946; "Orkidee", cat 1922; "Pale Black", tm 1948/1945; "Parachute", tm 1946/1945;
"Per Alta", cat 1922; "Persistence", tm 1934/1934; "Philine", cat 1922; "Picnic', tm 1940/1940; "Pink Party", tm 1940/1940; "Plaid", tm 1937/1937; "Princess Mary", cat 1922; "Quint-Essence", tm 1941/1938; "Rampant", tm 1946/1946; "Ransom", tm 1944/1944; "Realization", tm 1937/1937; "Red Lilac", ad 1958; "Repartee", tm 1950/1949; "Réunion", tm 1946/1944; "Ripple", tm 1961/1958; "Risque Tout", tm 1936/1935; "Rose des Rose", cat 1922; "Royal Caprice", tm 1924/1912; "Scotch Mist", tm 1936/1935; "Sec Marguerite", cat 1922; "Secret Fanchon", cat 1922; "Seersucker", tm 1945/1945; "Shanghai", ad 1936; "Simpatico", tm 1946/1945; "Skylark", tm 1940/1939; "Small Talk", tm 1946/1946; "Smoke", tm 1938/1938; "Sometime", tm 1946/1946; "Soon", tm 1938/1938; "Sourire de France", tm 1924/1924; "Sous-Zéro", tm 1941/1941; "Stepping Out", tm 1949/1948; "Tanbark", ad 1941; "Three Silent Messengers", tm 1934/1934; "Tombola", tm 1942/1942; "Tomorrow", tm 1939/1939; "Trouble", tm 1946/1945; "Turban", tm 1948/1946; "Turf", tm 1935/1934; "Tweed", tm 1936/1935; "Vagabond", tm 1935/1935; "Vieille France", tm 1941/1939; "Violette Orchidée", tm 1924/1912; "Vivid Black", tm 1947/1946; "Voom", tm 1946/1946; "Wildfire", tm 1941/1941.
LEON, Paris, France: "Lucky Scents", tm 1924/1924.
LEONARD, Paris, France: "Eau Fraiche", new 1974; "Fashion", new 1970; "Tamango", new 1977.
LERYS, Paris, France; Long Island, NY: "Belle Jolie", Fr. ad 1922; "Le Presentoir", ad 1926; "Lucidité", ad 1928; "Or Bruni", tm 1926/1924; "Pour Blonde", art 1927; "Pour Brune", art 1927.
LEONID DE LESCINSKIS, NY, NY: "Charmanka", tm 1947/1946; "Eau de Fleurs", ad 1944; "No. 9", ad 1944; "Reine de Nuit", tm 1940/1940.
LESQUENDIEU, Paris, France: "Flo", tm 1925/1923; "Optimiste", tm 1951/1948; "Pinoflor", tm 1926/1926; "Remember Me", ad 1939. (See also: TUSSY, LEHN & FINK).
ROBERT LEURENT, Paris, France: "Tendre Accord", tm 1947/1944.
LEVER BROTHERS, Port Sunday, England; NY, NY: "Coral", tm 1898/1893; "Dreamy", tm 1953/1952; "Happy Time", tm 1953/1952; "Night Letter", tm 1953/1952; "Private Wire", tm 1953/1952; "Q-Tol", tm 1925/1925; "State Secret", tm 1953/1952; "Sunbeam", tm 1889/1885; "Sunshine", tm 1889/1884; "Wedding Ring", tm 1953/1952; "Why Talk?", tm 1953/1952.
MAURICE LEVY, NY, NY: "Honoré Payan", tm 1932/1854; "Phenomenal", tm 1945/1945.
GEORGE B. LEWIS, Oxford, NY: "Lomerita", tm 1926/1925.
FRANCOIS LIBISCH, Paris, France: "Amado", tm 1924/1922; "Lytée", tm 1923/1901.
LIEBERT DISTRIBUTORS, NY, NY: "Cross My Heart", tm 1942/1942.
LILI, Bermuda: "Easter Lily", ad 1940; "Eve", ad 1939; "Moon Mad", ad 1941; "Oleander", ad 1940; "Passion Flower", ad 1940; "Wild
Jasmine", ad 1940.
ADOLF D. LINDEMANN, NY, NY: "Florette", tm 1920/1915; "Michoice", tm 1920/1915.
JOSEPH S. LINDEMANN, NY, NY: "De Linet", tm 1927/1921.
LINETTI, Venice, Italy: "Notte Di Venezia", tm 1959/1948.
LINK'S LABORATORIES, Dallas, TX: "Mary Elizabeth", tm 1928/1928.
LINNEA PERFUMES, Chicago, IL: "Lucia Night", tm 1947/1944.
LIONCEAU, Paris, France: "Brise D'Arabie", tm 1925/1925; "Brise des Indes", tm 1926/1925; "Chanson D'Automne", tm 1925/1925; "Flor de España", tm 1924/1923; "La Saison des Fleurs", tm 1925/1925; "Le Fleuve Bleu", tm 1925/1925; "Le Temps Des Fleurs", ad 1924; "Lune de Venise", tm 1928/1928; "Nuit D'Egypte", tm 1925/1925; "Pierre Precieuse", tm 1928/1927; "Poème Arabe", ad 1928; "Place De L'Opéra", tm 1925/1925; "Premiéres Fleurs", tm 1926/1925.
NINA DE LISLE (ELIZABETH NORRIS), NY, NY: "Heartstrings", tm 1947/1947.
LEONARD E. LISNER, NY, NY: "Petites Ondes", tm 1945/1936; "Serenade", tm 1944/1923.
LISSAR, San Pedro Makati, P. I.: "Première Nuit", tm 1940/1937.
LITTLE PRINCESS PRODUCTS, NY, NY: "My Little Princess", tm 1950/1945.
ROBERT G. LITTLES, NY, NY: "Beau Tarte", tm 1929/1928.
HERMAN LOEB & CO., NY, NY: "Armant Perfumes", tm 1889/1888.
GUSTAV LOHSE: "Gloriantes", art 1942.
LOKI, Yonkers, NY: "Loki", ad 1951.
G. LOMBARD, Paris, France: "Alydea", tm 1924/1922.
J. L. LOMBARDO CO., Buffalo, NY: "Amourette", tm 1927/1907; "Gailis", tm 1927/1907.
LONDON HOUSE, NY, NY: "Bathes", tm 1938/1933; "Toddy", tm 1937/1937.
LONTREL, Chicago, IL: "Sertine", tm 1955/1954.
LORD & TAYLOR, NY, NY: "J'en Réve", tm 1927/1927; "L'Esprit Du Printemps", tm 1927/1927.
L'OREAL, Paris, France: "Chromo", tm 1956/1953; "Clarissima", tm 1962/1960; "Elnett", tm 1962/1959; "Flone", tm 1962/1960; "Imédia", tm 1951/1950; "L'Oréaline", tm 1926/1926; "Orealor", tm 1956/1953; "Reclair", tm 1962/1960; "Régé", tm 1956/1952.
LORENZ, Toledo, OH: "East Orange, NJ: "Triumph", tm 1901/1900; "Lotus Lilly", 1889/1887; "Wild Grape Blossom", tm 1894/1891; "Mountain Mist", tm 1885/1885; "Angel Flower", tm 1885/1885; "St. Trelody Pink", tm 1886/1883; "Lady Claire", tm 1888/1887.
LORIE, Los Angeles, CA: "Adrienne", tm 1948/1927.
L'ORLE, NY, NY: "Argentina", ad 1940; "Craftsman", tm 1946/1946; "Doeskin", 1946/1941; "Embroidery", tm 1946/1946; "Fiesta", ad 1940; "Goldcraft", tm 1946/1946; "Gold Flask", tm 1947/1946; "It's A Date", ad 1944; "Landscape", tm 1947/1946; "Libido", ad 1941; "Lodorante", tm 1951/1938; "My Nemesis", ad 1944; "Pinbuds", tm 1952/1948; "Scenario", ad 1940;

"Silvercraft", tm 1946/1946; "Silver Flask", tm 1947/1946; "Sportswoman", tm 1948/1941; "Wine, Women, And Song", 1940/1938.

LORNA-JEAN, Jackson Heights, NY: "Coy", tm 1958/1956.

LORRAINE CO., Denver, CO: "Fleur de Lorraine", tm 1924/1915.

LORRAINE, Paris, France; NY, NY: "Rhée de Jaunesse", tm 1924/1924.

JEAN-PASCAL LORRIAUX, Paris, France: "Monastère", tm 1948/1946; "Oh! Oui Paris", tm 1950/1946; "Oh! Please", tm 1948/1946; "Parfumeur Masque", tm 1948/1942; "Radar", tm 1950/1945.

LOS ANGELES SOAP CO., Los Angeles, "Cosmic Ray", tm 1937/1937; "Kolandol", tm 1937/1937; "Nadji", tm 1933/1932.

LOUIS PHILIPPE, Paris, France; NY, NY: "Angélus", tm 1921/1915; "Je Pense A Vous", tm 1923/1915; "La Midinette", tm 1924/1923; "L'Extase Des Fleurs", tm 1923/1915.

AUDREY LOUISE, NY, NY: "Accolade", tm 1941/1939; "Décolleté", tm 1941/1939.

LOURNAY, Paris, France; NY, NY: "Fleur de Mignon", ad 1920; "Fleur Vivant", ad 1920; "L'Ile d'Amour", ad 1921; "Qui Sait", ad 1920; "Vivante", tm 1924/1923.

WILLIAM H. LOVELAND CO., NY, NY: "Jardin D'Amour", tm 1936/1935; "Speedee", tm 1937/1935.

LOVINS LABORATORIES, Denver, CO: "La Viola", tm 1953/1932.

LOVLITONE CO., Detroit, MI: "Lovli", tm 1931/1929.

WILLIS H. LOWE, Boston, MA: "Delight Kiss", cat 1922; "Mary Elizabeth", cat 1922; "Mexican Lily", cat 1922; "Parma Violet", cat 1922; "Rose Claire", cat 1922; "Sweet Orchid", cat 1922; "Violet Adorable", cat 1922.

LOWELL CO., NY, NY: "Primrose", tm 1925/1921.

LUBIN, Paris, France; NY, NY: "Abronia", cat 1922; "Acacia", cat 1922; "Ahazar", cat 1922; "Alpine Rose", cat 1922; "Amaryllis", tm 1925/1922; "Ambrosie", cat 1922; "Arabella", tm 1923/1920; "Au Soleil", tm 1925/1912; "Azalea", cat 1922; "Benjoin", cat 1922; "Bergamote", cat 1922; "Bouquet de Papillons", ad 1919; "Bouquet d'Osborne", cat 1922; "Bouquet d'Oxford", cat 1922; "Bouquet du President", cat 1922; "Bouquet du Printemps", cat 1922; "Bouquet Pompadour", cat 1922; "Bridal Bouquet", cat 1922; "Brise de Mai", cat 1922; "Cachemere Bouquet", cat 1922; "Californian Flowers", cat 1922; "Camelia", cat 1922; "Canelle", cat 1922; "Caprice de la Mode", cat 1922; "Cassie", cat 1922; "Cedrat", cat 1922; "Chevreveuille", cat 1922; "Chypre", tm 1923/1920; "Citronella Rose", cat 1922; "Clavel", cat 1922; "Crème Kissiah", tm 1925/1912; "Damask Rose", cat 1922; "Darling Bouquet", cat 1922; "Delice de Boudoir", cat 1922; "Diapris", cat 1922; "Douce France", tm 1923/1920; "Duchesse", cat 1922; "Edelweiss", cat 1922; "Eglantine", cat 1922; "Empress of India", cat 1922; "Enigma", tm 1925/1898; "Epidor", tm 1923/1912; "Esterhazy Bouquet", cat 1922; "Eva", tm 1923/1920; "Evening Star", cat 1922; "Ferveur", tm 1947/1928; "Fleurs d'Amanadier", cat 1922;

"Fleurs de France", cat 1922; "Fleurs des Indies", cat 1922; "Friendship's Offering", cat 1922; "Fumée de Lubin", tm 1951/1934; "Genets d'Espagne", cat 1922; "Gin Fizz", tm 1954/1947; "Girofflee", cat 1922; "Heather Bells", cat 1922; "Hedyosmia", cat 1922; "Heno", cat 1922; "Honey Moon", cat 1922; "Iris Ambre", cat 1922; "Jacinthe", cat 1922; "Jardin Secret", Fr. ad 1929; "Jonquille", cat 1922; "Kigriz", cat 1922; "Kiravi", cat 1922; "Kismet", art 1921; "Kiss Me Quick", cat 1922; "Lacdor", tm 1925/1922; "Lierami", cat 1922; "Lilliput", cat 1922; "Lis", cat 1922; "L'Ocean Bleu", tm 1929/1926; "Love Me Dear", cat 1922; "Lubinette", tm 1923/1912; "Madreselva", cat 1922; 'Magda", tm 1923/1921; "Marechale", cat 1922; "Mekong", ad 1936; "Mignardises", cat 1922; "Mille Fleurs", cat 1922; "Monbrosia", tm 1925/1925; "Monjoly", ad 1928; "Morning Star", cat 1922; "Mousseline", cat 1922; "Mugualba", cat 1922; "Musc", cat 1922; "Myrtida", cat 1922; "Narcisse du Japon", cat 1922; "Nard", cat 1922; "Newport Breeze", cat 1922; "Nube", cat 1922; "Nuit de Longchamp", tm 1949/1935; "Ocean Spray", cat 1922; "Oeillet Soleil", cat 1922; "Ouvrez Moi", ad 1937; "Pampres d'Or", cat 1922; "Parfum de la Coeur", cat 1922; "Perfect Gem", cat 1922; "Pervenche", cat 1922; "Pomeliane", cat 1922; "Pot Pourri", cat 1922; "Quatre-Fleurs", cat 1922; "Reine de Pres", cat 1922; "Rose de Chine", cat 1922; "Sain Foin", cat 1922; "Sierra Morena", cat 1922; "Sola Mia", tm 1925/1898; "Souvenir de Lubin", tm 1925/1925; "Star Of India", cat 1922; "Suzette", cat 1922; "Suzon", cat 1922; "Tanit", cat 1922; "Thimelia", cat 1922; "Tibi", cat 1922; "Tubereuse", cat 1922; "Upper Ten", cat 1922; "Vanille", cat 1922; "Verveine", cat 1922; "Violalba", cat 1922; "Violette des Aples", cat 1922; "Wall Flowers", cat 1922; "Wedding Bouquet", cat 1922; "West End", cat 1922; "Widow Machree", cat 1922.

CHARLES LUBRECHT, Brooklyn, NY: "Circassian", tm 1878/1878; "Imperial", tm 1877/1877.

LUCKY HEART, Memphis, TN: "Be Happy", tm 1942/1941; "Belldine", tm 1940/1920; "Good Luck", tm 1944/1916; "This Is Love", tm 1947/1946.

LUCKY STRIKE PERFUMERIES, NY, NY: "Miss Lucky", tm 1953/1949; "Mr. Lucky', tm 1953/1949.

LUCIEN. (See DERMAY).

LUNDBORG, London, England; NY, NY: "Admiration", tm 1920/1919; "Arborea", tm 1917/1905; "Ayli", tm 1897/1897; "Cake Walk", tm 1904/1903; "Cher Ami", tm 1918/1916; "Clovera", ad 1902; "Corsage", tm 1890/1890; "Dearie", tm 1907/1907; "Edeol", tm 1904/1903; "Fairy Frond", tm 1897/1897; "Fascination", tm 1928/1874; "Golden Jasmine", ad 1902; "Goya Lilly", tm 1888/1888; "Helio-Violet", tm 1890/1890; "Jockey Club", tm 1934/1877; "Lure", tm 1919/1918; "Nada", tm 1892/1892; "Oct 1, 1918", tm 1920/1918; "Opal", tm 1890/1890; "Pixie", tm 1918/1917; "Princess Ada", tm 1899/1899; "Sakura", tm 1918/1910; "Stolen Secret", ad 1944; "Sweet Spray", tm 1890/1890;

"Tally Ho", tm 1934/1878; "Trianon", tm 1895/1895; "Violet Dew", tm 1900/1900.

JULIO M. LUPUS, NY, NY: "Valencia", tm 1927/1926.

LUXANA, Barcelona, Spain: "Czarda", tm 1948/1943; "Gran Mogol", tm 1948/1942.

LUXOR, Chicago, IL: "American Beauty", ad 1940; "Bouquet", ad 1942; "Krasny", tm 1927/1926; "La Richesse", ad 1942; "Vision", ad 1942.

LUYNA, France: "Cadeau de Paris", tm 1930/1928; "Chanson d'Ete", ad 1922; "Fleur Ardente", ad 1922; "La Violette", ad 1923; "Le Jasmin", ad 1923; "Maya", ad 1923.

LUYTIES, St. Louis, MO: "Florja", tm 1915/1915; "Frivole", tm 1916/1915.

LUZIERS, Kansas City, MO: "Faithfully Yours", tm 1948/1946; "Poppaea", tm 1959/1938; "Shiraz", 1959/1938; "Si-Bella", tm 1958/1958; "Sumalee", tm 1962/1960.

LYBOZO (SIMON KLEINKRAMER), NY, NY: "Dutch Flowers", tm 1943/1941; "Old Delft", tm 1943/1941.

LYDES, Paris, France: "Bibelot", ad 1927; "Dans La Chevelure", Fr. ad 1928; "Diamant Noir", Fr. ad 1926; "La Fleur Du Lac", Fr. ad 1928; "L'Ambre Des Pagodes", new 1919; "L'Heure Du Baiser", Fr. ad 1925.

LYNETTE, NY, NY: "Apple Blossom", cat 1944; "Blue Sapphire", ad 1944; "Conspiracy", tm 1945/1945; "Fantasia", ad 1943; "Hampshire", tm 1946/1945; "Manito", tm 1945/1943; "Notorious", tm 1945/1944; "Shangrila", ad 1943; "Spellbound", tm 1944/1943; "Spice Bouquet", cat 1944.

LYSANDRA, NY, NY: "Bouquet", ad 1945; 'Carnation", ad 1945; "Neika", ad 1945.

LYTEE, Paris, France: "Amado", Fr. ad 1923.

J. E. MCBRADY (FULLER PRODUCTS CO.), Chicago, IL: "Gay Love", tm 1956/1955; "Gift Of Love", tm 1956/1948; "Perfect Night", tm 1958/1946; "Velvet Love", tm 1957/1956.

B. W. MCCANDLESS, Los Angeles, CA: "Fay-Mus", tm 1912/1912.

R. H. MCDONALD DRUG CO., NY, NY: "Odora", tm 1888/1888.

IRVING MCEWEN, Omaha, NE: "Cadet Club", tm 1927/1926; "Preshus", tm 1927/1927; "Twilight", tm 1927/1927.

MCKESSON & ROBBINS, Bridgeport, CT: "Aluria", cat 1922; "Canterbury House", tm 1936/1936; "Florise", cat 1922; "Khama", cat 1922; "Lynx", tm 1947/1946; "Rosemary", tm 1941/1941.

JOHN N. MCMATH, Larchmont, NY: "Bridal Night", tm 1930/1930; "Kis-Again", tm 1930/1929; "Wild Flowers Of Old England", tm 1961/1942.

M. G.: Kadour", ad 1927; "Kesako", ad 1927.

MACY. (See SUZY).

R. H. MACY & CO., NY, NY: "Amrita", tm 1924/1923; "Old Herbary", tm 1939/1938; "Scarlet', tm 1939/1939.

MADAME HELENE TOILET CO., Chicago, IL: "Garden de Marie", cat 1922; "Lotus Blossom", cat 1922; "Safrinar Fleurs", cat 1922; "Violet La France", cat 1922.

MADAME ISEBELL'S TOILET MFG. CO., Chicago, IL: "Ambree Exquisite", cat 1922; "Cupid's Kiss", cat 1922; "Destiny", cat 1922; "Favorite Bouquet", cat 1922; "Orchard Blossom", cat 1922; "Southern

Nights", cat 1922; "Tweetie Dear", cat 1922; "Udearie", cat 1922; "Viviani", cat 1922.

MAIN STREET TRADING, NY, NY: "Embrace Me", tm 1946/1944.

MAINBOCHER, NY, NY: "Djinn", tm 1950/1949; "Jardin Blanc", tm 1950/1947; "White Garden", tm 1949/1947.

MAISON CHOPARD CO., NY, NY: "Indolence", tm 1945/1944.

MAISON DE LUPO, Brooklyn, NY: "Love Bait", tm 1955/1953; "Royal Touch", tm 1954/1953.

MAISON DE PARIS, NY, NY: "A Jamais", tm 1930/1930.

MAISON D'OR, NY, NY: "Fleur D'Or", tm 1926/1925.

MAISON MENDESSOLLE, San Francisco, CA: "Fontainbleau Royal", tm 1925/1924.

MAJESTIC PERFUME CO., NY, NY; "Nashville, TN: "American Beauty", tm 1891/1889; "Van Winkles", tm 1892/1891.

MALVY, NY, NY: "Demi-Parfum", tm 1940/1939; "Phenomena", tm 1939/1939; "S'il Vous Plait", tm 1939/1939.

EMILIENNE MANASSE, Paris, France: "Un Peu De Vous", tm 1927/1926.

MANDEL BROTHERS, Chicago, IL: "Poujol", tm 1914/1912.

G. MANDELBAUM & CO., NY, NY: "Rhea Bouquet", tm 1890/1889.

MANFORD PHARMACAL, St. Louis, MO: "Living Flowers", tm 1924/1920.

LEO MANN & CO., Boston, MA: "Secret Garden", tm 1950/1940.

MANNING CO. (PAUL MANNING), West Springfield, MA: "Istar", tm 1928/1923; "Istarol", tm 1928/1922.

MAYBELLE MANNING, NY, NY: "Co Co", tm 1926/1923.

MANSON, Chicago, IL: "Casbah", tm 1943/1943; "Kiss And Tell", tm 1943/1943; "Misbehaving", tm 1943/1943.

MAQUESA, Chatham, NJ: "Fleurinda", tm 1959/1958.

MARCEAU, Paris, France; NY, NY: "Ambre Noir", ad 1925; "Baiser de Colombine", tm 1924/1922; "Damayanti", tm 1925/1924; "Diables Bleus", ad 1925; "Koura", tm 1916/1916; "Lilas", ad 1925; "Madouka", ad 1925; "Narcisses de Nikylla", ad 1925.

MARCEL. (See MARCEL RAFFY).

CHARLES MARCHAND, NY, NY: "Suspense", tm 1939/1938.

L. MARCHANDISE, Paris, France: "Cosmydor", tm 1886/1884.

MAREVA, NY, NY: "Appeau", tm 1956/1954.

RICHARD MARIANN, Chicago, IL: "Lady Connis", tm 1945/1944.

MARICATTE ET CIE: "Red Rose", cat 1922; "Treko", tm 1917/1897; "White Heliotrope", cat 1922.

MARIE DE FRANCE LABORATORIES INC., NY, NY: "Rojane", tm 1926/1925.

MARILYN SHOPPE, Rye, NY: "Cairo Loot", tm 1951/1946; "Dream Stuff", tm 1950/1946.

MARINELLO, La Crosse, WI: "Arvel", cat 1922; "Blue Ameryl", tm 1924/1923; "Egyptian Lily", cat 1922; "Idalia", cat 1922; "Marinello Girl", cat 1922; "Nardys", cat 1922; "Vic", cat 1922.

MARIO & FREDERICK INC., NY, NY: "Patrician", tm 1929/1919.

ALEXANDRA DE MARKOFF (MARTIN DE BOTELITO), NY, NY: "Alexandra de Markoff", ad 1939; "Spring Goddess", tm 1940/1940; "Tiara", ad 1955; "Virgin Flower", tm 1940/1940; "Water Nymphs", tm 1940/1940; "Woodland Shrine", tm 1940/1940.

MARLY, Paris, France; "NY, NY: "Adagio", ad 1932; "Flambeau de Marly", tm 1935/1934; "Gardenia", ad 1930; "Jasmin de France", ad 1930; "Lilas", ad 1930; "Lutétia", ad 1930; "Muguet", ad 1930; "Oeillet de France", ad 1930; "Parfum Impérial", ad 1930; "Rêve Aimé", ad 1930; "Rose de Frnace", ad 1930; "Swagger", tm 1934/1934; Tendresse", ad 1930; "Violette de France", ad 1930; "Vous et Mois", ad 1930.

MAROMAY: "Bal de Tete", ad 1954.

MARQUAY, Paris, France: "Coup De Feu", tm 1958/1957; "Elected", tm 1952/1951; "Le Couturier", tm 1956/1953; "Prince Douka", tm 1952/1951; "Rock And Rolls", tm 1957/1956; "The Chosen One", tm 1958/1957.

MARQUES DE ELORZA, Paris, France; NY, NY; "Newark, NJ: "Aperitiff", tm 1954/1951; "Argentina", ad 1929; "Bleu-Blanc", ad 1929; "Legion D'Honneur", ad 1929; "Maitresse", ad 1929; "Marche Nuptiale", tm 1953/1929; "Ming Jade", tm 1959/1955; "Spring Madness", tm 1954/1951; "Sweet Peas de Printemps", ad 1929; "Taj Mahal", tm 1953/1951; "Valencia", ad 1929; "White Enchantment", ad 1951.

MARSHALL FIELD, Chicago, IL: "Blue Rose", tm 1912/1912; "Cabaret", tm 1927/1926; "Flair", tm 1926/1923; "Ishtar", tm 1923/1922; "Senorita", tm 1927/1923.

LOUISE F. MARSHALL, NY, NY: "Monte Christo", tm 1891/1879.

ARNOLD MARTE, NY, NY: "Dervish", tm 1945/1936; "Envy", tm 1946/1931.

MARTIAL ET ARMAND, Paris, France: "Ambre", ad 1926; "Chez Martial et Armand", tm 1929/1928; "Chypre", ad 1926; "Place Vendome", ad 1926; "Un Rien", tm 1928/1925.

MARTON FRERES INC., NY, NY: "Nonchalant", tm 1937/1936.

ALFRED MARTORY, Paris, France: "Et Coetera", tm 1927/1927; "Feuille Noire", tm 1927/1927; "Juditt", tm 1927/1927; "Mi Fa Sol", tm 1927/1927; "Solweig", tm 1927/1927.

MARX & KUSHNER, NY, NY: "Corinthia", tm 1938/1937; "Quadrille", tm 1938/1938.

MARY LYNNE, Cleveland, OH: "Gypsy Violin", tm 1961/1959; "Persian Nights", tm 1959/1950; "Touch Of Spring", tm 1961/1940.

MARIE FRANCOISE MASCLET, Paris, France: "Modeline", tm 1950/1946.

HANS H. MASIE, NY, NY: "Casa Blanca", tm 1944/1943; "Happy Return", tm 1945/1944; "Old Europe", tm 1944/1942.

DAVID MASON, NY, NY: "Belle Heaven", tm 1928/1928.

MASSENET, Paris, France; NY, NY: "Altesse de Massenet", tm 1942/1941; "Bouquet-Americain", ad 1942; "Liquid Flowers", tm 1944/1944; "Mandalay", tm 1944/1942; "Rhapsodie", tm 1943/1942; "Sheherazade", tm 1946/1944.

MATE INC., Philadelphia, PA: "Dear O'Dreams", tm 1926/1925; "Jasmin-Malle", tm 1926/1925; "L'Embrasse D'Amour", tm 1927/1927; "Maid O' Flowers", tm 1926/1925; "Moguet-Volant", tm 1926/1925; "Nuit Joyeuse", tm 1925/1925; "Tout "En Vleur", tm 1926/1925.

MAXIMILLAN P. MATTHIAS, Forest Hills, NY: "Bois de Boulogne", tm 1931/1931.

MAUDY, Paris, France: "Chère Petite Chose", art 1928.

MAUPASSANT, Brooklyn, NY: "Thous Shalt Not", tm 1945/1944.

MAURELLA PRODUCTS CO., NY, NY: "Xandra", tm 1947/1937.

PHILLIP MAURICE, West Haven, CT: "Blossom Time", tm 1941/1931.

MAX, Paris, France: "Le Parfum Max", Fr. ad 1927.

MAXANDRE, NY, NY: "Maju", tm 1945/1943.

MAXIM'S, Paris, France: "Maxim's de Paris", new 1985.

MAXIME DRUG CO., Chicago, IL: "The Charm Of Youth", tm 1924/1923; "Torment", tm 1945/1934.

MAXINE PRODUCTS CO. INC., Detroit, MI: "Baby's Breath", tm 1932/1927; "Blue Heaven", tm 1928/1928.

JEROME F. MAY, Asbury Park, NJ: "Capture", tm 1947/1939; "Habanita", tm 1947/1939; "Noblesse", tm 1947/1939; "Oui-Ou-Non", tm 1945/1939; "Sugar Blossom", tm 1945/1942; "Tambor", tm 1947/1939; "Voulez-Vous?", tm 1945/1941.

MAY DEPARTMENT STORES CO., Los Angeles, CA: "Anita", tm 1927/1888; "Jolira", tm 1930/1929; "Qudinet", tm 1930/1929.

M. E. MAYER, Vienna, Austria: "Mayami", tm 1926/1923.

MAYFAIR PERFUMERS, NY, NY: "Lalique", tm 1946/1944.

MAYNARD INC., Chicago, IL: "Beautiful Lady", tm 1934/1933.

MEIER & FRANK CO., Portland, OR: "Propre", tm 1925/1925.

MELBA, Chicago, IL: "Adorme", tm 1921/1919; "Ambre de Melba", cat 1922; "Ariette", cat 1922; "Brema", tm 1917/1917; "Fleurs", ad 1925; "Glory", cat 1922; "Grape Blossom", cat 1922; "Isis", cat 1922; "Jollygood", cat 1922; "Lilac", ad 1925; "Lov'Me", tm 1914/1913; "Melbaline", cat 1922; "Sarene", cat 1922; "Shamrock", cat 1922.

MELLIER, St. Louis, MO; NY, NY: "Belle Of Roses", tm 1899/1899; "Belle Of Violets", tm 1899/1899; "Dardanella", tm 1920/1920; "Floressence", tm 1902/1902; "Frivole", tm 1924/1917; "Juliet", tm 1929/1899; "La Rosa De Guadalupe", tm 1930/1922; "Vogue", tm 1934/1902.

MELROSE MFG. CO., New Haven, CT: "Na-Hallar", tm 1926/1925.

MEM INC., NY, NY: "Citrange", tm 1941/1932; "Pedigree", tm 1945/1941; "Point Vert", tm 1943/1924.

MEMPHIS DRUG CO., Memphis, TN: "Temtacion", tm 1923/1916.

MENDESSOLLE, San Francisco, CA: "Fontainbleau", tm 1944/1922.

MENNEN CO., Morristown, NJ: "Coronet", tm 1954/1952.

MERITOL INC., Des Moines, IA: "Isa Meritol Perle", tm 1931/1915.

MERRIT DISTRIBUTORS (NATIONAL

TOILET CO.), Paris, TN: "Gay 16", tm 1944/1942.

BEATRICE MEYER LTD., NY, NY: "Manana", tm 1925/1924.

MIAHATI, NY, NY: "Audacious", tm 1945/1944; "Blue Fox", tm 1945/1944; "El Morocco", ad 1942; "Honolulu", ad 1939; "Jaunty", ad 1955; "Ka Lani Keia", tm 1944/1939; "My Francy", ad 1955; "Perhaps", ad 1941; "Pikaki", ad 1939; "Soul Of Flowers", ad 1939; "Tarantelle", tm 1960/1955; "Tomorrow", ad 1941; "Two Lips", ad 1941; "Waikiki", ad 1939; "Ye Olde Wishing Well", ad 1941.

MICHEL COSMETICS, Long Island, NY: "Message D'Amour", tm 1952/1949.

MICHELE PERFUMER, Hollywood, CA: "Mink", tm 1947/1941.

JOHN A. MIESSE CO., Philadelphia, PA: "La Fré", tm 1926/1926.

WALTER MILDNER, Buenos Aires, Argentina: "Vindobona", tm 1933/1925.

F. J. M. MILES, Sunland, CA: "Desert Verbena", tm 1933/1932; "Esquire", tm 1934/1933.

H. MILGRIM & BROS., NY, NY: "Salymil", tm 1930/1929.

MILKMAID INC., Paterson, NJ: "Michaelmas Daisy", tm 1943/1943.

MILLER BROTHERS, NY, NY: "Amaranth Bouquet", tm 1875/1874.

ALVIN MILLER, NY, NY: "Tutu", tm 1951/1950; "Vedette", tm 1951/1950.

H. W. MILLER COSMETIC, Glendale, CA: "Gold Lucette", tm 1946/1945.

I. MILLER & SONS, INC., Long Island, NY: "Millertaire", tm 1927/1927.

MILLIN DRUG CO., Memphis, TN: "Karma", tm 1925/1921.

F. MILLOT, Paris, France: "Altitude", tm 1935/1933; "Chere Madame", tm 1949/---; "Cher Monsieur", tm 1962/1959; "Crêpe de Chine", tm 1929/1929; "Ganteline", tm 1960/1959; "Impertinence", tm 1960/1953; "Insolent", tm 1959/1947; "Joyeuse Nuit", tm 1952/1948; "Partner", tm 1962/1959; "Recital", tm 1938/1931; "Regards", tm 1939/1938; "Revelry", tm 1951/1948; "Tanagra", tm 1962/1951.

MILSON CO., Cincinnati, OH: "Enticement", tm 1925/1925; "La Mysteree", tm 1928/1928.

EVELYN MIMS, Ft. Worth, TX: "Blue-Bonnet", tm 1936/1935; "Texanita", tm 1936/1935.

MINX MODES, St. Louis, MO: "Taffeta", tm 1948/1946.

MIRO-DENA, Paris, France; NY, NY: "Chantecler", cat 1922; "Cinesca", cat 1922; "CLematite", cat 1922; "Eleasia", cat 1922; "Fleur Charmante", cat 1922; "Heliotrope Bleu", cat 1922; "Jasmin de Paris", cat 1922; "L'Envie", cat 1922; "Lilas de Paris", cat 1922; "Muguet des Champs", cat 1922; "Rareniss", cat 1922; "Regent Violette", cat 1922; "Rose d'Amour", cat 1922; "Soiree Enchantee", cat 1922; "Violette Delicieuse", cat 1922.

MISENTA PINE PRODUCTS, Buffalo, NY: "Pine Vivo", tm 1939/1938.

MISSION BEAD CO., Los Angeles, CA: "California Nugget", tm 1932/1931; "Charm Of Love", tm 1925/1925.

MISSONI: "Missoni", new 1981.

LOUIS J. MISURACA, Glendale, CA: "Eternal Triangle", tm 1947/1944.

GEORGE E. MITCHELL, Lowell, MA: "Mitchell's Memorial", tm 1876/1876.

MOCQ, BURNIER & CIE, Paris, France; NY, NY: "Bouquet Fleuryea", cat 1922; "Eraine", tm 1924/1917; "Glorieux", ad 1920; "Meditation", cat 1922; "Perf", tm 1922/1921; "Soixante Quinze", cat 1922.

LOUIS MOCQ, NY, NY: "Rejuvia", tm 1930/1930.

MO-JO PRODUCTS CO., Chicago, IL: "Lucky Spirit", tm 1932/1932.

MOLINARD, Grasse, France; Paris, France: "1811", tm 1937/1936; "Ambre", art 1919; "Bacchantes", tm 1937/1931; "Calendal", tm 1948/1929; "Christmas Bells", tm 1927/1926; "Chypre", art 1919; "Concreta", tm 1948/1925; "Fleurettes", tm 1948/1935; "Habanita", art 1920; "Iles d'Or", tm 1948/1938; "Jasmin", ad 1936; "La Rose", art 1917; "Le Baiser du Faune", tm 1933/1930; "Le Mimosa", tm 1925/1923; "Les Iscles D'Or", art 1930; "Les Violettes", art 1917; "Madrigal", tm 1937/1936; "Molinard de Molinard", new 1980; "Nirmala", new 1955; "Orval", cat 1946; "Toute La Provence", tm 1948/1938; "Violette du Roi", ad 1936.

MOLINELLE, London, England: "Beau Geste", tm 1937/1930; "English Roses", ad 1930; "Gardenia", ad 1935; "Lilac", ad 1933; "No. 29", ad 1930; "Streamline", ad 1935; "Venez-Voir", tm 1936/1936.

DAVID ANTHONY MOLINARI, San Francisco, CA: "Gypsy Maiden", tm 1949/1941; "Sweet Dreams", tm 1948/1941.

MOLYNEUX, Paris, France: "3", ad 1925; "5", ad 1925; "14", ad 1925; "Charm de Molyneux", tm 1932/1928; "Connu de Molyneux", tm 1931/1927; "Fête", new 1962; "Fête de Molyneux", tm 1928/1927; "Gauloise", new 1981; "Le Chic de Molyneux", tm 1930/1929; "Le Parfum Connu", tm 1951/1929; "Magnificence de Molyneux", tm 1947/1947; "Quartz", new 1977; "Rue Royale", tm 1936/1935; "Une Idée de Molyneux", tm 1930/1930; "Vague", tm 1930/1930; "Viore", tm 1931/1931; "Vivre", new 1971.

MONEAU, NY, NY: "Discovery", tm 1942/1941; "If...", tm 1944/1944; "Rare Moments", tm 1958/1956.

HENRI MONET, Atlanta, GA: "Always In My Heart", tm 1945/1932; "Dresden", tm 1946/1937; "Gypsy Belle", tm 1949/1928; "Heart Break", tm 1946/1933; 'I Wonder Who?', tm 1949/1932; "Provocative", tm 1946/1932; "Somebody Loves Me!", tm 1947/1932; "Song Of India", tm 1945/1927; "Tantrum", tm 1945/1931.

MONICO: "Christmas In July", ad 1958.

MONNA VANNA, Paris, France: "Lilas D'Or", Fr. ad 1919; "L'Oiseau Bleu", Fr. ad 1919; "L'Oiseau Bleu", Fr. ad 1919; "Magnatic", Fr. ad 1919; "Pavlova", Fr. ad 1919.

MONNE, Paris, France: "Toute l'Egypte", art 1917.

MONOGRAM SOAP CO., Hollywood, CA: "Hi Mom", tm 1946/1944.

MONROE PRODUCTS CO., Los Angeles, CA: "Flamingo", tm 1932/1932.

MONS, Los Angeles, CA: "Night Song", tm 1952/1952.

MONTE CHRISTO COSMETIC, NY, NY: "Colorex", tm 1925/1916.

GERMAINE MONTEIL, NY, NY: "Fleur

Sauvage", tm 1954/1953; "Frou Frou", tm 1942/1941; "Gigolo", tm 1951/1951; "Laughter", tm 1941/1941; "New Love", tm 1941/1941; "Nostalgia", tm 1941/1941; "Nouvel Amour", tm 1952/1951; "Rigolade", tm 1952/1949.

JOHN HUDSON MOORE, NY, NY; Jersey City, NJ: "Jubilant", tm 1943/1943; "Sportswoman", tm 1946/1945; "Submission", tm 1943/1943; "Tall Story", tm 1953/1952.

MORDAUNT, Hoboken, NJ: "Midnight Rose", tm 1927/1927.

ADELE MOREL, NY, NY: "Paradise Garden", tm 1939/1939.

MORET PARFUMEUR, Washington, DC: "Mille Amours", tm 1927/1927.

MORETT & CIE, Paris, France: "Empress Josephine", cat 1922.

MORGENSTERN & CO., NY, NY: "Ilede", tm 1925/1925.

MORI, Paris, France: "Rève A Amour", ad 1932.

MORNY, London, England; Paris, France: "Chaminade", ad 1922; "June Roses", cat 1922; "Mysterieuse", cat 1922; "Nuit de Carnival", cat 1922; "Tentation", tm 1936/1926; "Yesha", cat 1922.

MORTON MANUFACTURING, Lynchburg, VA: "Voice Of Flowers", tm 1945/1945.

MAMIE L. MOSLEY, Philadelphia, PA: "Ever Lasting", tm 1952/1951.

MOUILLERON, INC.: "Flodorys", tm 1927/1926; "Royalis Flor", tm 1927/1926.

EUGENE MOULIE, Jacksonville, FL: "Maiden's Dream", tm 1892/1880; "Mission Memories", tm 1915/1915; "Ponce de Leon", tm 1914/1914.

J. G. MOUSON & CO., Frankfurt, Germany: "Mit der Postkutsche", tm 1953/1935; "Mouson", tm 1954/1798; "Tai-Tai", tm 1926/1921.

CHARLES M. MUNSCH, Portland, PA; NY, NY: "Eau de Alsace Vis-A-Vis le Ballon", tm 1927/1918.

MULHENS & KROPFF—GLOCKENGASSE NO. 4711, Cologne, Germany; NY, NY: "American Beauty Rose", ad 1922; "Amorena", art 1911; "Arie", tm 1927/1924; "Blaugold", tm 1932/1930; "Chintz", tm 1935/1935; "Cologwelle", tm 1957/1954; "Colognerics", tm 1958/1954; "Cordiale", cat 1922; "Double", art 1925; "Elan", tm 1958/1953; "Eldorado", cat 1922; "Eminence", tm 1909/1909; "Esthéta", tm 1930/1930; "Frisco", tm 1937/1937; "Friscologne", tm 1956/1953; "Gabi", 1927/1924; "Gavotte", tm 1929/1929; "Gral", tm 1927/1920; "Jaspis", tm 1927/1924; "Karat", tm 1936/1935; "La Baronesse", tm 1901/1899; "La Ronda", tm 1954/1952; "L'Offrande", ad 1922; "Luxus", cat 1922; "Marquise", tm 1904/1902; "Mascota", tm 1958/1935; "Mistral", tm 1927/1920; "Mon Muguet", cat 1922; "Nenita", tm 1927/1913; "Oriviola", cat 1922; "Pro Fume", tm 1932/1928; "Revue", tm 1927/1924; "Rhine", tm 1886/1884; "Rhine Gold", tm 1929/1914; "Russe", tm 1927/1926; "Santair", cat 1922; "Seven Mountains", tm 1886/1885; "Sevillan", cat 1922; "Sir", tm 1934/1933; "Sparta", tm 1934/1932; "Terci", tm 1936/1922; "Tizian", tm 1933/1924; "Tosca", tm 1931/1928; "Toscara", tm 1960/1958; "Troika", tm

1935/1920; "Tuchten", tm 1932/1931; "Viola Violetta", cat 1922; "Waldmeister", tm 1886/1885; "Yolai", tm 1936/1935.

JUDITH MULLER, Haifa, Israel: "Bat-Sheba", ad 1967.

CHAS. E. MULLIN, Camden, NJ: "Le Rêve", tm 1926/1921.

HENRI MURAOUR, Grasse, France: "Ambrée", ad 1921; "Caresse d'Amour", ad 1921; "Chypre", ad 1921; "Coeur de Gitane", ad 1921; "Hésitation", ad 1921; "Hors La Brume", ad 1921; "Jasmin", ad 1921; "L'Ambre", ad 1921; "Le Lilas", ad 1921; "L'Occident", ad 1921; "Narcisse Bleu", tm 1924/1923; "Révélation", ad 1921.

MURY, Paris, France: "Amadis", tm 1926/1926; "Cap A La Vie", tm 1948/1940; "Caresse d'Amour", art 1917; "Con Amore", tm 1926/1926; "Eté Fleuri", tm 1949/1940; "Le Beau Soir", tm 1924/1923; "Le Jardin De Ma Soeur", tm 1924/1923; "Narcisse Bleu", Fr. ad 1925; "Notturno", tm 1926/1926; "Patricia", tm 1926/1926; "Risk", ad 1935; "Siva", ad 1922; "Violetera", tm 1924/1923.

LEONARD MUSIC, NY, NY: "Dainty Dabs", tm 1938/1938.

MUSSET, Paris, France: "Poeme", new 1928; "Royal Gardenia", ad 1928; "Royal Pois de Senteur", ad 1928.

MYON, Paris, France: "3 Passions", ad 1933; "1000 Joies", ad 1933; "Coeur de Femme", art 1928; "Exaltation", ad 1934.

BARNEY MYROLEUM CO., Portsmouth, NH: "Perpetual", tm 1886/1884.

MYRURGIA, Barcelona, Spain: "Chippendale", tm 1946/1942; "Clavel de España", tm 1946/1936; "Embrujo de Sevilla", tm 1945/1933; "Flor de Blason", tm 1927/1926; "Flores Del Mal", tm 1927/1922; "Goyesca", tm 1936/1919; "Joya", tm 1956/1954; "Joyel", tm 1954/1954; "Junglas", ad 1944; "Maderas de Oriente", tm 1929/1920; "Maja", tm 1945/1918; "Morisca", tm 1930/1917; "Orgia", tm 1927/1922; "Perfume Alado", tm 1927/1926; "Señorial", tm 1959/1941; "Suspiro de Granada", tm 1929/1922; "Toison", tm 1958/1930.

NADIAR PARFUMS, Los Angeles, CA: "Shameless", tm 1944/1943.

THE NAMM STORE, Brooklyn, NY: "Valide", tm 1932/1931.

NARDAU LTD., NY, NY: "Blue Of The Night", tm 1945/1943.

NARDAU, NY, NY: "Princesse Lili", tm 1946/1945; "Tête A Tête", tm 1945/1944.

NASSOUR STUDIOS, Los Angeles, CA: "Diamonds And Mink", tm 1959/1958; "Royalty", tm 1959/1958.

JEAN NATE: "1-4-3", ad 1944.

NATIONAL OIL PRODUCTS CO., Harrison, NJ: "Admiración", tm 1933/1918.

NATIONAL PERFUMERY, Waterbury, CT: "Genius", tm 1924/1924.

NATIONAL SCIENTIFIC LABORA-TORIES, Richmond, VA: "Bal Dore", tm 1929/1929.

NATIONAL TOILET CO., Paris, TN: "Southern Flowers", tm 1926/1925.

NATONE, Los Angeles, CA: "Cent Fleurs", tm 1958/1957.

NATTIER, Paris, France: "Oiseau de Feu", tm 1946/1944.

GRACE V. NEFF, Chicago, IL: "The Language Of Flowers", tm 1944/1943.

NEIMAN-MARCUS CO., Dallas, TX: "A'Toi", tm 1927/1926; "Fauve", tm 1963/1958; "N M", tm 1952/1951.

NELSON PARFUMS, NY, NY: "Gold And Velvet", tm 1955/1954.

NELSON, BAKER, & CO., Detroit, MI: "Blossom Time", tm 1926/1926; "Fleurs du Midi", tm 1926/1926; "Spring Blossoms", tm 1926/1926.

NEMEEIA, Paris, France: "Nemesis", new 1910.

NEMOURS, NY, NY: "Biriatou", tm 1948/1946; "Ciel de France", tm 1948/1946.

NESTLE-LE MUR CO., NY, NY: "Fleur De France", tm 1957/1915.

NESTLY, Paris, France: "Chypre", ad 1929; "Gardenia", ad 1929; "Jasmin", ad 1929; "Numero 7", ad 1929; "Sweet Pea", ad 1929; "Violetta", ad 1929.

NETHERCUTT LABORATORIES, Santa Monica, CA: "First Kiss", tm 1948/1946; "Golden Feather", tm 1956/1953; "Jonquiljoy", tm 1953/1947; "Merlita", tm 1948/1946; "Resort", tm 1951/1950; "Tulaire", tm 1953/1935.

MORTON G. NEUMANN, Chicago, IL: "Lodestone", tm 1940/1932; "Sweet Georgia Brown", tm 1928/1927.

NEUVEE, Los Angeles, CA: "Crystalette", tm 1929/1927.

NEW PROCESS CO., Warren, PA: "Princess In Exile", tm 1938/1937.

NEW YORK & LONDON DRUG CO., NY, NY: "Nygracia", tm 1911/1910; "Nylotis", tm 1911/1910.

NEW YORK FRENCH EXPORTS, NY, NY: "Perfumettes", tm 1922/1921.

NEW YORK MAKE-UP CORP., NY, NY: "Jardy", tm 1941/1941; "Le Saucy", tm 1941/1941.

NEW YORK SHIELD CO., NY, NY: "Imprevu", tm 1917/1916.

NEW YORKER COSMETIC CORP., NY, NY: "Sophisticate", tm 1933/1932.

PAUL D. NEWTON, Newark, NY: "Peggy Newton", tm 1953/1941; "Slightly Wicked", tm 1950/1949.

NIELCO PRODUCTS CO., Detroit, MI: "Fleur de Lune", tm 1926/1926; "Mai' D'Honeur", tm 1925/1924.

HENRY NIER, San Francisco, CA: "Mopecco", tm 1924/1924.

A. NIGGI & C., Imperia, Italy: "Lavanda Coldinava", tm 1953/1939.

NIPOLA CO., Minneapolis, MN: "Swee-Tone", tm 1926/1926.

NISSERY, Paris, France: "Coeurs et Fleurs", ad 1925.

NISSY, NY, NY: "Casbah", tm 1943/1943; "Mei-Ling", tm 1944/1943.

NEANNE NOEL, NY, NY: "Texas Bonnet Bleu", tm 1951/1949.

NONANTUM WORSTED CO., Newton, MA; Boston, MA: "Lady Grey", tm 1888/1888; "Long Branch", tm 1888/1888.

NORANTE, Melun, France: "Scenario", tm 1948/1935; "Wally", tm 1949/1936.

ETHEL LEA NORE INC., Brooklyn, NY: "Lea — Secret Of Fifth Avenue", tm 1947/1935; "Lea — To Bac", tm 1947/1942.

NORMAN NORELL, NY, NY: "Norell", ad 1968.

MERLE NORMAN, Los Angelesj CA: "Constantly", tm 1963/1957; "Lasting Spring",

tm 1963/1963.

NORMITOL, Norwalk, CT: "Mystol", tm 1936/1920.

NORTHWEST FLOWER EXTRACTIONS CO., Seattle, WA: "De Glaceme", tm 1930/1930; "Glacial", tm 1931/1929.

NUDRU CO., Bayonne, NJ: "Nu-Bu-Ty", tm 1924/1922.

NU-VITA PRODUCTS, Pittsburg, PA: "Reveille", tm 1954/1931.

NYAL CO., Detroit, MI: "Blue Dusk", tm 1939/1939; "Dalon", tm 1931/1928; "Impulse", tm 1939/1939; "Innuendo", tm 1940/1940; "Intimacy", tm 1940/1940; "June Mist", tm 1939/1939; "Piccadilly", tm 1926/1925; "Ravish", tm 1940/1940.

NYLA LABORATORIES, Evansville, IN: "Princess Nyla", tm 1957/1935.

O-SAN, St. Louis, MO: "Lady-Grace", tm 1924/1917.

OAKLEY SOAP AND PERFUMERY, NY, NY: "Blue Ribbon", tm 1895/1894; "Bouquet Finesse", cat 1922; "Bouquet Nydia", cat 1922; "California Roses", cat 1922; "Lakewood", tm 1893/1893; "Ma Cherie", tm 1923/1909; "Yvette", cat 1922.

ODESANT. (See MARIE RICHELIEU).

ODO-FLOR LABORATORIES, Chicago, IL: "Blue Acacia", tm 1928/1927.

HARRY OHAYON, NY, NY: "Princess Sultana", tm 1938/1925.

OHIO COSMETICS CO., Fremont, OH: "Pledge", tm 1939/1938.

OLD 97 MANUFACTURING CO., Tampa, FL: "Hellen Blazes", tm 1954/1949; "King Gasparilla", tm 1952/1950.

OLD EMPIRE MANUFACTURING CHEMISTS, Newark, NJ: "En Garde", tm 1954/1952; "Moment D'Or", tm 1954/1952.

OLD LUCK CO., Memphis, TN: "Lucky Love", tm 1947/1947.

OLD SOUTH (CAMPANA SALES), NY, NY; Batavia, IL: "Cotton Blossom", ad 1941; "Plantation Garden", ad 1941; "Star Fire", tm 1950/1948; "Woodland Spice", ad 1941.

OLIVETTE LABORATORY, Providence, RI: "Spring Flowers", tm 1926/1924.

OMNIUM, Paris, France: "Etincelle", tm 1947/1937; "Excentric", tm 1949/1938; "La Fleur Folle", tm 1949/1938.

ORALEE FRERES, NY, NY: "Hollywood Nights", tm 1930/1930.

OR-BLOS CO., Jacksonville, FL: "Flower Of Youth", tm 1926/1925.

OREON PARFUMEUR, NY, NY: "L'Autre Femme", tm 1946/1945.

ORIENTAL HERB REMEDY CO., NY, NY: "Ohrco", tm 1930/1927.

ORIENTAL PERFUMERY, Stapleton, NY: "Egyptian Beauty", tm 1928/1928.

HEDWIG ORLIK, NY, NY: "Sans Nom", tm 1939/1938.

ORLOFF (JEAN VIVAUDOU CO.), NY, NY: "American Blossoms", ad 1941; "Attar Of Petals", cat 1945; "Carnation Imperiale", ad 1939; "Extrait de Cologne Russe", ad 1939; "Gardenia Russe", ad 1939; "Indies Spice", ad 1941; "Nikki", ad 1939.

ADELAIDE ORTEGAT, Paris, France: "Heures Mysterieuses", tm 1930/1930; "Je Suis Aimêe", tm 1930/1930; "Pinacle", tm 1930/1930; "Vibrations", tm 1930/1930.

ORTOSAN CO., NY, NY: "Just You", tm 1929/1929.

FLORENCE OSBORNE, Cleveland Heights, OH: "Creon", tm 1937/1933; "Simpson's Royal Family", tm 1937/1933.

OSTHEIMER BROTHERS, Philadelphia, PA: "Lafittè", tm 1890/1889.

OUCHY. (See D'OUCHY).

OUTDOOR GIRL: "Dawn", cat 1935; "Night", cat 1935; "Noon", cat 1935.

OVERTON-HYGIENIC MFG. CO., Chicago, IL: "High-Brown", tm 1924/1905.

PACOMA, Paris, France: "Ego", new 1978; "Ego 2", new 1981.

PAGE PERFUMER, NY, NY: "Beauty Youth", tm 1933/1931; "English Garden", new 1940; "Persian Lilac", new 1940; "Rose", ad 1917; "Violet", ad 1917; "Wistaria", ad 1917.

PERCY E. PAGE, NY, NY: "Corylopsis", ad 1918; "Fairy's Dream", tm 1923/1923; "Floral Bloom", new 1923; "Floral Dream", tm 1924/1923; "Rose", ad 1918; "Violet", ad 1918; "Wistaria", ad 1918.

MAURICE PAILLARD, Marne, France: "Vénusane", new 1947/1945.

THE PALAIS ROYAL INC., Washington, DC: "Miss Washington', tm 1927/1927.

GENE PALMER, Los Angeles, CA: "Malibu", tm 1937/1936.

KATHRYN PALMER INC., NY, NY: "I Do", tm 1947/1946.

SOLON PALMER, NY, NY: "Alberta", tm 1907/1907; "Apple Leaves", cat 1922; "Ariston", tm 1904/1903; "Baby Ruth", tm 1893/1892; "Brocade", tm 1939/1926; "Centennial Bouquet", ad 1947; "Chautauqua Bouquet", tm 1885/1885; "Curio", tm 1904/1904; "Dress Parade", tm 1939/1939; "Egyptian Lotus", cat 1922; "Fashion", tm 1914/1898; "Fiesta", tm 1928/1928; "Gardenglo", tm 1913/1913; "Gardenia", ad 1933; "Garland", tm 1896/1896; "Garland Of Roses", tm 1908/1905; "Garland Of Violets", tm 1908/1905; "Gem Rose", cat 1922; "Glenecho", tm 1923/1923; "Gold Leaf", tm 1929/1929; "Ihlang Ihlang", cat 1922; "India Bouquet", tm 1892/1878; "Lilac Sweets", tm 1891/1890; "Locust Sweets", cat 1922; "Marvel Of Peru", cat 1922; "May Bloom", tm 1889/1887; "Narcisfleur", tm 1925/1925; "Orchid Lily", tm 1926/1925; "Our Jack", tm 1894/1894; "Pink Fleur", tm 1926/1925; "Red Clover", ad 1922; "Rob Roy", tm 1895/1895; "Rose Fleur", tm 1926/1925; "Rose Girl", tm 1908/1906; "Sandalwood de Oriente", cat 1922; "Vio Fleur", tm 1925/1925; "Violet Girl", tm 1908/1906; "White Rose" ad 1934.

PALMERS LIMITED, Montreal, Canada: "3 Secrets", tm 1951/1948; "Ariola", tm 1921/1920; "Derny's 3 Secrets", tm 1932/1931; "Mandalay", tm 1927/1925; "Petal-Tone", tm 1935/1934.

PALMOLIVE CO., Chicago, IL: "Fanchon", tm 1927/1922.

PAQUIN, London, England; Paris, France: "9 X 9", tm 1955/1939; "Ever After", tm 1941/1939; "No. 9", tm 1949/---.

PARA TI CORP., NY, NY: "Anoche", tm 1947/1945; "Tuya", tm 1942/1942.

PARAMOUNT COSMETICS, NY, NY: "9 'til 6", tm 1945/1940.

PAREGIAN, Glen Olden, PA: "Wedding Nite", tm 1956/1955.

PARERA, Barcelona, Spain: "Madronos", tm 1956/1953; "Varon Dandy", tm 1955/1951.

PARFA, Zurich, Switzerland: "Cil Duc", tm 1948/1935.

PARFAIR, Chicago, IL: "Kick Off", tm 1947/1946; "Thorobred", tm 1946/1946.

PARFISE INC., NY, NY: "Cypria", tm 1926/1925.

PARFUMS PARIS HOUSE, NY, NY: "Cellarette", ad 1941.

PARIS LABORATORIES, INC., NY, NY: "Countess Maritza", tm 1933/1931; "La Tesh", tm 1925/1925; "Mildred Jolson", tm 1931/1931; "Sweet Whiffs", tm 1926/1918.

PARIS TOILET CO., Paris, TN: "Golden Peacock", tm 1925/1923.

PARISTYLE NOVELTY CO. INC., NY, NY: "Aivlys", tm 1932/1929.

PARK AVENUE PERFUMERS ASSOCIATES, Detroit, MI: "Wild Innocence", tm 1953/1951.

PARK AVENUE SALES CO. INC., NY, NY: "Pent House", tm 1936/1933.

PARK & TILFORD, NY, NY: "Adventure", tm 1937/1937; "Cherish", tm 1938/1938; "Eve d'Adam", tm 1959/1957; "Faoen", tm 1926/1926; "High Heels", tm 1948/1947; "My Desire", tm 1958/1957; "No. 3", tm 1933/1931; "No. 12", tm 1933/1931; "No. 19", tm 1933/1932; "No. 44", tm 1934/1934; "Scotch Glen", tm 1959/1957; "Sharp!", tm 1946/1946; "Vain", ad 1957; "Wild Harvest", tm 1948/1947; "Woody Glen", tm 1958/1957.

PRISCILLA PARKER, NY, NY; St. Paul, MN: "Hopeton House", tm 1949/1948.

PARKINSON-LECOURT, Katonah, NY: "Buttons & Bows", tm 1951/1950; "Dinner-Date", tm 1952/1951.

GEORGE R. PARKINSON, NY, NY: "Eros", tm 1947/1946.

JEAN DE PARYS, Paris, France; NY, NY: "Sous Le Gui", Fr. ad 1925.

ALICE PASCANET, Paris, France: "Secret de Maharani", tm 1935/1934.

LOUIS PASKIN, NY, NY: "Picardy", tm 1933/1933; "Seeress", tm 1932/1931; "Soprano", tm 1933/1933.

MICHEL PASQUIER, NY, NY: "Tobruk", art 1952; "Wall Street", tm 1947/1939.

PATANWALLA: "Bhagwan", art 1929.

JEAN PATOU, Paris, France: "Adieu Sagesse", tm 1926/1925; "Ambition", tm 1954/1953; "Amour Amour", tm 1929/1925; "Angostura", tm 1930/1922; "Anything Goes", tm 1957/1955; "Aparté", tm 1929/1928; "Bar A Parfums", tm 1931/1929; "Brandy Of Flowers", tm 1936/1936; "Câline", new 1964; "Cocktail Dry", tm 1931/1930; "Cocktail Sweet", tm 1931/1930; "Colony", tm 1937/1937; "Companion", tm 1952/1950; "Folie Divine", tm 1931/1931; "For Her... ...For Him", tm 1931/1931; "Happy Lovers", tm 1931/1930; "Heureux Amants", tm 1931/1930; "Holidays", tm 1934/1934; "Huile de Chaldée", tm 1931/1927; "Invitation", tm 1932/1932; "Joy", tm 1949/1931; "L'Amour Est Roi", tm 1931/1930; "L'Heure Attendue", tm 1946/1945; "La Joie de Jean Patou", tm 1931/1930; "Lasso", tm 1957/1955; "Le Sien", tm 1929/1928; "Lift", tm 1930/1930; "Love Appeal", tm 1931/1930; "Makila", ad 1961; "May-Be", tm 1931/1925; "Moment Suprême", tm 1931/1929; "Normandie", new 1935; "Olé", tm 1955/1954; "Patou's

Own", tm 1931/1930; "Que Saisje", new 1925; "Snob", tm 1950/1950; "The Awaited Hour", tm 1949/1945; "Toilet Brandy", tm 1935/1935; "Tout Va", tm 1957/1955; "Vacances", tm 1934/1934; "Vin De Toilette", tm 1935/1935.

PATRICIA COSMETICS, Chicago, IL: "Tico-Tico", tm 1946/1945.

D. P. PAUL & CO., NY, NY: "Nuit de Marriage", tm 1927/1926.

PAYOT, Paris, France: "Pavlova", new 1976.

PECK & PECK: "Pour le Sport", tm 1927/1926.

PIERRE PELISSARD, Casablance, Morocco: "Tiulak", tm 1958/1957.

PENINSULAR CHEMICAL, Detroit, MI: "Garden Court", tm 1917/1917; "Moorland", tm 1914/1913; "Sylvodora", tm 1912/1912.

J. C. PENNEY CO., Wilmington, DE: "Chalon", tm 1932/1932; "Corlon", tm 1933/1932; "Leelon", tm 1933/1932.

MARY D'ESTE PERCH, NY, NY: "Deste", tm 1924/1911.

PERFUMERIES DISTRIBUTORS, Hamilton, Bermuda: "Bermuda Blue", tm 1955/1952.

DOROTHY PERKINS, St. Louis, MO: "Conquest", tm 1950/1932; "Curtsy", tm 1963/1962; "Dry Wine", tm 1963/1962; "Full Sail", tm 1963/1962; "Identity", tm 1963/1962; "Memoirs", ad 1944; "Moment De Paris", tm 1963/1963; "Patio", tm 1963/1962; "Sea Talk", tm 1963/1962.

PEROXIDE CHEMICAL CO., St. Louis, MO: "Vi-Jon", tm 1927/1924.

ANDRE PERROUD, Lyons, France: "Xerol", tm 1901/1895.

PERSIAN COSMETIC CO., Chicago, IL: "Donna Wayne", tm 1935/1933.

PERUGIA, Paris, France: "Après Midi", ad 1929; "Atmosphere", ad 1938; "Matin", ad 1929; "Soir", ad 1929.

HELENE PESSL, NY, NY: "Dutch Treat", tm 1957/1956; "Go Dutch", tm 1957/1956; "Lady Deb", tm 1957/1956; "Little Lady", tm 1945/1944; "Melinda", tm 1945/1945; "Pink Popsicle", tm 1956/1954; "Toy-Letries", tm 1949/1948.

PETRIN CO., NY, NY: "Sables And Pearls", tm 1937/1937.

PFALTZ & BAUER INC., NY, NY: "Falbafleur", tm 1937/1936.

PHILLIPS MANUFACTURING, Philadelphia, PA: "Paramount", tm 1924/1918.

S. TOM PHILLIPS, NY, NY: "Barbizon", tm 1945/1940.

JEANNE PIAUBERT, Paris, France: "Vive La Vie", tm 1948/1946.

PICARD, NY, NY: "Cheetah", ad 1946; "Scanty", tm 1942/1941.

PALOMA PICASSO: "Paloma Picasso", new 1984.

GEORGE PICKRELL LABORATORY, Chicago, IL: "Gai-Dai", tm 1946/1944.

S. S. PIERCE CO., Boston, MA: "Arosa", tm 1927/1927; "Bewilderment", tm 1945/1944; "C'est Vous", tm 1941/1927; "Le Temps des Fleurs", tm 1925/1924.

PIERRE: "Number X", ad 1928.

ROBERT PIGUET, Paris, France: "Augure", tm 1946/1945; "Baghari", tm 1946/1945; "Bandit", art 1944; "Brigand", tm 1947/1946; "Calypso", ad 1959; "Cattleya", tm 1945/1942; "Dark Herald", tm 1947/1946; "Dingo", tm 1946/1945; "Dona Sol", tm 1947 1940; "Esclave", tm 1947/1945; "Estampe", tm 1948/1946; "Fou", tm 1946 1945; "Fracas", tm 1946/1945; "Gambade", tm 1946/1945; "Grande Epoque", tm 1947/1946; "Hirondelle", tm 1947/1946; "Messanger", tm 1952/1939; "Mimo", tm 1947/1940; "Rollon", tm 1947/1945; "Visa", tm 1946/1945.

PILLET, Paris, France; NY, NY: "As de Pique", tm 1927/1926.

ED. PINAUD, Paris, France: "A La Corbeille Fleurie", tm 1887/1840; "Akita", cat 1922; "Ambretta", tm 1896/1896; "Ammunitia", tm 1943/1943; "Anemone De France", tm 1895/1894; "Apple Blossom", ad 1939; "Aurora Tulip", tm 1893/1892; "Bitter Sweet", tm 1930/1930; "Blue Nymphia", tm 1897/1896; "Boomerang", tm 1943/1943; "Bouquet Marie Louise", art 1903; "Brazilia", tm 1943/1943; "Bridge", tm 1911/1910; "Brinda", cat 1922; "Brisa De Las Pampas", tm 1887/1878; "Brise Embaumee", ad 1906; "Brise Embaumee Violette", ad 1906; "Brise Embaumee White Rose", ad 1906; "Campeador", cat 1922; "Canter", tm 1937/1937; "Capri", cat 1922; "Captive", tm 1944/1943; "Celestis", tm 1897/1896; "Christmas Carol", tm 1941/1941; "Christmas Tree", tm 1944/1943;"Clubman", tm 1937/1933; "Comme Toi", ad 1922; "Corbeille Fleurie", tm 1877/1876; "East Is West", tm 1929/1929; "En Sorceleuse", new 1944; "Essence Pravia", cat 1922; "Excellence", tm 1945/1943; "Exultis", tm 1896/1896; "Feline", tm 1944/1943; "Flirt", tm 1937/1910; "Flirtation", tm 1944/1944; "Fol Amour", tm 1944/1943; "Foscarina", tm 1903/1901; "French Carnation Pink", cat 1922; "Her Secret Weapon", tm 1944/1944; "Ixora Breonia", cat 1922; "Jacintheroy", cat 1922; "Jasmin De France", tm 1895/1894; "Jasmin Roy", cat 1922; "Joliveté", tm 1944/1943; "La Corrida", ad 1906; "Lilas De France", tm 1928/1890; "Lilianelle", tm 1944/1944; "lis De France", tm 1895/1894; "Madreselva", tm 1937/1932; "Moskova", tm 1945/1945; "Moss Rose", cat 1922; "Muscara", tm 1896/1896; "Obsession", tm 1944/1943; "Paquita Lily", tm 1893/1893; "Parfums Debay", tm 1939/1938; "Persian Amandia", tm 1897/1896; "Playtime", tm 1944/1943; "Pravia", art 1912; "Preface", tm 1937/1937; "Prelude", tm 1930/1930; "Roman", cat 1922; "Royal Lavender", tm 1937/1900; "Scarlett", tm 1941/1937; "Set-Up",tm 1937/1937; "Show Boat", tm 1929/1929; "Show Girl", tm 1929/1929; "Stay-Up", tm 1937/1937; "Theodora", ad 1902; "Thisbe", cat 1922; "Végétal", tm 1938/1857; "Violet Roy", cat 1922; "Violette Princesse", tm 1897/1895; "Whoopee", tm 1929/1929.

L. T. PIVER, Paris, France; NY, NY: "Ambre Duale", cat 1922; "Astris", tm 1927/1908; "Aventurine", cat 1922; "Azurea", ad 1907; 'Baccara", tm 1960/1959; "Bel Flor", tm 1924/1910; "Carminade", tm 1928/1928; "Ciel d'Eté", tm 1960/1959; "Corylopsis du Japon", cat 1922; "D'Aventure", Fr. ad 1931; "Dolme", art 1910; "Espéris", tm 1911/1903; "Fétiche", tm 1925/1925; "Floramye", tm 1923/1905; "Gao", art 1925; "Ilka", tm 1913/1912; "Le Tréfle Incarnat", new 1898; "Mascarade", tm 1928/1928; "Mismelis", tm 1924/1921; "Misti", tm 1927/1923; "Pompeia", cat 1922; "Rêve d'Or", tm 1930/1929; "Rocroy", tm 1927/1927; "Rosiris", cat 1922; "Safranor", cat 1922; "Scarabee", cat 1922; "Un Parfum D'Adventure", tm 1931/1931; "Vallee Des Rois", Fr. ad 1923; "Velivole", tm 1924/1913; "Violette Duale", cat 1922; "Vivitz", cat 1922; "Volt", tm 1923/1922.

PLASSARD, Paris, France: "De Fleur En Fleur", ad 1927; "Dyne", Fr. ad 1928; "Une Femme Passa", art 1911.

JEANNE PLAUBERT, Paris, France: "Très en Forme", tm 1949/1946.

PLEVILLE, Paris, France; Detroit, MI: "Charme Caressant', tm 1924/1923; "Flamme de Floire", tm 1924/1923; "Flamme d'Or", tm 1924/1923; "Flânerie", tm 1924/1923; "Jardin d'Or", tm 1927/1927; "Le Secret de la Perle", ad 1926; "Mah Jongg", tm 1924/1923; "Plaisir d'Orient", tm 1927/1927; "Triomphe de Pléville", tm 1925/1923.

PLEXO PREPARATIONS, INC., NY, NY: "Maidenglo", tm 1929/1929.

PLOUGH INC., Memphis, TN: "Cupid's Kiss", tm 1934/1882.

POLYPHASE CORP., NY, NY: "Prima Donna", tm 1932/1932.

ELIZABETH POST (LANDER CO.), NY, NY: "Samedi Soir", tm 1958/1952.

POTTER & MOORE, London, England: "Mitcham", tm 1935/1888.

JOHN ROBERT POWERS, NY, NY: "Esprit De Nuit", tm 1961/1959; "Excité", tm 1961/1959; "Osé", tm 1961/1959; "Pas de Deux", tm 1960/1959; "Susceptible", tm 1952/1951; "Tocatta", tm 1962/1959.

JOSEPH VAN PRAAGH, London, England: "Bougance", tm 1925/1924.

DELBERT E. PRALL, Saginaw, MI: "Banzai", tm 1906/1906.

PREMET, Paris, France: "Etrange Inconnu", ad 1925; "Le Secret de Premet", tm 1931/1930; "Pour Un Oui", tm 1931/1930.

PRESTON CO., NY, NY: "Queen Elizabeth", tm 1926/1925.

JOHN L. PRIESS, Chicago, IL: "Caliph", tm 1945/1941; "Madcap", tm 1945/1941; "Scheherazade", tm 1945/1941; "Tip Top", tm 1945/1941.

PRIMROSE HOUSE, NY, NY: "Chiffon", tm 1947/1938; "Flowery Bank", tm 1945/1945; "Petal Garland", tm 1945/1945; "Witchery", tm 1946/1945; "Witches Brew", tm 1947/1946.

PRINCE ALEXIS ROMANOFF, Fishkill, NY: "Lubler", tm 1954/1953.

PRINCE DE BOURBON: "Flame d'Amour", ad 1943.

PRINCE DE CHANY, Paris, France; "Beverly Hills, CA: "Emotion", ad 1935; "Lost Orchid", tm 1936/1935; "Mystery Gardenia", tm 1936/1934; "Orchidée Perdue", ad 1935. (See also: VIMAY).

PRINCE GAGARIN: "Bouquet", ad 1935; "Lilac", ad 1935; "Special", ad 1935.

PRINCE GEORGE OF RUSSIA (MARTIN DE BOTELHO), NY, NY: "Elixir", ad 1936; "Tiara", tm 1938/1937.

PRINCE MATCHABELLI, Paris, France; NY, NY: "Abano", ad 1938; "Added Attraction", tm 1956/1956; "Ambre Royal", ad 1927; "Apassionata", tm 1956/1954; "Avance", tm 1962/1962; "Ave.

Maria", tm 1929/1926; "Beloved", ad 1950; "Beloved Moment", tm 1960/1960; "Cachet", new 1970; "Call To Arms", tm 1942/1942; "Carnation", ad 1935; "Cherokee", tm 1936/1936; "Christmas Angel", tm 1956/1955; "Christmas Rose", ad 1940; "Crown Duet", tm 1946/1943; "Crown Jewel", tm 1946/1945; "Crown Prince", tm 1947/1946; "Crown Princess", tm 1947/1946; "Duchess Of York", ad 1934; "Easter Bonnet", tm 1943/1943; "Firelight", tm 1955/1953; "Gay Suggestion", tm 1957/1956; "Golden Autumn", tm 1959/1948; "Grace Moore", ad 1934; "Guiding Star", tm 1955/1953; "Gypsy Pattern", tm 1942/1942; "Honey Suckle", ad 1935; "Imperial Violet", ad 1927; "Infanta", tm 1937/1937; "Jingle Bell", tm 1937/1937; "Katherine The Great", tm 1935/1935; "Lilac", ad 1935; "Lilith", tm 1955/1953; "Muguet", ad 1935; "Odyssey", tm 1955/1953; "Potpourri", tm 1940/1940; "Prince Georges", tm 1936/1935; "Princess Marie", ad 1933; "Princess Nina", ad 1927; "Princess Norina", tm 1929/1926; "Princess Of Wales", ad 1939; "Queen Of Georgia", tm 1928/1926; "Reprise", tm 1955/1953; "Sceptre", tm 1936/1936; "Sheer Madness", tm 1960/1959; "Snowball", tm 1936/1936; "Spring Fancy", tm 1956/1955; "Stradivari", ad 1950; " Summer Frost", ad 1947; "Summer Shower", tm 1954/1953; "Sybarite", tm 1957/1956; "Wind Song", tm 1954/1953.

PRINCE OBOLENSKI, NY, NY: "Bouquet de Fleurs", ad 1947; "Credo", tm 1946/1943; "Le Parfum Homage", tm 1947/1946.

PRINCESS MARCELLA BORGHESE, Rome, Italy: "Ecco", ad 1961.

PRINCESS PRODUCTS, Newark, NJ: "Princess Edwina", tm 1949/1947.

LUCE PRINTAMP: "Rive Droite", ad 1930; "Rive Gauche", ad 1930.

PRINTEMPS, Paris, France; Baltimore, MD: "FLeur de Lys", tm 1952/1924.

PROKA PARFUMERIE, Vienna, Austria: "Royale Bouvardia", tm 1926/1924.

PARFUMERIE PROVENCAL, NY, NY: "French Provincial", tm 1952/1950.

EMILIO PUCCI, Paris, France: "Vivara", ad 1966; "Zadig", ad 1973.

PUIG, Paris, France: "Estivalia", new 1976.

LILLY PULITZER: "Lilly #1", ad 1968.

PUREX, Lakewood, CA: "Hob Nail", tm 1963/1937.

PUREX PRODUCTS, Baltimore, MD: "Hysterical", tm 1946/1944.

PURITAN: "Gardenia", cat 1935; "Jasmine", cat 1935.

PURITAN COSMETICS, St. Louis, MO: "Allure", tm 1956/1914; "Brown Derby", tm 1935/1934; "Vivian Trent", tm 1935/1934.

QUALITY PRODUCTS, NY, NY: "Garden Walk", tm 1945/1945; "Love Lace", tm 1947/1946; "Mimoné", tm 1937/1936; "Night Fall", tm 1945/1945; "Sorrento", tm 1946/1945; "Wistful", tm 1945/1945.

QUEEN, Chicago, IL: "Crabapple", ad 1905; "Lily of the Valley", ad 1905.

QUENTIN'S (ELLWOOD B. CHAPMAN), Philadelphia, PA: "Lotos of the Nile", tm 1894/1893.

QUI SAIT, Linfield, PA: "Garden Fragrance", art 1937; "Yule Love", tm 1948/1946.

KATHLEEN MARY QUINLAN, NY, NY:

"After Dark", tm 1938/1938; "Forget Me Not", ad 1942; "Organdy", tm 1937/1937; "Rhythm, tm 1936/1936.

JOSEPH H. QUINTERO, Paris, France: "N'est-ce Pas?", tm 1925/1925.

R. J. S. LABORATORY, Chicago, IL: "Certified", tm 1924/1922.

RABANI CREATIONS, NY, NY: "C'est Si Bon", tm 1959/1955.

PACO RABANNE, Paris, France: "Calandre", ad 1969.

RACARMA, Paris, France; Detroit, MI: "Excentrique", ad 1916; "L'Esprit de Lilas", ad 1916; "L'Esprit de Rose", ad 1916; "Reine de Fleurs", ad 1916.

RACINE, Paris, France: "Eau de Soleilhas", ad 1957.

RAFFY (MARCEL J. RAFFY), Paris, France; NY, NY: "Adam et Eve", tm 1924/1923; "Chypre", ad 1930; "Encens Oriental", ad 1930; "Gardenia Bleu", tm 1927/1926; "Le Rubis", ad 1929; "Parfum R", ad 1930; "Parfum X", tm 1924/1924; "Rapsodie", tm 1930/1929; "Satan", ad 1930; "Shanghai", ad 1930; "Tour Eiffel", tm 1926/1926; "Tulipe", ad 1930; 'Voici Paris", ad 1929.

RALLET, Paris, France: "No. 1", Fr. ad 1930; "No. 3", Fr. ad 1930; "33", tm 1930/1930; "77", tm 1930/1930; "Confession", tm 1935/1934; "Floric", tm 1928/1927; "La Giroflée", tm 1937/1932; "Last Paradise", tm 1935/1935; "Le Succes de Rallet", ad 1937; "Maidou", Fr. ad 1930; "Xyris", tm 1928/1928.

RAMSES, Paris, France; Cairo, Egypt: "Ambre de Nubie", ad 1923; "Chypre", ad 1923; "Jasmin d'Egypte", ad 1923; "Lotus Sacré", art 1918; "Origan", ad 1923; "Ramses IV", art 1919; "Rose Antique", cat 1922; "Secret du Sphinx", art 1917; "Sidon", cat 1922; "Sphinx D'Or", cat 1922.

RAPHAEL, Paris, France: "Cynique", tm 1947/1944; "Feu De Paille", tm 1947/1944; "Réplique", tm 1946/1944; "Volontiers", tm 1947/1944; "Whisky", tm 1958/1957.

RAQUEL INC., NY, NY: "Le Menuet", tm 1927/1926; "L'Endeley", tm 1927/1927; "Olor de la Noche", tm 1925/1925; "Orange Blosso Fragrancia", tm 1926/1925.

RAUCOUR, Paris, France: "Calypso", ad 1946.

JEAN RAVAUD, NY, NY: "Neuilly, France: "Abdication", tm 1937/1936; "Royal Romance", tm 1937/1936.

RAVEL, NY, NY: "No. 9", tm 1958/1956; "Adagio", tm 1945/1945; "Faun", ad 1946; "L'Amour En Rose", tm 1956/1955; "Moments-De-Passion", tm 1957/1955; "My Fair Lady", tm 1957/1955; "Pagan", tm 1945/1945; "Pagoda", tm 1945/1945.

W. T. RAWLEIGH, Freeport, IL: "La Jaynees", tm 1924/1924.

RAY MANUFACTURING CO., NY, NY: "Ramaco", tm 1925/1910.

RAYMOND, London, England: "Teasie Weasie", tm 1956/1954.

A. RAYNAUD, Paris, France: "Oriza", tm 1879/1879.

READ DRUG & CHEMICAL CO., Baltimore, MD: "Lorty", tm 1926/1915.

REBOUX, Paris, France: "Black", ad 1929; "Green", ad 1929; "Red", ad 1929; "Yellow", ad 1929.

RECHERCHES, Paris, France: "Moulin Rouge", tm 1949/1910.

REDAU LABORATORY, Brooklyn, NY: "June Moon", tm 1930/1930.

FRANCAISE REDFERN, Paris, France: "Ocean D'Amour", tm 1930/1929; "Rouge Lointain", tm 1930/1929; "Soir Hindou", tm 1930/1929.

MAYO REESE, Chicago, IL: "Kolone Kanes", tm 1948/1946; "The Glass Menagerie", tm 1948/1946.

REGENT LABORATORIES, NY, NY: "Carousel", tm 1946/1945.

MARTHE REGNIER, Paris, France: "Elle A Passé Par Ici", tm 1925/1924; "Suivez-Moi Jeune Homme", tm 1926/1923.

OTTO REICHEL, Berlin, Germany: "Licht Herz", tm 1936/1933.

REICHMAN & FAUST, NY, NY: "May Flowers", tm 1926/1926.

FRANK C. REILLY, NY, NY: "Après-Midi", tm 1933/1931; "Caballero", tm 1934/1933; "Deep Night", tm 1931/1931; "Drezden", tm 1933/1932; "Easter Parade", tm 1935/1932; "First Night At The Empire", tm 1932/1931; "Guernsee", tm 1932/1930; "Hennessy", tm 1932/1931; "Jardin Des Baghdad", tm 1936/1935; "Jasmin 1929", tm 1936/1932; "Jerzee", tm 1932/1931; "L'heure du Thé", tm 1933/1931; "Le Message de Violette", tm 1936/1931; "Molnar", tm 1932/1931; "Moonlight & Roses", tm 1934/1932; "Moonlight On The Ganges", tm 1932/1931; "New Year's Eve In Havana", tm 1932/1931; "Nuit Profonde", tm 1932/1931; "Rose Ebène", tm 1934/1932; "Rose Noire", tm 1934/1932; "Roses Of Picardy", tm 1933/1932; "Strictly Dishonorable", tm 1932/1931; "Two Hearts In Waltz Time", art 1931.

REINE INC., NY, NY: "French Bleu", tm 1947/1946; "Nanouchka", tm 1944/1927.

REINHARDT & MCSWEENEY, NY, NY: "Screen Star", tm 1939/1938.

REJANE, NY, NY: "Canasta", tm 1950/1950; "Cascabel", tm 1948/1947; "Colibri", tm 1948/1947; "Flor de Insidia", tm 1948/1947.

REJUVIA, NY, NY: "Bull's I", tm 1947/1946; "Crossfire", tm 1947/1946.

REMBRANDT, Philadelphia, PA: "Carousel", tm 1945/1945.

REMILLER, NY, NY: "Basket Of Roses", cat 1922; "Billet Doux", tm 1924/1922; "Fleurs Joyeuse", tm 1924/1923; "Grecian Rose", cat 1922; "Léone", tm 1916/1916; "Lorina", tm 1925/1923; "Mirimbi Lily", cat 1922; "Mon Trésor", tm 1924/1922; "Narcé", tm 1924/1923; "Rose O'May", tm 1926/1926; "Varna", cat 1922.

REMOVA LABORATORIES, INC., Syracuse, NY: "Lady Jane", tm 1926/1925.

RENAUD, Paris, France; Montreuil, France; Boston, MA: "Bateau Ivre", tm 1947/1940; "Cour de Russie", tm 1925/1920; "Fleur de Manacao", tm 1925/1920; "Fleurs de Grasse", tm 1925/1920; "Forest of France", tm 1925/1920; "Glissade", tm 1947/1943; "Jardins Celestes", tm 1925/1920; "L'Ile de France", tm 1926/1919; "L'Isle", tm 1926/1919; "Lubentia", tm 1925/1920; "Parfums of Royalty", ad 1936; "Sur Deux Notes", tm 1947/1940.

RENDES (RENE DESSEIGNES), Paris, France: "Ting-Shang", tm 1925/1924.

RENEE, NY, NY: "Paris, France: "Baiser Discrit", ad 1923; "Mon Parterri", ad 1923; "Narcissus", ad 1923.

RENEL, Mt. Vernon, NY; NY, NY:

"Becoming", tm 1944/1944; "Etchings", tm 1944/1943; "Mandate", tm 1946/1945; "Provocative", tm 1943; "Roughing It", 1945/1944; "Roulette", tm 1943/1943.

RENOIR, Paris, France; NY, NY: "Alibi", tm 1943/1942; "Chi Chi", ad 1942; "Daring", tm 1943/1942; "Dõna Sol", art 1939; "Futur", new 1939; "Gambade", ad 1949; "Grande Epoque", ad 1953; "Impetuous", tm 1942/1941; "Messager", new 1939; "My Alibi", tm 1945/1942; "Paradox", tm 1944/1944; "Sheshe", tm 1947/1947; "Witchcraft", tm 1943/1942.

OSCAR DE LA RENTA, Paris, France: "Oscar de la Renta", new 1977.

MAURICE RENTNER, NY, NY: "Eight Thirty", tm 1946/1946; "Memento", tm 1957/1956; "So Chic", tm 1953/1951; "Twenty-One", ad 1945.

REUTER (LANMAN & KEMP-BARCLAY & CO.), NY, NY: "1808", tm 1945/1945; "Agua De Florida", tm 1948/1830; "Hasta Mañana", tm 1945/1945; "Restless", tm 1945/1945.

REVILLON, Paris, France: "4 Vents", tm 1955/1952; "Amou-Daria", tm 1935/1935; "Cantilene", new 1948; "Carnet De Bal", tm 1938/1935; "Detchema", tm 1955/1953; "Egoïste", tm 1938/1935; "Latitude 50°", tm 1935/1935; "Tornade", tm 1935/1935; "Turbulences", new 1981.

REVLON, NY, NY: "Aquamarine", tm 1959/1946; "Charlie", new 1973; "Intimate", new 1957; "Jontue", new 1975; "Majorca", tm 1957/1955; "Norell", new 1968; "Sea Isle", tm 1956/1955; "Splurge", tm 1954/1953; "That Man", tm 1959/1958.

LENA E. REYNOLDS, Lincoln, NE: "La Vrayne", tm 1942/1942; "Shangri-La", tm 1945/1942.

NINA RICCI, Paris, France: "Barbaresque", tm 1946/1943; "Bigarade", new 1971; "Capricci", new 1961; "Coeur-Joie", new 1946; "Eau de Fleur", new 1980; "Farouche", new 1974; "Fille d'Eve", new 1952; "Fleurs de Fleurs", new 1982; "L'Air Du Temps", new 1948; "Philers", new 1984; "Pigno Ricci", new 1966; "Melle Ricci", new 1965; "Nina", new 1987.

IVOR RICH, NY, NY: "Curzon", tm 1945/1943; "Mexican Hayride", tm 1944/1943; "Night of Stars", tm 1943/1942.

RICHEBOIS: "Scrupule", art 1942.

RICHELIEU: "Cardinal", cat 1933; "Gardenia", cat 1933; "Humoresque", cat 1933; "Or Leay", cat 1933; "Tete-A-Tete", cat 1933.

MARIE RICHELIEU PARFUM ODESANT, NY, NY: "Black Jade", tm 1946/1941; "Curtain Call", tm 1946/1941; "Deceit", tm 1946/1941; "Duk-Duk", tm 1947/1944; "Kikki", tm 1947/1944; "Pink Lilac", tm 1946/1944; "Saddle Bow", tm 1946/1941; "Sand & Spray", tm 1946/1941.

RICHEY INC., Chicago, IL: "Daring", tm 1945/1941; "Sentiment", tm 1945/1943; "Spice O' Life", tm 1945/1941.

RICHMOND-PHILLIPS, NY, NY: "Fleur de Barbezon", tm 1946/1945.

THEO RICKSECKER, NY, NY; Hoboken, NJ: "Attar Tropical", cat 1922; "Golden Gate", new 1884; "La Vie", cat 1922; "Lily of the Valley", new 1884; "Mizpah", new 1884; "Ping Pong", cat 1922; "Seven Roses", cat 1922; "Subroga", new 1884.

S. A. RIDER CO., Chicago, IL: "Arabay", tm 1925/1924.

PAUL RIEGER, San Francisco, CA: "Alcazar", cat 1922; "Coronado", cat 1922; "Countess Spencer", cat 1922; "Flower-Drops", ad 1910; "Garden Bloom", cat 1922; "Garden Queen", cat 1922; "Honolulu Bouquet", cat 1922; "Jazarimba", cat 1922; "Mariposa Lily", cat 1922; "Mon-Amour", tm 1912/1911; "Mon Desir", cat 1922; "Palo Alto Pink", cat 1922; "Parfum Rienzi", cat 1922; "Rahma", cat 1922; "Reve des Fleurs", cat 1922; "Romanza", cat 1922; "Royal Cherry Buds", 1906/1906; "Sweet Kiss", cat 1922.

WILHELM RIEGER, Frankfort, Germany: "Nirvana", tm 1895/1893; "Parzival", tm 1892/1890.

RIFA-NEW YORK INC., NY, NY: "Rosanthol", tm 1937/1936.

RIGAUD, Paris, France; NY, NY: "Alizé", tm 1945/1945; "Azur Nuit", tm 1925/1925; "Cantate", tm 1947/1946; "Cher Souvenir", tm 1925/1925; "Des Roses", tm 1924/1908; "Eau De Kananga Du Japon", Fr. ad 1932; "Evereve", tm 1957/1955; "Féerie Moderne", tm 1938/1938; "Fragrant Breeze", tm 1951/1948; "Geraldine Farrar", tm 1913/1912; "Golden Narcissus", tm 1926/1923; "Igora", tm 1931/1931; "Kananga Flowers", tm 1882/1882; "L'Air de France", tm 1948/1947; "Lilac", ad 1913; "Lilas de Rigaud", ad 1913; "Mary Garden", tm 1910/1910; "Minena", tm 1923/1909; "Ombrages", tm 1947/1946; "Outre Mer", ad 1938; "Parade", tm 1933/1932; "Parfum Tendre", Fr. ad 1925; "Près de Vous", tm 1946/1945; "Ruse", tm 1945/1945; "Soupirs D'Amour", tm 1925/1925; "Souviens-Toi", tm 1925/1925; "Spirale", tm 1947/1946; "Style", tm 1947/1946; "Téméraire", tm 1945/1945; "Trentini", tm 1911/1911; "Tumultes", tm 1947/1946; "Typhon", ad 1938; "Un Air Embaumé", tm 1925/1915; "Vers La Joie", tm 1927/1927; "Violettes de Toulouse", ad 1957.

RIGO CHEMICAL, Nashville, TN: "Alice Dale's Crest", tm 1924/1923.

WM. B. RIKER & SON, NY, NY: "Charmona", tm 1907/1907.

RIKER & HEGEMAN, NY, NY: "Incensia", tm 1915/1911.

RILLING-DERMETICS, NY, NY: "Dotted Swiss", tm 1954/1953.

RIMMEL, London, England; Paris, France; NY, NY: "Art Moderne", tm 1926/1925; "Fraxi", tm 1925/1925; "Golden Fern", ad 1911; "Les Capucines", art 1923; "Ma Mie Annette", art 1923; "Onyka", tm 1930/1930; "Velvetis", tm 1932/1925; "Vocalise", art 1923.

RINELLI: "No. 9", ad 1936; "No. 10", ad 1936; "Scent Eternal — No. 7", ad 1936.

RITORNELLE, NY, NY: "Coming Attraction", tm 1955/1955; "Mona Lisa", tm 1961/1949.

RITZ COSMETIC, Elizabeth, NJ: "Joalene", tm 1933/1933; "Joanel", tm 1932/1931.

RIZIK BROS., Washington, DC: "Fleur Divine", tm 1926/1926.

ANATOLE ROBBINS, Los Angeles, CA: "Autumn Leaves", tm 1948/1940; "Forty Thieves", tm 1947/1940; "Wanderlust", tm 1952/1951; "Woodfield", tm 1948/1946.

ROBERT, NY, NY: "Best Wishes", tm 1946/1945; "Hubba-Hubba", tm 1946/1945; "Lady of Leisure", tm 1933/1932; "Thinking of You", tm 1947/1946.

ROBIEN, NY, NY: "Decision", ad 1946.

ROBJ., Paris, France: "Le Secret de Robj", tm 1927/1925.

ROCCA, Paris, France: "Brise d'Or", ad 1920; "Divin Muguet", ad 1926; 'Eveil Des Roses", ad 1920; "Mon Succes", ad 1921; "Oliane", ad 1921; "Wonderful", tm 1948/1897.

GUILLEMETTE ROCHAID, Paris, France: "Madame X", tm 1963/1961.

ROCHAMBEAU, NY, NY: "Clochettes Parfumées", tm 1925/1923.

MARCEL ROCHAS, Paris, France: "Air Jeune", ad 1936; "Audace", ad 1936; "Avenue Matignon", tm 1937/1936; "Femme", art 1945; "La Rose", ad 1949; "Lumière", new 1984; "Macassar", new 1980; "Madame Rochas", tm 1962/1960; "Mouche", tm 1950/1948; "Mousseline", tm 1949/1947; "Moustache", art 1947; "Mystère", new 1978.

ROCHESTER LABORATORIES INC., Rochester, MN: "American Venus", tm 1926/1925.

E. RODIER & CIE, Paris, France; Courbevoie, France: "Lydés", tm 1921/1919.

CHARLES RODITI, Paris, France: "Raquel Meller", tm 1927/1925.

ROELLY CHEMICAL, NY, NY: "Beatrice", cat 1922; "Carissima", cat 1922; "Gardenia", cat 1922.

ROGER ET GALLET, Paris, France: "Ambrerose", cat 1922; "Anthéa", tm 1940/1892; "Ausonia", tm 1926/1905; "Aveu", tm 1947/1946; "Bouquet des Amours", tm 1924/1898; "Bouquet des Roses", cat 1922; "Bridalis", cat 1922; "Challenge", tm 1935/1935; "Cigalia", cat 1922; "Delicia", tm 1926/1890; "Diamelia Pompadour", cat 1922; "Dim Innuendo', tm 1946/1945; "Dogwood", tm 1942/1941; "Ess Bouquet", cat 1922; "Feu-Follet", tm 1931/1930; "Feux Follets", tm 1931/1930; "Fleurs D'Amour", tm 1923/1902; "Fleurs du Passe", cat 1922; "Flors de Tokio", cat 1922; "Foin Nouveau", cat 1922; "Frivolités", tm 1936/1934; "Fugue", tm 1938/1832; "Gallia", tm 1929/1886; "Giroffflee", cat 1922; "Gloire de Paris", tm 1924/1906; "Initiation", tm 1935/1935; "Innuendo", ad 1946; "Kali", tm 1943/1943; "Lavande", new 1896; "Le Jade", tm 1923/1923; "Lioris", cat 1922; "Marechale", cat 1922; "Marque Noire", new 1891; "Missive", tm 1934/1932; "Muguet de Mai", cat 1922; "Narkiss", cat 1922; "Nemora", cat 1922; "Night of Delight", tm 1948/1938; "Nuit D'Extase", tm 1939/1938; "Oeillet Blanc", cat 1922; "Oeillet Bleu", tm 1939/1939; "Oeillet de Paris", cat 1922; "Paquerettes", cat 1922; "Partir", tm 1948/1927; "Pavots D'Argent", tm 1926/1926; "Persana", tm 1926/1911; "Pervenche", cat 1922; "Pourpre d'Orient", tm 1930/1929; "Prestige", tm 1943/1943; "Rose Paul Nevron", cat 1922; "Salvia", cat 1922; "Santal", new 1978; "Soins D'Eau", new 1981; "Soloïl", tm 1930/1928; "Souvenir de la Cour", cat 1922; "Stephanotis", cat 1922; "Tentation", tm 1925/1923; "Vera-Violetta", tm 1893/1892; "Vetyver", new 1974; "Violette Amoree", cat 1922; "Violette Rubra", art 1911.

VIRGINIA NICHOLSON ROGERS, Memphis, TN: "Make Believe", tm 1947/1946; "Mother O'Mine", tm 1947/1946.

MIMI ROGET, Short Hills, NJ: "Till Then", tm 1954/1953.

ROGIER, Paris, France: "Aida", ad 1921; "Argonne", ad 1921; "Broken Blossoms", ad 1921; "Lilac", ad 1921; "Lily", ad 1921; "Rose", ad 1921; "Violette", ad 1921.

RO-JO CURIO CO., Chicago, IL: "Indian Love Call", tm 1944/1943.

ROLLEE, NY, NY: "Today", tm 1925/1925.

ROLLEY, San Francisco, CA: "Barbary Coast", tm 1953/1946; "Cable Car", tm 1953/1949; "China Doll", tm 1960/1952; "Décolleté", tm 1947/1945; "Frantic", tm 1946/1945; "Haunting", tm 1953/1935; "Immortal", tm 1953/1951; "Inspiration", tm 1960/1945; "Response", tm 1946/1942; "Torrid", tm 1953/1938.

PARFUMS ROMANCE, NY, NY: "Tales of Love", ad 1941.

CHARLES J. ROMER, NY, NY: "Prince Charmant", tm 1938/1934.

RONA, Chicago, IL: "Hour Glass Cologne", ad 1940.

PARFUMS RONNI INC., NY, NY: "Rare Orchid", tm 1935/1934.

RONSARD PERFUMERS, Paris, France; NY, NY: "Blue Haze", tm 1947/1945; "Grignan", tm 1948/1945; "Mexicali", tm 1947/1945; "Vieux Paris", tm 1947/1945.

ROOSA & RATLIFF, Cincinnati, OH: "Love's Dream", tm 1923/1920; "Margie Lou", tm 1933/1930.

ROPHON INC., NY, NY: "Extravagance", tm 1941/1941.

ROSAL LABORATORIES, Miami, FL; Philadelphia, PA: "Shai", tm 1944/1943; "Shy", tm 1957/1936.

MINNA ROSE, NY, NY: "L'Orlé", tm 1935/1934.

ROSELEY PERFUMERY SHOPPE, INC., Newark, NJ: "Mary Alden", tm 1932/1931.

ISAAC ROSENBLATT, NY, NY: "Fajon", tm 1926/1926.

AL ROSENFELD, NY, NY: "Beau Catcher", tm 1941/1941; "Fountain Spray", tm 1948/1947.

EDMOND ROSENS, Paris, France: "Amorial", tm 1947/1939; "Fringant", tm 1947/1939; "La Clef de Pierre Dune", tm 1947/1946; "Privilège", tm 1947/1939; "Vous Seule", tm 1947/1939.

NETTIE ROSENSTEIN, NY, NY: "After Hours", tm 1947/1946; "Fleurs D'Elle", tm 1962/1961; "Odalisque", tm 1946/1946; "Tianne", tm 1949/1948.

ROSINE (PAUL POIRET), Paris, France: "1925", tm 1927/1926; "Aladin", tm 1923/1919; "Antinea Ou Au Fond De La Mer", art 1922; "Arlequinade", tm 1925/1924; "Avenue Du Bois", tm 1927/1926; "Borgia", tm 1925/1922; "Chez Poiret", ad 1913; "Coeur En Folie", tm 1927/1924; "Connais Tu Le Pays?", tm 1927/1925; "Coraline de Rosine", tm 1925/1918; "Es Palier Du Roy", ad 1913; "Hahna L'Etrange Fleur", tm 1925/1922; "La Coupe D'Or", tm 1925/1921; "La Rose De Rosine", tm 1925/1924; "La Rose Grand Modele", cat 1922; "La Tulipe", ad 1913; "Lait de Junon", tm 1925/1921; "Le Balcon", tm 1925/1922; "Le Bosquet D'Apollon", tm 1925/1923; "Le Fruit

Defendu", cat 1922; "Le Minaret", cat 1922; "Maharadjah", tm 1925 1922; "Mea Culpa", cat 1922; "Mou Choir De Rosine", cat 1922; "Nuit De Chine", tm 1923 1913; "Pelosine", tm 1927 1926; "Pierrot", cat 1922; "Pot Au Rose", tm 1927 1924; "Qui es-tu", tm 1927 1926; "Sa Chambre", tm 1927 1924; "Toute La Foret", tm 1925 1921.

CATHERINE G. ROSS, Chicago, IL: "Kremay", tm 1947 1934.

BENEDICT A. ROTOLO, Brooklyn, NY: "Jessica", tm 1925 1924.

L. ROUFF, Paris, France: "L. Rouff", art 1927.

MARY SCOTT ROWLAND, LTD., Jersey City, NJ: "Sinless Passion", tm 1933 1932.

ROWOLA PARFUMERIE INC., Chicago, IL: "Bridal Bouquet", tm 1926 1923.

ROX-TAN, NY, NY: "Allies", cat 1922; "Bouquet Egyptien", cat 1922; "Chin Wah", cat 1922; "Fleurs des Pris", cat 1922; "Jaquinette", cat 1922; "Mimosa de Nice", cat 1922; "Tandor", cat 1922; "Tanty", cat 1922; "Yassara", cat 1922.

ROXEY, Paris, France; NY, NY: "Chinwah", ad 1919.

ROYAL LUXURY PERFUME, NY, NY: "Entendu", tm 1958 1957; "Pardon", tm 1958 1957.

ROYANA (MANSON DIST.), Chicago, IL: "Disturbing", tm 1945 1944.

ROYCEMORE TOILETRIES, Chicago, IL: "Trellis", tm 1946 1940.

JOHN RUBEL CO., NY, NY: "Amphora", tm 1945 1944.

RUBICON INC., NY, NY: "Cupid-Lite", tm 1947 1946; "Frontier Girl", ad 1942; "Lamp Lite", ad 1941.

CARL Z. RUBIN, Chicago, IL: "Chicquita", tm 1929 1928.

SAMUEL RUBIN, NY, NY: "Chambray", tm 1941 1940; "Demi-Drams", tm 1939 1937; "Dramettes", tm 1938 1937; "Red Rhumba", tm 1943 1941; "Strawhat", tm 1939 1938; "Tigress", tm 1939 1938.

RUE DEE: "Witching Hour", ad 1935.

FERDINAND RUGGIERO, Boston, MA: "Lady Eve", tm 1948 1946.

CLARE RUMBALL (CLARE R. MILLOY), Erie, PA: "Bold Venture", tm 1955 1945; "Night Flight", tm 1955 1944.

DR. MARGARET RUPPERT, Philadelphia, PA: "Mi-Rita", tm 1933 1913.

RUTLAND'S (RUTLAND BROTHERS), St. Petersburg, FL: "Orange Blossom", tm 1936 1925.

D. FRANK RYAN INC., Cambridge, MA: "Penzance", tm 1926 1926.

SONIA RYKIEL, Paris, France: "Septième Sens", new 1979.

HELENA RUBINSTEIN, NY, NY: "715", ad 1937; "Baroque", tm 1943 1936; "Best Seller", tm 1952 1946; "Bonne Chance", tm 1940 1939; "Cologne Foam", tm 1954 1953; "Command Performance", tm 1948 1946; "Country", ad 1936; "Distinction", tm 1948 1947; "Emotion", ad 1966; "Enchanté", ad 1934; "Flower Julep", tm 1953 1949; "Flower Shop Bouquet", tm 1938 1938; "Fourth Dimension", tm 1953 1953; "Gala Performance", tm 1940 1940; "Garden Party", tm 1948 1947; "Green Jade", tm 1941 1941; "Green Velvet", tm 1948 1947; "Heaven Sent", tm 1946 1941; "Love In Bloom", tm 1947/

1946; "Mahatma", ad 1928; "Noa-Noa", tm 1953 1953; "O, Promise Me", tm 1941 1941; "One Dozen Roses", tm 1943 1943; "Orchid", ad 1939; "Princess Helena", tm 1961 1960; "Rambling Rose", tm 1947 1946; "Rebel Rose", tm 1947 1946; "Ring Me", tm 1941 1940; "Rose Magnolia", tm 1949 1946; "Secret Garden", tm 1947 1946; "Slumber Song", tm 1938 1938; "Something Blue", tm 1943 1943; "Town", ad 1936; "Vis-A-Vis", tm 1962 1960; "Water Lily", ad 1934; "White Flame", tm 1942 1942; "White Magnolia", tm 1952 1949; "Wood Fern", tm 1960 1958. (See also GOURIELLI).

S F LABORATORIES, Boston, MA: "Stane", tm 1951 1948.

SAENZ, BRIONES, & CIA, Buenos Aires, Argentina: "Fru-Fru", tm 1947 1942; "Mal Maison", tm 1947 1943; "Ninoska", tm 1946 1942; "Rêve Fleuri", tm 1947 1931.

SAHYUN LABORATORIES, Santa Barbara, CA: "Guided Missile", tm 1956 1954.

SAINT-CYR, Paris, France; NY, NY: "Homme de Paris", tm 1949 1926; "Love In Paris", tm 1949 1926; "Toujours Ou Jamais", tm 1949 1926.

SAINT DENIS, Paris, France; NY, NY: "B 18", tm 1933 1932; "Affection", tm 1937 1937; "Au Revoir", ad 1935; "Auf Wiedersehen", tm 1932 1932; "Birch", tm 1926 1925; "Birch Buds", tm 1925 1925; "Blue Carnation", tm 1926 1925; "Blue Sapphire", tm 1941 1941; "Candle Light", tm 1936 1936; "Chivalry", tm 1937 1936; "De Tout Mon Coeur", tm 1933 1932; "Dirnd'l", tm 1937 1937; "Eau de Cologne Royale", tm 1936 1926; "Gardenia Royal", tm 1935 1933; "Gay Nineties", tm 1937 1936; "Hyde Park", tm 1938 1936; "Jaunty", tm 1941 1941; "Jeunesse Vivante", tm 1927 1926; "La Royale", ad 1936; "Les Fleurs De Jasmin", ad 1935; "Liebestraum", tm 1932 1932; "Lily Of France", tm 1934 1934; "Loyalty", tm 1937 1936; "Madonna", tm 1936 1936; "New Mown Hay", ad 1939; "Non-At-All", tm 1933 1933; "Old Fashioned Bouquet", ad 1936; "Orchid", ad 1936; "Parlez Moi D'Amour", tm 1934 1934; "Pine Rest", tm 1932 1931; "Rose Garanium", ad 1935; "Royal Guard", tm 1935 1934; "Saints Release", tm 1937 1936; "Syncopation", tm 1937 1936; "The Grenadier", tm 1935 1934; "Turandot", tm 1928 1928; "Tyrolean Pine", tm 1938 1937; "Valse de Champagne", tm 1936 1934; "Vigorettes", tm 1928 1928; "Votre Beauté", tm 1936 1936; "Yankee Doodle", tm 1933 1933; "Zombie", tm 1946 1940.

YVES SAINT LAURENT, Paris, France: "Opium", new 1977; "Paris", new 1983; "Rive Gauche", new 1971; "Y", new 1964.

SAKS, NY, NY: "High Hat", tm 1932 1932; "Wee Moderns", tm 1960 1959.

JEAN BAPTISTE SALARNIER, Crepieux Rillieux, France: "Harmelle", tm 1930 1904.

G. SALEVA & CO., NY, NY: "Tropic-Isle", tm 1939 1939; "Tropicale", tm 1940 1939.

SALOMON FRERES, Pantin, France: "Valoy", tm 1948 1942.

SALTZMAN & BROMBERG, NY, NY: "Aube d'Amour", tm 1931 1930.

SAMAR COSMETIC CO., Syracuse, NY: "Convicted", tm 1952 1950; "My Destiny", tm 1952 1951.

LOUIS ALBERT SAMSTAG, NY, NY: "Duchess Of Windsor", tm 1937 1937.

SAMURAI PERFUME, NY, NY: "Mura", tm 1912 1911.

SANOPOL, Seine, France: "Marietta Enikson", tm 1948 1945.

SARAVEL INC., NY, NY: "Nuance", tm 1939 1939; "Seductive", tm 1954 1953; "Sirocco", tm 1939 1939; "Touchant", tm 1939 1939; "White Christmas", tm 1954 1943.

SARDEAU, NY, NY: "Suspicion", ad 1945; "Zebra", tm 1945 1939.

SARDI, Chicago, IL: "Incendiari", tm 1951 1949; "Tres Menée", tm 1950 1949.

SAUZE FRERES, Paris, France; Colombes, France: "Altea", cat 1922; "Brin de Mousse", cat 1922; "Chevreveuille", cat 1922; "Chypre", Fr. ad 1928; "Exotis", cat 1922; "Feu Rouge", tm 1954 1953; "Feuilles de Violettes", cat 1922; "Fleuris La Flouve", cat 1922; "Fleurs de Lys", cat 1922; "Fleurs de Mousse", cat 1922; "Floraison", cat 1922; "Grand Siècle", tm 1950 1943; "Imperial Acacia", cat 1922; "Imperial Russe", cat 1922; "La Flouve", cat 1922; "Lauris", cat 1922; "Liane Fleurie", cat 1922; "Lys de Domremy", cat 1922; "Prestigs de Paris", tm 1950 1947; "Sèvres", tm 1939 1936; "Simple Bouquet de Roses", cat 1922.

SAVAGE INC., Chicago, IL: "Jungle", tm 1934 1934.

SAVILLE, Watford, England: "Gallant", ad 1941; "June", tm 1940 1927; "Mischief", tm 1937 1935; "Seventh Heaven", tm 1940 1938; "Tutu", tm 1956 1955.

SCAGLIA, Kansas City, MO: "Night Blooming Cereus", tm 1956 1954; "White Savage", tm 1954 1952.

J. SCHANZENBACH & CO., NY, NY: "Sis-Ozon", tm 1925 1925.

SCHARMOUCHE, Chicago, IL: "Jabali", tm 1946 1946.

SCHERICK, Paris, France: "Nabu", tm 1935 1935; "Tempest", tm 1935 1935.

SCHERK (LUDWIG SCHERK), Berlin, Germany; NY, NY: "Arabian Nights", new 1919; "Arabifche Nächte", tm 1925 1919; "Briza", tm 1926 1918; "Intermezzo", tm 1930 1929; "Mimikri", tm 1927 1926; "Mysticum", tm 1926 1910; "Mystikum", tm 1925 1910; "Purple Rose", tm 1945 1920; "Renaissance", tm 1940 1921; "Trisena", tm 1926 1913.

WALTER SCHERK, Neuilly, France: "Danses", tm 1957 1953.

JEAN-LOUIS SCHERRER, Paris, France: "Jean-Louis Scherrer", new 1979; "Scherrer 2", new 1986.

SCHETTLER DRUG CO., Detroit, MI: "Enfin", tm 1928 1928.

SCHIAPARELLI, Paris, France: "Chloro-Cologne", tm 1955 1952; "Le Roy Soleil", tm 1946 1946; "Radiance", tm 1947 1943; "Salud de Schiaparelli", tm 1934 1934; "Sans Souci", tm 1943 1943; "Schiap", tm 1934 1934; "Seraphique", tm 1946 1945; "Schocking", tm 1937 1936; "Schocking You", new 1977; "Si", tm 1959 1957; "Silence", tm 1942 1942; "Sleeping", tm 1938 1938; "Snuff", tm 1942 1940; "Sotto Voce", tm 1948 1947; "Soucis de Schiapa-

relli'', tm 1934/1934; ''Spanking'', tm
1942/1942; ''Spring 'N Summer'', tm
1957/1956; ''Stratosphere'', tm 1946/1946;
''Succès Fou'', ad 1953; ''Voyageur'', tm
1960/1958; ''Zut'', ad 1949.

GEORG SCHICT, Aussig, Czechoslovakia:
''Elida'', tm 1928/1921; ''Leda'', tm
1930/1901; ''Polynol'', tm 1926/1923.

IRA SCHIEBER, NY, NY: ''La Enamorade'',
tm 1935/1934.

SCHIEFFELIN, NY, NY: ''Calista'', tm
1908/1908; ''Charade'', cat 1922; ''La
Luzerne'', cat 1922; ''Neuya'', cat 1922;
''White Bells'', cat 1922.

SCHIMMEL & CO., Miltitz, Germany;
Leipzig, Germany: ''Clykosma'', tm
1929/1928; ''Extrol'', tm 1926/1926;
''Jasmilan'', tm 1927/1926; ''Neoviolon'',
tm 1909/1908.

HERMAN V. SCHLOSS, NY, NY: ''Oomph'',
tm 1940/1940.

JULIUS SCHMID, INC., NY, NY: ''Milrone'',
tm 1929/1928; ''Santro'', tm 1927/1927.

SCHNEFEL BROS., Newark, NJ: ''Jewel
Mist'', tm 1954/1953; ''La Cross'', tm
1950/1922; ''Naylon'', tm 1949/1941.

EDWARD SCHNYDER, Zurich, Switzerland:
''Honey'', tm 1953/1949.

MAURICE SCHOEPFER, Paris, France:
''Dixor'', tm 1923/1922.

EDITH SCHULTZ, Chicago, IL: ''Mitzi's
Charm'', tm 1927/1922.

LIGHTFOOT SCHULTZ CO., NY, NY;
Hoboken, NJ: ''Avaderma'', tm 1946/1945;
''Clover'', ad 1936; ''Mordaunt'', tm
1930/1915; ''Mural-Scent'', tm 1928/1928;
''Royal Oak'', tm 1945/1942.

WILLIAM L. SCHULTZ, NY, NY: ''Alice In
Wonderland'', tm 1934/1933.

P. J. SCHUMACHER CO., NY, NY: ''La
Musa'', new 1920.

F. A. SCHWANNECKE, NY, NY: ''Doucette'',
tm 1925/1923.

GUSTAV SCHWARZ, Chicago, IL: ''Secrets
Of Paris'', tm 1941/1940.

J. F. SCHWARZLOSE, Berlin, Germany:
''Rose Royalin'', art 1911; ''Violette
Royalin'', art 1911.

R. & F. SCHWEICKHARDT, St. Louis, MO:
''Violacynth'', tm 1904/1903.

SCOTCH PRODUCTS INC., NY, NY: ''Yes'',
tm 1937/1937.

SCOTT'S LABORATORIES, Chicago, IL:
''Marquita'', tm 1924/1924.

HYMAN SEGER, Brooklyn, NY: ''Mme
Ada'', tm 1929/1919.

SEGHERS. (See DE SEGHERS).

SELWYN IMPORTING, NY, NY: ''La
Feria'', tm 1904/1902; ''Tintoret'', tm
1904/1901.

MARGUERITE SELZ, Paris, France:
''Calixte'', tm 1946/1944; ''Manege'', tm
1946/1944.

RALPH F. SENESE, Brooklyn, NY: ''Ever-
stay'', tm 1930/1913.

SEREY, Paris, France: ''La Nuit du Samedi'',
art 1932.

SERON, Long Island, NY: ''Georgette'', tm
1944/1940.

BERNARD SEROY, NY, NY: ''Dolie'', tm
1930/1929.

SHANDRA, NY, NY: ''Devil May Care'', ad
1947; ''Halcyon Nights'', ad 1947; ''Three-
Quarter Time'', ad 1947.

EVE SHANNON, NY, NY: ''Misteria'', tm
1950/1948.

H. B. SHAPIRO, Miami, FL: ''I'm Loved'',
tm 1955/1954.

SHEFFIELD CO., New London, CT: ''Tut
Tut'', tm 1938/1937.

SHERBROOKE CO., Philadelphia, PA:
''Sherbron'', tm 1956/1955.

JEAN R. SHERMAN, NY, NY: ''Du Vée'', tm
1936/1936.

SHISEIDO, Japan: ''Hanae Mori'', ad 1969;
''Inoui'', new 1959; ''Murasaki'', new 1980;
''Nombre Noir'', 1982; ''Zen'', ad 1969.

KABUSHIKI SHOTEN, Tokyo, Japan:
''Lait'', tm 1920/1906.

SHULTON, NY, NY; Clifton, NJ: ''Always
Date Lovely'', tm 1942/1942; ''Early
American'', tm 1937/1937; ''Early American
Gardens'', tm 1939/1939; ''Early American
Heartbeat'', tm 1940/1939; ''Early American
Roundelay'', tm 1940/1939; ''Escapade'',
tm 1955/1954; ''Friendship's Garden'', tm
1940/1939; ''handsome is as handsome
does'', tm 1938/1937; ''Old Spice'', tm
1938/1936; ''Page One'', tm 1955/1954;
''Picaresque'', tm 1945/1944; ''Sandra'', tm
1936/1935; ''Taji'', ad 1965; ''Tropical
Night'', tm 1936/1936; ''Verve'', tm
1955/1953.

H. R. SIBNER CO., NY, NY: ''His Nibs'', tm
1947/1945.

SILKA, Paris, France: ''Caricia'', tm 1924/
1910; ''Coy de Paris'', tm 1947/1946;
''Flamme Parfumée'', tm 1924/1912;
''Konia'', art 1919; ''Lunasol'', art 1928;
''Viens A Moi'', ad 1930.

SILVER MOON CO., New Orleans, LA:
''Witching Moon'', tm 1930/1929.

ALBERT SIMON, NY, NY: ''Happiness'',
tm 1924/1922.

FRANKLIN SIMON, Paris, France: ''Révér-
ence'', new 1982.

FRANKLIN SIMON & CO., NY, NY: ''Rêve
de Chine'', tm 1924/1921; ''Telise'', tm
1931/1931.

SIMONETTA, Rome, Italy: ''Incanto'', ad
1955.

ALBERT SIMONSON, NY, NY: ''Capitole'',
tm 1882/1882.

ADELE SIMPSON, NY, NY; Miami, FL:
''Collage'', ad 1969; ''Exotic'', tm 1935/
1935; ''Introduction'', tm 1946/1944.

ROY M. SINGER, Los Angeles, CA:
''Chanteur'', tm 1938/1934.

JOSEF SJOSTROM, Stockholm, Sweden:
''Prince of Parma'', tm 1929/1928.

SKIN TESTED DRUG PRODUCTS, NY,
NY: ''Montego'', tm 1954/1953;
''Romanelle'', tm 1954/1953.

E. T. SLATTERY CO., Boston, MA: ''Marie
Antoinette'', tm 1926/1920.

SMITH, KLINE, & FRENCH, Philadelphia,
PA: ''Blue Danube'', tm 1912/1911;
''Eskay'', tm 1891/1891; ''Idealia'', tm
1891/1891; ''Scottish Queen'', tm 1891/
1891.

SMITH BROS., Brooklyn, NY: ''Princess
Jeannette'', tm 1929/1928.

ALBERT L. SMITH, Palatine, IL: ''Lovine'',
tm 1889/1880.

FREDERICK K. SMITH, NY, NY: ''La
Victoire'', tm 1919/1917.

OLIVE SMITH, Chicago, IL: ''Chinita Mia'',
tm 1946/1946; ''Tuteame'', tm 1945/1945;
''Wayfarer'', tm 1947/1947.

SMITH VICTORY CORP., Buffalo, NY:
''Bright Christmas'', tm 1957/1948.

SNOW WHITE, Lynchburg, VA: ''Lady

Wayne'', tm 1954/1938; ''Love Magic'', tm
1948/1947.

SOCIALITE COSMETICS INC., NY, NY:
''Cosmopolitan'', tm 1946/1945;
''Jamboree'', tm 1946/1945.

SOCIETE DU LOURE, Paris, France:
''Studia'', tm 1927/1923.

**SOCIETE FRANCAISE DES PRODUCTS
DE BEAUTE,** Paris, France: Citroneige'',
tm 1926/1922; ''Neige des Cévennes'', tm
1923/1920; ''Reine de Paris'', tm 1926/1926;
''Sous Les Neiges'', tm 1926/1924.

SOCIETE HYGIENIQUE, Paris, France:
''Arnaga'', cat 1922; ''Bronx Park'', cat
1922; ''Chant d'Amour'', cat 1922;
''Cythise'', cat 1922; ''Dazy'', cat 1922;
''Eryda'', cat 1922; ''Griserie'', cat 1922;
''Heliosa'', cat 1922; ''Incroyable Bouquet'',
cat 1922; ''Japara'', cat 1922; ''Joye du
Coeur'', cat 1922; ''Kiou-Li'', cat 1922;
''Krocusia'', cat 1922; ''Lait de Violettes'',
cat 1922; ''Laurosa'', cat 1922; ''Lilas
Cottan'', cat 1922; ''Muguet de France'', cat
1922; ''Musidora'', cat 1922; ''Myrte d'Or'',
cat 1922; ''Rosilda'', cat 1922; ''Si Jolie'',
cat 1922; ''Very Violet'', cat 1922; ''Violettes
Derby'', cat 1922.

**SOCIETE PARISIENNE D'ESSENCES
RARES ET DE PARFUMS,** Paris, France:
''A Travers La Voilette'', tm 1926/1923;
''Ambre De Carthage'', tm 1926/1924;
''Bleu de Chine'', tm 1926/1924; ''Trésor
Caché'', tm 1926/1925; ''Venise La Belle'',
tm 1926/1925.

SOCIETE VIRGINIA, Monte Carlo:
''Giglio'', art 1961.

ANTON DEPPE SOHNE, Hamburg,
Germany: ''Schloss-Marke'', tm 1912/1906.

SOLIS, Habana, Cuba: ''El Encanto'', tm
1940/1888.

SOPRANO PERFUME CO., NY, NY:
''Proposal'', tm 1945/1943.

ROGER DE SORIA, Clichy, France:
''Elesbé'', tm 1923/1922.

MIGUEL BIENVENIDO SORRIBES, Paris,
France: ''Amor Brujo'', tm 1950/1948.

SOUTHLAND PERFUME CO., NY, NY:
''Jacksonville, FL: ''Carmita'', ad 1918.

SOVEREIGN PRODUCTS, Chicago, IL:
''Evening Star'', tm 1936/1935.

SPANISH TRADING CORP., NY, NY: ''Old
Madrid'', tm 1937/1925.

SPEAR & SUSSKIND, Providence, RI:
''World's Fair'', tm 1938/1936.

SPECIAL PREPARATIONS CO., NY, NY:
''Entrancement'', tm 1956/1953.

SPECIAL PURPOSE PERFUME CO.,
Chicago, IL: ''Birthday Perfume'', tm
1939/1939.

SPENCER PERFUME CO., South Bend, IN:
''L'Odeur'', tm 1926/1922; ''Mai-Ton'', ad
1923; ''Vadis'', tm 1920/1919.

ADOLPH SPIEHLER, Rochester, NY:
''Aurora'', cat 1922; ''Chic'', cat 1922;
''College Queen'', cat 1922; ''Fleur de
Marie'', cat 1922; ''Florodora'', cat 1922;
''Japanese Tea Rose'', cat 1922; ''Madelon'',
tm 1929/1887; ''March Violet'', cat 1922;
''Picked Violets'', cat 1922; ''Queen Anne'',
cat 1922; ''Thirza'', cat 1922.

SPOONER, NY, NY: ''Americana'', tm
1939/1937; ''Charleston Red'', tm 1926/
1925; ''Elice White'', tm 1931/1930;
''Genesse'', tm 1930/1928; ''Helen Jay'', tm
1933/1932; ''Honeymoon'', tm 1924/1914;
''Jean Royce'', tm 1931/1930; ''Lucille

Lee'', tm 1934/1931; "Southern Girl'', tm 1930/1929.

SPORTLINE INC., NY, NY: "Casual'', tm 1947/1945.

CONSTANCE SPRY, NY, NY: "Blue Flowers'', tm 1942/1941.

STADDON & KILBOURN, Montreal, Canada: "Halcyon Nights'', tm 1948/1946; "Scimitar'', tm 1948/1946; "Vagrant'', tm 1948/1946.

STAFFORD-MILLER CO., Brooklyn, NY: "Melard'', tm 1934/1934.

STANIS, Chicago, IL: "Chez Paree'', tm 1939/1934; "Evening of Romance'', tm 1939/1938; "Night of Love'', tm 1939/1936.

STANLEY HOME PRODUCTS, Westfield, MA: "Lady Catherine'', tm 1953/1952; "Lady President'', tm 1953/1952; "Party Date'', tm 1962/1960; "Sweater 'n Skirt'', tm 1961/1959.

FREDERICK STEARN, Detroit, MI: "Chin Chin'', tm 1917/1916; "Concress'', tm 1910/1910; "Czarina'', tm 1899/1896; "Day Dreams'', tm 1918/1917; "Desirez Moi'', tm 1940/1935; "Eterno'', tm 1914/1914; "Eudora'', tm 1903/1903; "Fluffy Ruffles'', tm 1907/1907; "Four Roses'', cat 1922; "Golden Dawn'', tm 1928/1928; "Jazz'', tm 1919/1919; "L'Amusette'', tm 1919/1919; "Lamballe'', tm 1909/1908; "Lorna'', tm 1901/1901; "Pompadour'', tm 1906/1905; "Sadira'', tm 1921/1920; "Suprema'', tm 1901/1901; "Synthetol'', tm 1910/1910; "Thelma'', tm 1905/1905; "Yolande'', tm 1903/1902.

CARL V. STEHLE, NY, NY: "Aromette'', tm 1924/1924.

STEIN AND BLAINE, NY, NY: "Ambassador'', tm 1925/1925.

STEINFELS FRERES, Vincennes, France: "Chanson D'Ete'', tm 1924/1922; "Fleur Ardente'', tm 1924/1920.

STEINWAY PERFUMERY SHOP, Long Island City, NY: "Or Buern'', tm 1928/1928.

STERLE, Paris, France: "Huit-Huit'', Fr. ad 1955.

STERN BROTHERS, NY, NY: "Pamela'', tm 1931/1931.

CHAS. A. STEVENS & BROS., Chicago, IL: "a la primavera'', tm 1928/1927; "C'est Ca!'', tm 1927/1927; "Ci-Cix'', tm 1927/1927; "durante el invierno'', tm 1927/1927; "el ano perfumado'', tm 1927/1927; "en el verano'', tm 1927/1927; "parael otono'', tm 1927/1927; "Tears'', tm 1927/1927.

JOHN H. STEVENS, Newark, NJ: "Foma'', tm 1910/1909.

RUTH C. P. STEVENSON, Rockcliffe Park, Canada: "Planetary'', tm 1929/1928; "Zodiacal'', tm 1929/1928.

GEZA STIASSNEY, NY, NY: "Nirvana'', tm 1946/1945.

STIX, BAER, AND FULLER, St. Louis, MO: "Arline'', tm 1943/1932; "Josanne'', tm 1925/1925.

STORFER LABORATORIES, NY, NY: "Guimet'', tm 1925/1925; "Valois'', tm 1926/1925.

STORZ LABORATORIES, Chicago, IL: "Miss America'', tm 1927/1927.

STOYANOFF, GERLI, & CO., Sofia, Bulgaria; NY, NY: "Kara Rosa'', tm 1927/1924.

STRANGE LABORATORIES, Tucson, AR: "Kuan Yin'', tm 1948/1943.

EDWARD STRECKER, NY, NY: "Cinderella'', tm 1939/1939.

J. STRICKLAND & CO., Memphis, TN: "Aloma'', tm 1954/1947; "Leap Year'', tm 1949/1948; "Red Plush'', tm 1949/1948; "Royal Crown'', tm 1954/1953; "Rustic'', tm 1954/1953; "Thunderbolt'', tm 1949/1948.

JEAN STUART COSMETICS INC., New Haven, CT: "Charm Box'', tm 1929/1928; "Country'', tm 1930/1930; "Junior Deb'', tm 1929/1928; "Town'', tm 1930/1930.

STUART, St. Paul, MN: "Bed of Roses'', tm 1941/1940; "Dutch Girl Perfumes'', ad 1940; "Floral Quintuplets'', tm 1936/1935; "Hi-Lights'', ad 1940; "Perfumador'', ad 1940; "Perfume Topics'', ad 1941; "Perfume Vanity'', ad 1940; "Teez'', tm 1952/1937; "Whatnot Perfumes'', ad 1940. (See also: KAROFF).

STUART-CHASE CO., North Bergen, NJ: "Covettes'', tm 1951/1950.

STUDIA, Paris, France: "Sim Viva'', Fr. ad 1928.

STUDIO COSMETIC CO., Los Angeles, CA: "Early Californian'', tm 1945/1939; "Fashion of Hollywood'', tm 1934/1932.

SUBLIME, Chicago, IL: "My Love'', tm 1937/1936.

SUPERIOR PRODUCTS CORP., Elizabeth, NJ; NY, NY: "Annette'', tm 1926/1926; "Volupté'', tm 1927/1926.

SUTTON COSMETICS, NY, NY: "Blue Capri'', tm 1957/1954; "Ebony'', tm 1957/1956.

SUZANNE (SUZANNE PERICHON), Paris, France; NY, NY: "Bright Christmas'', ad 1947; "Le Secret de Suzanne'', tm 1929/1924; "Permettez Moi'', tm 1947/1946; "Tout de Suite'', tm 1939/1938.

SUZANNE LABORATORIES, Paterson, NJ: "Chastity'', tm 1952/1950; "Destine'', tm 1953/1950.

SUZY, Paris, France: "Bandbox'', ad 1942; "Ecarlate de Suzy'', ad 1940; "Golden Laughter'', tm 1941/1941; "Madrigal'', tm 1944/1944.

SWAN LUXURIES CO., NY, NY: "June Swan'', tm 1935/1934.

SYLVA-CROSS LABORATORIES, INC., NY, NY: "June Daon'', tm 1933/1932; "René Chevalle'', tm 1933/1932; "Yolayne'', tm 1933/1932.

SYLVANIA PERFUME CO., Philadelphia, PA: "Aromas of the Orient'', tm 1927/1922.

SYNDICATE-ARKWRIGHT, NY, NY: "Rojane'', tm 1948/1926.

SYNTOMATIC CORP., NY, NY: "Geranidar'', tm 1951/1950.

J. SUZANNE TALBOT, Paris, France: "J'', art 1925; "S'', art 1925; "T'', art 1925.

TANTY, Freeport, NJ; NY, NY: "Fleurs des Prés'', tm 1918/1917.

J. B. TALABOT, San Diego, CA: "Ultima'', tm 1924/1921.

HERMAN TAPPAN, NY, NY: "Dime'', cat 1920; "Little Casino'', cat 1920; "Sweet Bye & Bye'', tm 1881/1881.

TATTOO INC., NY, NY: "Coral Sea'', tm 1952/1946.

EVERETT F. TAWNEY, Winona, MN: "Nite Club'', tm 1927/1927.

TAYLOR LABORATORIES, Liverpool, NY: "Adorable'', tm 1935/1933.

ALFRED B. TAYLOR, Philadelphia, PA: "Twenty-Five Scent Cologne'', tm 1877/1876.

TEBOE PERFUMERS, NY, NY: "Fancy Free'', tm 1944/1944.

RETA TERRELL, Chicago, IL: 'Blanc De Chine'', tm 1947/1943; "Russian White Violet'', ad 1936.

TERRI COSMETICS INC., NY, NY: "Entre Nous'', tm 1932/1931; "Erotique'', tm 1932/1927; "Fenwicke'', tm 1933/1931; "Intrigue'', ad 1928; "La Terri'', tm 1931/1931; "Rapture'', tm 1932/1927; "Terri Deb'', tm 1932/1931.

HENRY TETLOW CO., Philadelphia, PA: "Blue Moon'', tm 1925/1919; "Floridena'', tm 1893/1892; "Floroleum'', tm 1883/1883; "Holly Blossom'', tm 1894/1893; "Pussywillow'', tm 1916/1916; "Theme Song'', tm 1929/1929.

THAYER PHARMACAL, Chicago, IL: "Carle'', tm 1930/1929.

THOEN, NY, NY: "Allure'', ad 1941; "Scent O Lite'', tm 1942/1940; "Soirée'', ad 1941; "Whimsy'', ad 1941.

THERMOPIN LABORATORIES: "Sarong'', tm 1943/1943.

SUZANNE THIERRY, Paris, France: "Beauroy'', tm 1959/1958; "Ondine'', tm 1956/1954.

ROGER THIRION & CIE, Paris, France: "Très Bien'', tm 1947/1943.

H. GREGORY THOMAS, NY, NY: "Coronation'', tm 1936/1936.

WILLIAM S. THOMSON, London, England: "Ambroline'', tm 1895/1894; "Crab-Apple Blossoms'', tm 1887/1886; "Karilpa'', tm 1891/1890; "Matsukita'', tm 1894/1892; "Orchidia'', tm 1888/1887.

RENEE THORNTON, NY, NY: "Mistress of the Night'', tm 1930/1929.

JAY-THORPE INC., NY, NY: "Exciting'', tm 1938/1937; "Hearts & Flowers'', tm 1940/1940; "Jaytho'', tm 1927/1921; "Pensees d'ewe'', tm 1926/1926; "This With That'', tm 1938/1937.

THURSTON-HELME, INC., NY, NY: "Thinc'', tm 1927/1927.

TILFORD. (See PARK & TILFORD).

C. I. TOGSTAD CO., Kokomo, IN: "Charmaine'', tm 1928/1928; "Mariet'', tm 1938/1920.

TOKALON, Paris; NY, NY: "Adurea'', cat 1922; "Buda'', cat 1922; "Chateav d'Azvr'', tm 1928/1926; "Chateav'', tm 1928/1926; "D'Ara'', tm 1924/1923; "Demon Chateav'', tm 1928/1927; "Fascination'', cat 1922; "Flor Azur'', tm 1914/1912; "Mon Chateau'', tm 1928/1926; "Mysteria'', tm 1914/1912; "Petalia'', tm 1925/1923; "Ponette'', cat 1922; "Serie Classique'', cat 1922; "Songe D'Orient'', cat 1922.

TORRENTE, Paris, France: "Madame Torrente'', new 1976; "Or De Torrente'', new 1981; "Torrente'', new 1978.

TOUJENAIS, Los Angeles, CA: "Congo'', ad 1944.

TOURNEUR, NY, NY: "Furcur'', tm 1938/1937.

TOVOTE, NY, NY: "Anxious'', tm 1944/1944; "Fleur de Mon Coeur'', ad 1944.

TOWEY CO., Minneapolis, MN: "Radio Girl'', tm 1925/1924.

NETTIE TRACER COSMETICS, NY, NY: "Muska'', tm 1951/1948.

JOHN J. TRACEY, Chicago, IL: "Flaroma'', tm 1939/1937.

TREBOR, Detroit, MI: "Black Diamond'', tm

1959 1959; "Eldorado", tm 1959/1959; "Furs", tm 1954/1941.

TRE-JUR, NY, NY: "Carnation", cat 1936; "Cha-Lai", tm 1928/1927; "Charvai", tm 1927/1926; "El-Vera", tm 1930/1929; "Gardenia", cat 1936; "Follow Me", tm 1942/1925; "Lilac", cat 1936; "Nonchalant", tm 1943/1936; "Special Occasion", tm 1951/1949; "Suivez Moi", tm 1925/1925; "Varva", tm 1942/1938.

TRESOR, NY, NY: "Cygnet", ad 1946; "Jabiru", ad 1946; "Siléne", ad 1946.

TRIPOLI BARBER SUPPLY CO., INC., Philadelphia, PA: "Tripco", tm 1931/1930.

TROISVILLE: "Bridal Satin", ad 1952.

DR. M. H. TROSSY, NY, NY: "American Youth", tm 1928/1926.

HUGH B. TROTTER, Evanston, IL: "Bag O' Tricks", tm 1953/1950; "Intense", tm 1954/1954; "Masterpiece", tm 1953/1951; "Riptide", tm 1953/1950; "Zenana", tm 1954/1954; "Zsa Zsa", tm 1954/1950.

MARI TRUDEAU CO., St. Paul, MN: "Aero Queen", tm 1927/1926.

TRUSSARDI, Italy: "Trussardi", new 1980; "Uomo", new 1984.

TRUVY INC., NY, NY: "Evening Myst", tm 1926/1925; "Evening Shade", tm 1926/1925; "Morning Myst", tm 1926/1925; "Night Myst", tm 1926/1925; "Night Shade", tm 1926/1925; "True Myst", tm 1926/1925; "Tulipe d'Or", tm 1927/1925.

TRYLON PRODUCTS, Chicago, IL: "Myth", tm 1946/1944.

TUSSY, Paris, France; Bloomfield, NJ: "Bright Secret", ad 1954; "Charme Rose", art 1951; "Midnight", cat 1950; "Optimiste", ad 1949; "Rouge et Noir", ad 1935; "Safari", tm 1940/1937; "Terpsichore", art 1947; "Tres Jolie", tm 1960/1960. (See also: LEHN & FINK; LESQUENDIEU).

TUVACHE, NY, NY: "Algiers", ad 1940; "Arabia", ad 1944; "Cossack", tm 1946/1938; "Highlander", tm 1945/1938; 'Jasmin From Egypt', ad 1945; "Jungle Gardenia", new 1932; "Lilac Royal", ad 1940; "Love Of Your Life", tm 1946/1946; "Moroccan Rose", ad 1940; "Nectaroma", tm 1960/1960; "Reve de Paris", tm 1947/1946; "Sumatra", ad 1940; "Tuvara", tm 1947/1946; "Ze Zan", tm 1945/1938.

UNGARO, Paris, France: "Diva", new 1983.

UNGERER & CO., NY, NY: "Rose D'Or", tm 1924/1890.

UNION FRANCAISE DE PARFUMERIE ET DE MAROQUINERIE, Nice, France: "Brin de Rêve", tm 1925/1920; "Divine Chanson", tm 1925/1920; "Le Coeur de Mimi", tm 1925/1920; "Le Jardin en Fête", tm 1925/1920; "Tout l'Azur", tm 1925/1920.

UNION PRODUCTS CO., Detroit, MI: "Queen-O-Beauty", tm 1932/1919.

UNITED CHINA TRADING CO., Los Angeles, CA: "Gung Ho", tm 1947/1946; "Hollywood Secret", tm 1947/1946; "Lady of Hollywood", tm 1947/1946.

UNITED DRUG, Boston, MA: "Alma Zada", cat 1922; "Bouquet Dazira", tm 1915/1915; "Cara Nome", tm 1919/1918; "Coeur d'Or", tm 1924/1917; "Dazira", cat 1922; "Fleur des Bois", cat 1922; "Harmony", cat 1922; "Intense", cat 1922; "Jonteel", Ad 1918; "Juneve", tm 1923/1921; "Nacre", cat 1922; "Shari", tm 1925/1925; "Truflor", tm 1919/1918.

UNITED TOILET GOODS CORP., NY, NY: "18th Century", tm 1939/1939.

UNIVERSAL HYGIENIC CORP., NY, NY: "Sul-Ker", tm 1934/1933.

UNIVERSAL LABORATORIES, Dallas, TX: "Blue Charm", tm 1931/1930; "Cynthia", tm 1929/1924; "Elsye Paree", tm 1931/1930.

SAMUEL C. UPHAM, Philadelphia, PA: "Liberty Bell", tm 1875/1875.

VADSCO SALES INC., Long Island, NY: "Anulodor", tm 1936/1919; "Baby Comfort", tm 1936/1916; "Djer Lady", tm 1932/1927; "Djer One", tm 1932/1927; "Encor", tm 1936/1920; "La Jeunesse", tm 1935/1919; "Mai D'Or", tm 1936/1920; "Mai Vou", tm 1936/1921; "Melbaline", tm 1934/1933; "Myrtis", tm 1936/1920; "Ninique", tm 1930/1929; "Nuriss", tm 1937/1937; "Vivacité", tm 1936/1935; "Vivomint", tm 1936/1920.

VAIL BROTHERS, Philadelphia, PA: "Lucia", tm 1923/1918; "Orinda", tm 1898/1897.

ANGELO VAJ, Piacenza, Italy: "Ri=No=Va", tm 1953/1951.

VALDOME, NY, NY: "Your Highness", tm 1946/1943.

VALDOR, Puteaux, France: "Arcancil", tm 1939/1937; "Guitare", tm 1938/1935.

VALENTINA, NY, NY: "Valentina's My Own", tm 1946/1945.

VALENTINE LABORATORIES (WALGREEN CO.), Chicago, IL: "Amelita", tm 1937/1924.

VALENTINO, Paris, France: "Valentino", new 1977.

VALLI, Bridgeport, CT: "Ponjola", tm 1926/1924.

VALMOR PRODUCTS, Chicago, IL: "Hold Your Man", tm 1954/1937; "Paris Girl", tm 1930/1930; "True Love", tm 1954/1937.

VALORE, Greenwick, CT: "Blue Vision", tm 1955/1953; "Cyriaque", tm 1956/1953; "Sayonara", tm 1955/1953; "Solange", tm 1955/1953.

VALPO CO., Berwyn, IL: "Love Lane", tm 1926/1926.

VANAE CIE: "Narcisse", cat 1928.

GLORIA VANDERBILT CORP., NY, NY: "Da", tm 1947/1946; "Diamant Bleu", ad 1946; "Indian Orchid", tm 1947/1946; "Mon Beguin", tm 1947/1946; "Star of India", tm 1947/1946.

LUCRETIA VANDERBILT, NY, NY: "Gardenia", ad 1931; "Golden Butterfly", ad 1931; "Jasmine", ad 1931; "Muguet", ad 1931; "My Hero", tm 1944/1944; "Renée", ad 1943; "Sweet Pea", ad 1931.

VANITY IMPORT CO., NY, NY: "Tres Bien", tm 1926/1925.

A. A. VANTINE, NY, NY: "Clover", ad 1940; "Embassy", tm 1933/1933; "Flowery Kingdom", ad 1913; "Geisha Flowers", tm 1908/1908; "Hi Yang", tm 1908/1908; "Jafleur", ad 1922; "Japanese Lily", ad 1913; "Ka Sai", tm 1908/1908; "Lilac", ad 1940; "Lotus Flower", cat 1922; "O Lotus San", cat 1922; "Orange Blossoms", cat 1922; "Oriental Violet", cat 1922; "Rose Drops", cat 1922; "Turkish Rose", cat 1922; "Viorenta", tm 1908/1908; "Zanadu", tm 1928/1927.

VARRE INC., NY, NY: "Perfumates", tm 1939/1938.

VARVA, NY, NY: "Follow Me", ad 1943;

"Suivez-Moi", tm 1941/1938.

RALPH C. VAUGHN, NY, NY: "Trulip", tm 1933/1932.

VENDOME, Paris, France: "Jade d'Or", cat 1922.

LOUEY VENN, London, England; NY, NY: "Liaison", tm 1946/1945; "Time And Tide", tm 1946/1945.

NAAMLOOZE VENNOOTSCHAP, Amsterdam, Netherlands: "Azuloro", tm 1926/1920; "Fé", tm 1928/1926; "Invicta", tm 1926/1926.

VEOLAY. (See VIOLET).

VERCHERE (PARFUMS JEROME), Paris, France: "Cheek To Cheek", tm 1948/1947; "Désormais", tm 1947/1945; "Paddy", tm 1947/1945; "Toast", tm 1947/1945; "Vaudeville", tm 1957/1945.

JEAN VERGLAS, Paris, France: "Visiteurs Du Soir", tm 1946/1943.

VERLAINE: "Ame d'Orient", cat 1922; "Arginette", cat 1922; "Birial", cat 1922; "Bul Bul", cat 1922; "Des Fleurs", cat 1922; "Diali", cat 1922; "Tchin", cat 1922.

VERLAYNE, Paris, France: "Attente", art 1946; "Expérience", tm 1946/1944; "Lumière de Paris", tm 1947/1945; "Plaisirs", tm 1947/1944; "Sermaize", tm 1947/1945; "Tadla", tm 1947/1945.

ALBERT VERLEY, Linden, NJ; Chicago, IL: "Foolish Heart", tm 1959/1959; "Nicotinia", tm 1938/1937; "Shangri", tm 1938/1937.

VERNET, NY, NY: "Lover's Form", tm 1927/1927.

GIANNI VERSACE, Italy: "Gianni Versace", new 1982.

VERTRA, Paris, France: "Carnation", ad 1937; "Sourire de France", ad 1937.

VIBERT, Paris, France: "Bruyere", ad 1945.

VICHY, Vichy, France: "Secret De Vichy", tm 1959/1946.

VICTOIRE, Paris, France: "Lilac", ad 1921; "Violet", ad 1921.

VICTOR, Milan, Italy: "Acqua di Selva", tm 1950/1946; "Colonia Silvestre", tm 1950/1946; "Mixtail", tm 1956/1953; "Silvestre", tm 1957/1954.

SALLY VICTOR INC., NY, NY: "Private Stock", tm 1945/1943; "White Tie", tm 1942/1941.

VICTORIA, NY, NY: "et cetera", tm 1947/1946; "Ranger", tm 1943/1942; "Vice Versa", tm 1947/1946.

VIENNESE LABORATORIES INC., Brooklyn, NY: "Jadwiga", tm 1935/1929.

VIGNY, Paris, France: "Be Lucky", art 1925; "Beau Catcher", cat 1942; "Chambord", tm 1952/1949; "Chick-Chick", tm 1925/1923; "D'ou Vient-Il", cat 1922; "Douce Chose", art 1921; "Echo Troublant", tm 1951/1932; "Eloa", cat 1922; "Fleur Celeste", art 1922; "Golliwogg", tm 1925/1919; "Guili-Guili", ad 1934; "Heure Intime", tm 1934/1933; "Jamerose", tm 1926/1921; "L'Infidèle", tm 1926/1921; "Le Bosquet de Vigny", tm 1927/1921; "Le Narcisse De France", ad 1923; "Lionette", tm 1924/1923; "Musky", cat 1922; "Plain Soleil", cat 1922.

VI-JON, St. Louis, MO: "Night In Hong Kong", tm 1943/1943; "Night In Shanghai", tm 1940/1937; "Velvet Night", tm 1948/1944.

JUAN L. VILA, Havana, Cuba: "Orion D'Or", tm 1957/1945.

VILLON & VILLON, Brooklyn, NY: "Noël en Paris", tm 1932/1931.

VIMAY, Los Angeles, CA; "Culver City, CA: "Orange Petals", tm 1937/1935; "Sins of Hollywood", tm 1935/1935. (See also: PRINCE DE CHANY).

VINCHA, London, England: "Osiris", art 1914.

VIOLET (VEOLAY), Paris, France; NY, NY: "Abîme", tm 1930/1930; "Altys", ad 1920; "Ambre Royal", tm 1923/1900; "Amorosa", cat 1922; "Ancien", cat 1922; "Apogée", tm 1933/1932; "Bouquet Farnese", ad 1918; "Brise Ambre", cat 1922; "Brise De Violette", ad 1918; "Charmose", cat 1922; "Chypre", ad 1924; "Compliments", ad 1939; "Contes des Fées", ad 1939; "Cuir de Russie", ad 1939; "Curieux", cat 1922; "Ecoutez-Moi", tm 1937/1926; "Eternelle Chanson", tm 1928/1928; "Fastuosa", cat 1922; "Fleur de Giroflee", cat 1922; "Fougere d'Ecosse", cat 1922; "Gerbes Folles", tm 1937/1922; "Intelligence", tm 1947/1945; "Kassya", ad 1913; 'Kiloe", cat 1922; "L'Heure Jolie", cat 1922; "Les Sylvies", ad 1923; "Marechal", cat 1922; "Méalys", tm 1947/1892; "Musc", cat 1922; "Niobe", tm 1924/1915; "Oryane", cat 1922; "Pois de Senteur", ad 1928; "Pour Rêver", tm 1928/1926; "Pourpre d'Automne", Fr. ad 1924; "Prelia", ad 1918; "Prologue", ad 1939; "Rameau Fleuri", ad 1918; "Refrain", tm 1959/1953; "Rosamine", cat 1922; "Satan", tm 1937/1926; "Sketch", Fr. ad 1924; "Sylviane", cat 1922; "Tanagra", cat 1922; "Valreine", art 1911; "Viborg", cat 1922; "Ylang", cat 1922.

VION, Paris, France: "Bouquet", ad 1926; "Chypre", ad 1926; "Jasmin", ad 1926; "Lavion-ette", tm 1928/1927; "Narcisse", ad 1926; "Rose", ad 1926.

VITAPIL, Diekirch, Luxemburg: "Sénégol", tm 1939/1938.

VITA-RAY: "Gallivanting", ad 1944.

V. VIVAUDOU, INC., NY, NY; Los Angeles, CA: "Boditan", tm 1929/1928; "Boudoirette", tm 1924/1924; "Fleur de France", tm 1916/1915; "Flower Pot", tm 1940/1940; "Fortuna", tm 1916/1915; "Heure Passionnante", tm 1927/1926; "Jasmin Noir", tm 1924/1924; "Kyrill", tm 1926/1925; "La Sept Mysterieux", tm 1935/1934; "Lady Mary", new 1915; "Mavis", tm 1916/1915; "Myrtis", tm 1921/1920; "Narcisse de Chine", tm 1924/1923; "Nuit Folle", tm 1934/1934; "Parfum Park Lane", tm 1926/1925; "Parfumez-Vous", new 1920; "Pleasant Memories", tm 1925/1924; "Sivam", tm 1932/1923; "Vrai", tm 1929/1929. (See also: ARLY; DELETTREZ; PRINCE DE CHANY; VADSCO SALES CORP.).

VIVI INC., Paris, France; NY, NY: "Aroma", tm 1926/1925; "Carola", tm 1925/1925; "Carty", tm 1926/1925; "Ensueño", tm 1925/1925; "La Tulipe Noire", tm 1925/1925; "Parfum Touvi", tm 1925/1925; "Vicky", tm 1925/1925.

VIVIAN, NY, NY: "Champagne Mink", tm 1958/1957.

VIVILLE, NY, NY; Paris, France: "Baccara", tm 1930/1930; "Coeur de L'Ete", tm 1930/1930; "Dame de Lague", tm 1930/1930; "Ecaille", tm 1930/1930; "Laquer Lady", tm 1930/1930; "Peony", tm 1932/1930; "Prés de Moi", tm 1930/1930.

VIVINY PERFUMERS INC., West Haven, CT: "J. V. G.", tm 1934/1932; "Maurice", tm 1931/1931; "Paul Du Bois", tm 1931/1931; "Septol No. 6X", tm 1933/1932; "Sper", tm 1930/1926; "Velvex", tm 1935/1933; "Viennese Nights", tm 1934/1926.

VOGELER, SON & CO., Baltimore, MD: "Fedora", tm 1884/1884; "Lalla Rookh", tm 1887/1886.

VOLAY OF PARIS CO., Kalamazoo, MI: "L'Heur", tm 1948/1946.

VOLNAY, Paris, France; Suresnes, France: "Ambre de Siam", ad 1925; "Ambre Indien", ad 1922; "Cachucha", tm 1947/1937; "Cap d'Or", ad 1922; "Cerny", tm 1949/1919; "Choses du Passé", ad 1928; "Chypre", ad 1922; "Chypre Ambre", ad 1922; "Firefly", ad 1922; "Fleurs Vives", ad 1922; "Gri-Gri", ad 1922; "Iris Neige", ad 1928; "Jardinee", ad 1922; "Jasmin du Cap", ad 1922; "Le Parfum de Gabrielle Dorziat", ad 1925; "Lilas de Lorraine", ad 1922; "Maoni", ad 1922; "Mimeomai", ad 1922; "Mousse Ambrée", cat 1922; "Muguet", art 1919; "Napee", ad 1922; "Oeillet Kleber", ad 1922; "Perlerette", ad 1925; "Rose Brumaire", ad 1922; "Rosée des Bois", ad 1927; "Silas", art 1919; "Soir d'Ete", ad 1928; "Très Français", tm 1947/1937; "Un Gardenia", ad 1927; "Yapana", ad 1922.

WAHNA (JOHN WANAMAKER), NY, NY: "Ma Mie", tm 1921/1909; "Melisande", tm 1921/1909. (See also: JOHN WANAMAKER).

WALGREEN, Chicago, IL: "Amoray", tm 1940/1940; "Chambly", tm 1938/1930.

MORRIS WALHIMER, New Haven, CT; NY, NY: "Bryn Mawr", tm 1945/1943; "Chevy Chase", tm 1945/1943; "Whispering Willow", tm 1944/1943.

ABBE WALLACE COSMETICS INC., Atlanta, GA: "Dream Number", tm 1937/1937.

GANNA WALSKA, Paris, France: "Blue Ribbon", Fr. ad 1928; "Divorcons", tm 1929/1927; "Plasticrème", tm 1928/1927; "Pourlesport", Fr. ad 1928.

WALSTAN CO. (WALTER S. SOSIN), NY, NY: "Seasoned", tm 1947/1946.

CHESTER E. WALTON, Inglewood, CA: "Desert Flower", tm 1929/1929.

JOHN WANAMAKER, Philadelphia, PA: "Cartwright", tm 1889/1883; "C'est Paris", tm 1926/1926; "Charme d'Amour", tm 1924/1917; "Claire", tm 1948/1910; "Coin de Paris", tm 1923/1923; "Fleur D'Or", tm 1924/1910; "Fleurs Celeste", tm 1924/1921; "Le Beau Narcisse", tm 1926/1923; "Le Couquet", tm 1926/1926; "Orée", tm 1924/1910; "Red Leaf", tm 1924/1923; "Reine Marie", tm 1924/1910; "The Queen Mary", tm 1889/1881; "Tribout", tm 1935/1935; "Violette de Paris", tm 1924/1910; "Yu Yu", tm 1924/1910. (See also: WAHNA).

WARIN & CIE, Paris, France: "Ninon", tm 1925/1869.

WARNER & WARNER, Brooklyn, NY: "Cupid's Garden", tm 1926/1923.

PHILIP H. WARSHAW INC., NY, NY: "Virtus", tm 1926/1914.

WASHINGTON BARBER SUPPLY CO., NY, NY: "New Moon", tm 1929/1923.

J. R. WATKINS, Winona, MN: "A Fragment Of My Heart", tm 1947/1945; "Belle de Nuit", tm 1924/1924; "Concerto", tm 1944/1944; "Emblem", tm 1941/1940; "Garda", tm 1918/1917; "In The Mood", tm 1955/1952; "Jean Wade", tm 1933/1932; "Love Story", tm 1955/1954; "Mariel", tm 1945/1944; "Mary King", tm 1929/1929; "Ramona", tm 1929/1928; "So Tenderly", tm 1954/1953; "Sweeteen", tm 1956/1955; "Syr", tm 1925/1925; "Torch Song", tm 1960/1959; "Tropical Bouquet", tm 1926/1926; "Tropical Magic", tm 1947/1946; "Watko", tm 1927/1927; "White Blossom", tm 1955/1952.

WAVERLY LABORATORIES, NY, NY: "Champs de Fleurs", tm 1936/1936; "House of Flowers", tm 1939/1938.

WAYSIDE HOUSE, Painesville, OH: "Blossom Fragrance", tm 1940/1939.

WEAVER-JACKSON CO., Los Angeles, CA: "Desert Night", tm 1931/1930.

WILLIAM A. WEBSTER CO., Memphis, TN: "House Of Lord's", tm 1936/1935; "La Paro", tm 1926/1926; "Super Narcisse", tm 1927/1925; "The Talk Of The Town", tm 1929/1928; "Tru Test", tm 1926/1926.

WEIL, Paris, France: "Antilope", tm 1935/1931; "Bambou", tm 1934/1933; "Bundles For Beauty", tm 1942/1942; "Carbonique", tm 1937/1936; "Cassandra", tm 1935/1935; "Chinchilla Royal", tm 1931/1927; "Cobra", tm 1941/1941; "Evettes", tm 1948/1948; "Gentilhomme", tm 1962/1958; "Grigri", tm 1944/1943; "Hermine", tm 1931/1927; "Noir", ad 1937; Secret Of Venus", tm 1962/1942; "Violette Victorienne", tm 1937/1936; "Zibeline", tm 1931/1927.

WEILL & HARTMANN, NY, NY: "Dolores", tm 1934/1932.

WELDON INC., NY, NY: "Flower Garden", tm 1946/1946.

WELEDA, NY, NY: "Summer Woods", tm 1947/1944.

WEMBDON, NY, NY: "Wembdon Lavender", ad 1939.

WENDY PARFUMERIE, Cincinnati, OH: "Narcisse", tm 1926/1925; "The Charleston", tm 1926/1926.

HOUSE OF WENGER, Philadelphia, PA: "Chou-Chou", tm 1926/1925.

WESMAY: "Mae West Perfume", ad 1934.

WESTERN LABORATORIES, San Francisco, CA: "Chicago, IL: "Nannette", tm 1930/1927; "Sunset Maid", tm 1926/1925.

WESTERN SOAP & CHEMICAL CO., Los Angeles, CA: "Betsy Ross", tm 1927/1926; "Valley Queen", tm 1927/1926.

WEST INDIA COMMERCIAL CO. INC., NY, NY: "Khus-Khus", tm 1936/1936.

WEST INDIA MANUFACTURING, NY, NY: "Gold Seal", tm 1883/1883; "Green Seal", tm 1883/1883; "Orange Blossom", tm 1883/1883; "Violet", tm 1883/1883.

PAUL WESTPHAL, NY, NY: "Auxiliator", tm 1903/1882; "Lavandine", tm 1903/1887.

WETHERHOLT'S PERFUME CO., Chicago, IL: "Comanté", tm 1946/1945; "Could Be", tm 1946/1945; "Knight Of Armor", tm 1947/1942; "Majorette", tm 1946/1945; "Out Of This World", tm 1946/1942; "Pigtail Parade", tm 1949/1945; "Red, Lovely, And Dangerous", tm 1946/1945.

WEXFORD CO., NY, NY: "Belgravia", tm 1878/1878.

GEORGE H. WEYER, St. Joseph, MO: "3 Roses", tm 1923/1923.

WHITE MOUNTAIN PERFUMERS, Nashua, NH: "Baby Sweet", tm 1949/1947; "Specifik", tm 1947/1947; "Terrifik", tm 1947/1947; "White Lie", tm 1947/1947.

WHITEHALL PHARMACAL CO., NY, NY: "Louis Philippe", tm 1951/1928; "Princess Eve", tm 1952/1946; "Vaness", tm 1948/1940.

HAROLD P. WILLATS, Hollywood, CA: "Campus", tm 1941/1940; "Colonial Bouquet", tm 1940/1940.

WILLIAMS, DAVIS, BROOKS, Detroit, MI: "Dabrook's", tm 1893/1893; "Lace", tm 1900/1899.

WILLIAMS & WILLIAMS, Atlanta, GA: "Paris Bouquet", tm 1931/1930.

J. B. WILLIAMS, Glastonburg, CT: "Aqua", tm 1927/1926.

WILMA CO., NY, NY: "Desir De Toi", ad 1925.

WILSON CHEMICAL CO., Tyrone, PA; "Persian Garden", tm 1926/1905.

ARTHUR WINARICK, NY, NY: "Fore", tm 1930/1930; "Luzant", tm 1926/1926; "Omax", tm 1926/1926; "Sonora", tm 1926/1926.

WINDSOR HOUSE, Los Angeles, CA: "Castle Eire", tm 1944/1942; "Juliet", ad 1941; "Knight Errant", tm 1945/1942; "Opera Night", ad 1941; "Romeo", ad 1941.

WINDSOR PRODUCTS, Chicago, IL: "Florolite", tm 1941/1940.

WINKELMANN & BROWN DRUG CO., Baltimore, MD: "Dew Driplets", tm 1892/1892; "Japonita", tm 1892/1892; "Lilioptus", tm 1892/1892; "Pearls-Of-Violets", tm 1895/1895; "Violila", tm 1895/1895.

OLIVE CARMEAN WITZMAN, Kansas City, MO: "Lady Carmean", tm 1936/1934.

WOLF DRUG CO., Newark, NJ: "Swagger", tm 1949/1937.

FRANK WOLF, Brooklyn, NY: "Full-Dress", tm 1925/1924.

F. WOLFF & SOHN, Karlsruhe, Germany: "Black Forest Pine", tm 1930/1906; "Florasma", tm 1923/1909; "Phantasma", tm 1923/1909.

WOLFF FRERES INC., NY, NY: "Ambiance", tm 1949/1948; "Bathsheba", tm 1948/1948; "Crisance", tm 1950/1949; "Dew of Violets", cat 1922; "Divinia", cat 1922; "Elata", cat 1922; "Frisky", tm 1950/1949; "My French Cousin", tm 1948/1948; "Rose Marechal Neil", cat 1922; "Song of Songs", tm 1948/1948; "Vinda Alegre", cat 1922; "Violet Rococo", cat 1922.

BRONISLAWA WOLOCKO, Salem, MA: "Carib", tm 1953/1952.

WOOD BROTHERS, Detroit, MI: "Satin-Scent", tm 1896/1889.

VIVIANE WOODARD, Panorama City, CA: "Alter Ego", tm 1962/1958; "Baloo", tm 1962/1958; "Et Tu", tm 1962/1958; "Frévo", tm 1963/1960; "Je Pleur", tm 1962/1958; "Rikki Tavi", tm 1962/1958; "When In Rome", tm 1962/1961.

JOHN H. WOODBURY, Cincinnati, OH:

"Zia", tm 1942/1942.

H. A. WOODS, INC., Evansville, IN: "Marthé Jean", tm 1931/1931.

C. B. WOODWORTH & SONS, Rochester, NY: "Blue Liles", tm 1890/1887; "Centennial", tm 1875/1873; "Conceit", tm 1910/1909; "Diana", tm 1894/1894; "Fianceé", tm 1912/1912; "Garden Fragrance", tm 1917/1916; "Karess", ad 1922; "La Dansante", tm 1915/1914; "La Nocturne", tm 1915/1915; "Mandarin Rose", tm 1914/1913; "Nina", tm 1901/1900; "Pearl of Savoy", tm 1885/1885; "Santana", tm 1915/1912; "Spanish Lilac", tm 1890/1890; "Viegay", tm 1925/1925; "Violets of Sicily", tm 1908/1908; "Vivace", tm 1929/1929.

JULIE WORMSER, Paris, France: "Cheruit", tm 1925/1925.

WORTH, Paris, France: "By Request", tm 1946/1945; "Cologne Chest", tm 1948/1947; "Dans La Nuit", tm 1923/1920; "Fleurs Fraiches", new 1973; "Gardenia", ad 1939; "Honeysuckle", art 1931; "Imprudence", tm 1938/1938; "Je Reviens", tm 1932/1931; "Lilas", ad 1939; "Miss Worth", new 1977; "Oeillet", ad 1939; "Projets", tm 1937/1935; "Requete", tm 1945/1944; "Sans Adieu", tm 1930/1929; "Spotlight", tm 1943/1942; "Vers Le Jour", tm 1927/1926; "Vers Toi", tm 1934/1933.

IRVING WORTHMAN, Brooklyn, NY: "Kis-N-Make-Up", tm 1946/1945.

WRIGHT BEAUTY SUPPLY CO., Roanoke, VA: "Ermanée", tm 1932/1931.

ALFRED WRIGHT, Philadelphia, PA; NY, NY; Rochester, NY: "American Beauty", tm 1912/1889; "Grand Duchess", tm 1896/1877; "Juliet", tm 1899/1899; "Madame Butterfly", tm 1912/1902; "Mary Stuart", tm 1876/1876; "Maud Muller", tm 1894/1894; "Melodie", tm 1927/1908; "Priscilla", tm 1898/1898; "Reverie", tm 1924/1905.

WRISLEY (ALLEN B. WRISLEY), Chicago, IL: "Alpine Violet", cat 1922; "Apple Blossom", art 1940; "Blue Fern", ad 1942; "Carnation", art 1940; "Colonial", tm 1901/1895; "English Lilac", cat 1922; "Fez", ad 1936; "Frill Cologne", ad 1943; "Gaiete", tm 1962/1939; "Gardenia", art 1940; "Gold Tassels", tm 1948/1942; "Lorelei", cat 1922; "Magnetique", tm 1962/1961; "My Heart", tm 1960/1951; "Pink Coral", ad 1941; "Queen's Guard", ad 1936; "Reservation For Two", tm 1949/1944; "Rose Pom Pom", cat 1922; "San Toy", ad 1915; "Vicereine", cat 1922; "White Flower Cologne", ad 1942; "Wild Crab Apple Blossom", cat 1922.

D. WROBLEWSKI & CO., Brooklyn, NY: "Warszawianka", tm 1938/1914.

ESTELLE WYLER, NY, NY: "Magic Moment", tm 1954/1950.

YARDLEY, London, England: "April Violets", ad 1938; "Bond Street", tm 1918/1917; "Caricia", tm 1918/1917; "Charme De Cupidon", tm 1918/1917; "Damosel", tm 1935/1935; "Elegance", tm 1934/1932; "Enchantress", tm 1918/1912; "Flair", ad 1952; "Fragrance", ad 1934; "Gage D'Amour", tm 1918/1913; "Garden Whispers", tm 1918/1912; "Khadine", ad 1968; "La Plus Bell Des Fleurs", tm

1918/1913; "Ladies-In-Waiting", tm 1937/1937; "Lady Gay", tm 1918/1917; "Lavenesque", tm 1953/1951; "Le Beau Monde", tm 1918/1914; "Le Secret des Dieux", tm 1918/1913; "Lotus", ad 1948; "Loves' Secret", tm 1918/1917; "Mon Desir", tm 1918/1912; "Murmure De Forêt", tm 1918/1913; "Nell Gwynne", tm 1918/1910; "Old English Lavender", tm 1934/1894; "Orchis", ad 1931; "Poise", tm 1934/1934; "Red Rose", cat 1930; "Sans Souci", tm 1918/1917; "Scintilla", tm 1935/1934; "Source D'Or", tm 1918/1910; "Tête A Tête", art 1914; "Vanity Fair", tm 1920/1916.

YBRY, NY, NY; Paris, France: "Amour Sauvage", tm 1930/1929; "Désir du Coeur", tm 1932/1925; "Devinez", tm 1932/1927; "Femmes de Paris", tm 1925/1925; "French Bouquet", ad 1940; "Joie de Vivre", tm 1936/1935; "L'Amour Toujours", tm 1933/1932; "Les Bourgeons", tm 1929/1928; "Les Fleurs d'Ybry", ad 1929; "Mon Ame", tm 1932/1925; "Naturelle", ad 1940; "Odorade", tm 1940/1939; "Old Fashioned Garden", tm 1940/1939; "Palo Alto", tm 1944; "The Buds", ad 1944; "Toujours l'Amour", tm 1932/1931; "Un Soir de Ma Vie", tm 1930/1929; "Wild Daphne", ad 1940.

YOCUM LABORATORIES, Chariton, IA: "Cologne of the Month", tm 1941/1940.

YONA, Chicago, IL: "By Appointment", ad 1946.

YORK PHARMACAL CO., St. Louis, MO: "Jun-Nite", tm 1936/1935.

YOUNG, LADD, & COFFIN, NY, NY: "Alpine Violet", tm 1887/1883; "California Water", tm 1874/1874; "Criterion", tm 1877/1877; "Edenia", tm 1879/1879; "Fascination", tm 1874/1874; "Tally Ho", tm 1878/1878.

MIRA YOUNG: "Actif", tm 1949/1948.

RICHARD D. YOUNG, NY, NY: "Bouquet Araby", tm 1889/1888; "Lily Bells", tm 1889/1888; "Melaura", tm 1889/1888; "Prairie Wild", tm 1889/1888.

JAMES L. YOUNGHUSBAND, Chicago, IL: "Dissipation", tm 1937/1936; "Gay Bandit", tm 1938/1937; "Light Fantastic", tm 1952/1949; "Quickies", tm 1938/1936; "Sensual", tm 1938/1936; "Smoothie", tm 1938/1936.

YOUNG-QUINLAN CO., Minneapolis, MN: "J'Aime-Ca", tm 1928/1925.

YOUSSIF H. ZAKI, Akron, OH: "Persian Moon", tm 1946/1944.

YSIANE, Paris, France: "Saturnale", Fr. ad 1927.

ZANOL PRODUCTS, Cincinnati, OH: "Faith Avery", tm 1953/1930.

ZANZAR & CO., Brentwood, MO: "Oblivion", tm 1951/1948.

IRVIN S. ZELUFF, NY, NY: "Dante", tm 1927/1926.

ZODIAC HOUSE, Hollywood, CA: "Star Sent", tm 1948/1946.

ZOFALY, Paris, France: "Jeux D'Amour", tm 1947/1946; "Passion De Zofaly", tm 1947/1946; "Retour Charmant", tm 1947/1946.

ZSA ZSA, U.S.: "Zigzag", ad 1969.

Index

Price Guide

Key:

w/box = with box. Price stated includes an original box with the bottle.

set = Price stated includes all pieces of a set.

NPA = No price available. Due to the rarity of the bottle and constant market fluctuation of value, no price is stated.

Title Page—$125, $250
Page 8—NPA, $95 w/box
Page 9—$325 w/box
1 $125, $250
2 NPA
3 $20
4 $195
5 —
6 $40
7 $150
8 $275 w/box
9 $950
10 $85
11 $95
12 $45
13 $85 each
14 $95 w/box
15 $65
16 $10-$15
17 $20
18 $15
19 $10-$30 each
20 NPA
21 $65 w/box
22 $85
23 $125
24 NPA
25 $50 w/box
26 $85
27 $85
28 $350
29 $175
30 $40
31 $55
32 $65 w/box
33 $400
34 $45
35 $20
36 $65
37 NPA
38 $150 w/box

39 $45
40 $35
41 NPA
42 $125
43 $275 w/box
44 $325 w/box
45 $75
46 $75
47 $30 set
48 $65
49 $100
50 $10
51 $750
52 $125
53 $45
54 $15
55 NPA
56 $150
57 $45 w/box
58 $100
59 $30
60 $25
61 $20
62 $175
63 $20
64 $300
65 $1000 w/box
66 $325 w/box
67 $325
68 $125
69 NPA
70 $375
71 $325 w/box
72 —
73 $1200
74 NPA
75 $25
76 $175
77 $15, $25, $35
78 $150 w/box
79 $375

80 $100
81 $35
82 $45
83 —
84 —
85 $20
86 $325 w/box
87 NPA
88 $200 w/box
89 —
90 $300
91 NPA
92 $350
93 —
94 —
95 —
96 —
97 $325
98 $75
99 $75
100 $125
101 $200
102 $100
103 $225
104 —
105 —
106 $125
107 $75
108 $150 w/box
109 $275 w/box
110 $125
111 $45-$95 each
112 $175
113 $20-$60 each
114 —
115 —
116 —
117 $125
118 $35
119 $200
120 $225

121 $15 w/box
122 $300
123 $65 w/box
124 $650 w/box
125 —
126 —
127 $125
128 $200
129 NPA
130 $150
131 $35
132 $35
133 —
134 —
135 $40
136 $15 each
137 $550
138 $85
139 $250
140 $115
141 $85
142 $35
143a $100
143b $125
144 —
145 —
146 NPA
147 $450
148 $35
149 $225 w/box
150 $575 w/box
151 NPA
152 $450
153 $85
154 —
155 $50
156 NPA
157 $50
158 $250
159 $450
160 $175

161 $175
162 —
163 —
164 $200 each
165 $225
166 $100
167 NPA
168 $85 w/box
169 $1500
170 $350
171 $1200
172 $135
173 $300
174 $85
175 $200
176 $400-$450
177 $325
178 $25
179 $95
180 $45
181 $200
182 $125
183 $75
184 $325
185 $85 w/box
186 $85
187 $75
188 NPA
189 —
190 $30
191 $250 w/box
192 $145
193 $185
194 $20
195 $45 w/box
196 NPA
197 $125
198 $45
199 $85
200 $300
201 $85
202 —
203 $165
204 $40 w/box
205 $45
206 $375 w/box
207 $1500
208 $25
209 $75
210 $175 w/box
211 —
212 $350 w/box
213 $85
214 $65
215 NPA
216 NPA
217 $275 w/box
218 $275 w/box
219 $400 w/box
220 —
221 —
222 —
223 $25
224 $25 w/box
225 $375
226 $200
227 $125
228 $275
229 $20

230 $250
231 $650
232 $600
233 $125
234 $300
235 $250 w/box
236 $200
237 $300 w/box
238 $250
239 $250
240 $300
241 $200
242 $85
243 $25
244 $45
245 $85
246 $75
247 $90 w/box
248 $20
249 $30
250 $185
251 $15
252 $20
253 $25 w/box
254 —
255 $550
256 $225
257 $15
258 $125
259 $100 w/box
260 $45 w/box
261 $75 w/box
262 $45 w/box
263 $100 w/box
264 $125 w/box
265 $35
266 $275 w/box
267 $75 w/box
268 NPA
269 $225
270 $150 w/box
271 $5
272 $45
273 $150
274 —
275 $35
276 $225
277 $85
278 $100
279 $85
280 $75 set
281 $65 set
282 $75 set
283 $85 w/box
284 $125 w/box
285 $25
286 $250 w/box
287 $30
288 $10
289 $30 w/box
290 $5
291 $25
292 $10
293 $25 set
294 $15
295 $45 w/box
296 $85 w/box
297 $95
298 $10

299 NPA
300 $5
301 $20
302 $85
303 $20
304 $15
305 $20
306 $85
307 $45
308 $30
309 $125
310 $100
311 $100
312 $35
313 $65
314 $165 w/box
315 $30
316 $30
317 NPA
318 $40 set
319 $85
320 $40
321 $85 w/box
322 $95 w/box
323 NPA
324 $250 w/box
325 $350
326 $50 w/box
327 $125, $150
328 $65 w/box
329 $125
330 NPA
331 $175
332 $85 w/box
333 $55
334 $250 w/box
335 $85
336 $150
337 $85
338 $125
339 $35, $20
340 $85
341 $75 w/box
342 $45
343 $125
344 $250
345 $40
346 $55 w/box
347 $175
348 $125
349 $200 w/case
350 NPA
351 NPA
352 $500
353 —
354 —
355 —
356 $25
357 $25
358 $20
359 $175
360 $150 w/box
361 $35
362 $20 each
363 $20 each
364 $35 each
365 $35 each
366 $35
367 $85

368 $40 each
369 $300
370 $550 w box
371 $35
372 $175 w box
373 $25
374 $300
375 $45
376 NPA
377 —
378 $75
379 NPA
380 $40
381 $75 w box
382 $25
383 $250 w/box
384 $85
385 $125, $85
386 $55 w box
387 $85 w box
388 $125
389 $45 w box
390 $65
391 $125
392 $550 w/box
393 $35 w/box
394 $75
395 $200
396 $15
397 $65 w/box
398 $45 w/box
399 $45 w/box
400 $40 w/box
401 $25
402 $175
403 $10
404 $15
405 $25
406 $35
407 $35 w/box
408 $35
409 $45
410 $35
411 $35
412 $145 w/box
413 $125
414 $300
415 $45
416 $225 w/box
417 $25
418 $10-$20 each
419 $150 w/box
420 $75
421 $60
422 $35
423 $20
424 $28
425 $25
426 NPA
427 $250 w/box
428 $65
429 $20
430 $150 w/box
431 $25
432 —
433 $100 w/box
434 $125
435 $175 w/box
436 $250, $350

437 $85
438 $125 w/box
439 $350 w/box
440 $25
441 $225
442 $350
443 $100 w/box
444 $175, $225
445 $65
446 $35 w/box
447 $100
448 $25
449 $100
450 $85
451 $30
452 $20
453 $25
454 $28
455 $35
456 $20
457 $55
458 $45
459 $55
460 $45 set
461 $75 w/box
462 $200
463 $10
464 $55
465 $50 w/box
466 $10 w/box
467 $20
468 $35
469 $65
470 $95 set
471 $250 w/box
472 $10 w/box
473 $85
474 $225 set
475 $45
476 $550
477 $15
478 $45
479 $15 w/box
480 $35 set
481 $25

482 $55
483 $40
484 NPA
485 $5-$15 each
486 $65
487 $175 w/box
488 $85 w/box
489 $5
490 $20
491 $25
492 $75 w/box
493 $45 w/box
494 $35
495 $85
496 $25
497 $200
498 $75
499 $375
500 $45
501 $20
502 $400
503 $15
504 $425
505 —
506 $35 set
507 $60
508 $300
509 $200 w/box
510 $10
511 $45
512 $60 w/box
513 $25 w/box
514 $35
515 $65
516 $40 set
517 $75
518 $125
519 $25
520 $45
521 $100 set
522 $125
523 $75 w/box
524 $65 w/box
525 $65
526 $25, $15

527 $15
528 $100 w/box
529 $25
530 $30 w/box
531 $10-$20 each
532 $10-$15 each
533 $125 w/box
534 $35
535 $200 w/box
536 $30
537 $45 w/box
538 $150
539 $35
540 $225
541 $140
542 $35 set
543 $30 w/box
544 $65
545 $275 w/box
546 $25
547 $85
548 $75
549 $85 w/box
550 $225 w/box
551 $400 w/box
552 $150 w/box
553 $75
554 $25
555 $25 w/box
556 $20
557 $45 w/box
558 $175 w/box
559 $175
560 $65
561 $35 w/box
562 $65
563 $45
564 $25
565 $20
566 $10
567 $55
568 $25, $35
569 $85
570 $375 w/box
571 $85

572 $50
573 $85 w/box
574 $275 w/box
575 $65
576 $15
577 $15
578 $45 w/box
579 $85
580 $95 w/box
581 $45 w/box
582 $75 set
583 $40 w/box
584 $145 w/box
585 $200 w/box
586 $20
587 $75 w/box
588 $300 w/box
589 $100 w/box
590 $165 w/box
591 $45 w/box
592 $150
593 $15
594 $150
595 $300
596 $45 w/box
597 $20 w/box
598 $15
599 —
600 $200
601 $25
602 $15
603 $350
604 $300
605 $65
606 $25
607 $75 w/box
608 $35 set
609 $20
610 $85
611 —
612 $65
613 —
614 $75
615 $125
616 $50